The Complete Guide to Water Plants

Helmut Mühlberg

The Complete Guide to
Water Plants

A Reference Book

with 109 colour and 112 black-and-white photographs of plants
and 59 illustrations in the text

ep EP Publishing Limited

Translated from the German by Ilse Lindsay, London
Revised by Colin D. Roe, Solihull

Line drawings by Britta Matthies
© 1980 of the German edition and 1981 of the English translation by Edition Leipzig
© English edition 1982 EP Publishing Limited

ISBN 0 7158 0789 7
First printed 1982
Printed in the German Democratic Republic

Contents

6   Contents

Contents   7

8   Contents

Advice to the reader:
Numbers in italics refer to drawings in the text and numbers
in Roman type to photos.

Foreword by Bernard Pye

Very often the initial lack of success when growing plants, particularly those kept in an aquarium, can be attributed to the absence of sufficient relevant information. The novice may select a number of plants for his aquarium without being aware that in the wild they come from many different locations and consequently have different, and often incompatible, requirements. It is therefore not surprising that disappointment and disillusion often ensue, and the first venture into aquatic plant keeping is also the last. However, for those prepared to disregard early reverses, water plants offer an invariably interesting, sometimes frustrating but always engrossing occupation. The exchange of seeds and specimens, and the interchange of ideas will interest aquarists, plant growers and collectors alike.

With the importation of plants from various parts of the world becoming commonplace, a very large number and variety of species are now available, and there is an urgent need for a ready reference to determine the suitability or otherwise of a plant for a particular environment. This book, which covers nearly two hundred species of aquatic plants, gives through description and illustration a guide to most of the plants the reader is likely to encounter. It includes true aquatics as well as others which are generally considered marsh plants and which have hitherto rarely been described in popular literature on the subject, so will be of particular interest to aquarists, botanists and owners of garden pools to whom the details of cultivation and propagation will be especially valuable.

Much research on water plants has been carried out in Europe, particularly in Germany, by professionals and amateurs alike, and their findings have made a major contribution to recent literature on the subject. It is therefore very appropriate that this translation by Ilse Lindsay of Helmut Mühlberg's important book should appear now. It is a valuable reference work which should find a place on the bookshelves of all English-speaking plant lovers.

I. The Biology of Aquatic Plants

1. Aquatic Plants in the Wild

Many aquatic plants grow completely submerged or floating on the surface of the water. Some plants rooted at the bottom produce floating leaves or thrust their flowers above the surface. These plants are so dependent on the water as a habitat that they would die on land or develop stunted forms. Other aquatic plants colonize the border zone between water and land. These are often called marsh plants. They grow on wet soil around the edges of the water or in shallow water so that shoots and leaves develop in the air. Some marsh plants are able to withstand short periods of drought in their habitat, others can adapt to being submerged. It is not possible to make a clear division between the plants of the water and those of the border zone between land and water. Most of them are suitable for cultivation in a pond, a planthouse or an aquarium.

Distribution

All species of plants, in fact all classified groups such as genera and families, have their distinctive areas of distribution on the earth's surface. Equally this applies to aquatic plants as long as they are natural forms and not especially cultivated like many of the water lilies. Plant physiology is inherited. Thus plants need the right ecological conditions so that they can thrive. Often, however, the plants have to make the best of what their environment offers them.

Plant life depends on climate and a suitable habitat—water and marsh in the case of the aquatic plants. A plant family's history, evolution and ability to spread will have considerable influence on the position and size of the area of distribution.

Of the primary climatic factors, rainfall and temperature with their seasonal variations are of particular importance to plant life. From the equator towards the poles the temperature decreases, while annual fluctuations in temperature increase.

Rainfall depends to a large degree on the movement of the cloud masses in the atmosphere.

Put in simplified terms, there are three main climatic zones (Ill. *1*), but within each zone many variations occur. These depend on the size of the respective land masses, the tempera-

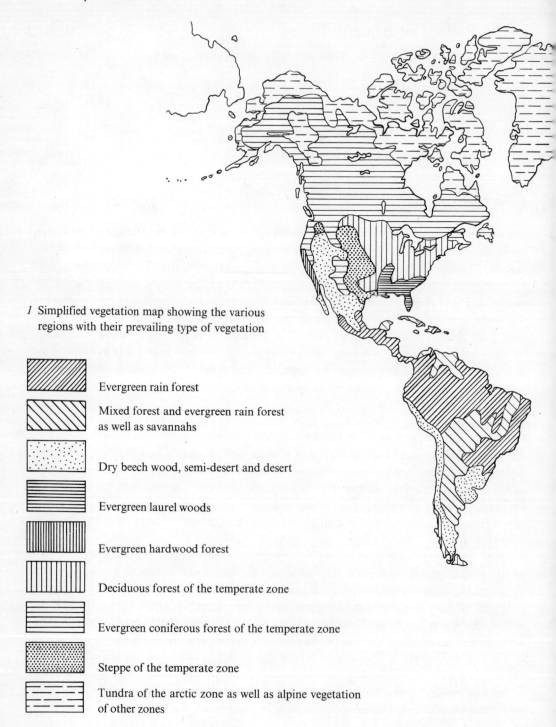

1 Simplified vegetation map showing the various
regions with their prevailing type of vegetation

Evergreen rain forest

Mixed forest and evergreen rain forest
as well as savannahs

Dry beech wood, semi-desert and desert

Evergreen laurel woods

Evergreen hardwood forest

Deciduous forest of the temperate zone

Evergreen coniferous forest of the temperate zone

Steppe of the temperate zone

Tundra of the arctic zone as well as alpine vegetation
of other zones

ture of the oceans surrounding the continents, and the influence exercised by high mountains. Thus, areas with characteristic vegetation are distributed within the different climatic zones.

Heavy seasonal rain and special air currents are typical for the tropical-subtropical region. When in spring and autumn the sun is in the zenith over the equator, the air heats very quickly and air currents rise. The air that has risen cools, and vapour contained in it condenses to fall to earth as rain. The air masses themselves blow away in higher altitudes. At some distance south and north of the equator airstreams sink towards the ground and blow towards the equator as 'Trade Winds'.

In summer, while the sun is directly overhead in the Tropics of Cancer and Capricorn, maximum rainfall shifts to the tropical latitudes. On the other hand, the rising air currents only move to latitudes of 15° and 5°C approximately north and south of the equator and, as a result, a corresponding displacement of the belt of Trade Winds occurs. But in summer and winter the Trade Winds blow in typical fashion over the oceans only. The summer heat of the large land masses causes the monsoon winds, particularly noticeable in East Africa and Asia.

With the exception of East Africa, the equatorial region of the tropical-subtropical zone possesses a warm, constantly moist climate. Annual temperatures vary little with the mean daily average being approximately 25° to 27°C. The region has no clearly definable seasons. Daylight hours also show little variation, the longest days having 12.5 hours of daylight and the shortest 11.5 hours. Thundery downpours occur every day. Maximum rainfall always occurs when the sun is in the zenith—in March/April and in September/October. The vast networks of the Amazon and Congo rivers lie in the equatorial zones of South America and Africa. A belt of tropical, evergreen rain forest is centred on the equator.

Areas with a variable tropical climate border both sides of the equatorial region—the north and the south. Maximum rainfall there also depends on the sun's being in the zenith; thus, the summer's rainy season is succeeded by a dry period in the cooler months. The dry periods become longer the further one moves away from the equator, but never exceed eight months of the year. Daytime hours vary between 10.5 and 13.5 hours. Some waters dry out temporarily. During short dry periods some trees in forests stay evergreen, while others shed their foliage. In prolonged periods of drought forests are bare but become green with the onset of the rainy season. On finely-grained soil forests may disappear altogether, grasses will grow in their place and such areas turn into savannahs.

In the adjoining subtropics, nearer the poles, the length of days varies from nine hours to fifteen hours. The earth's really dry areas are situated here. Owing to a high degree of radiation and a low degreee of air humidity annual as well as daily temperatures fluctuate considerably. Night frosts are not uncommon. If dry periods last for eight to ten months the typical vegetation will consist of sparse, low bushes. Less rainfall still is accompanied by transition to semi-deserts and finally deserts (where no rain may fall for years).

The tropical-subtropical zone is the main region in which aquatic plants have developed and spread, and which are suited for an indoor aquarium.

Cyclones bring rain to the temperate zones during all seasons of the year. Cyclones form in the areas where warm air meets the cold air blowing from the poles. Westerly winds are predominant. In a latitude of 60° daytime lasts from 5.5 to 18.5 hours.

Two main vegetation areas are distinguishable in the regions of the temperate zones immediately bordering the subtropics. These areas are dependent on local conditions of rainfall.

Monsoon regions, particularly the south-eastern part of the Asiatic mainland, are moist with fairly even temperatures. Most of the rainfall occurs in the summer months. Evergreen woods of large-leafed laurel are typical vegetation here.

Several other fringe areas of the temperate zone, e.g. the Mediterranean region and Cape Province in South Africa, are characterised by winter rain released by cyclones blowing through. Winters are mild and frosts are rare. Summers are dry and hot because, at that time, the descending air currents of tropical-subtropical origin are the decisive weather factor. Evergreen forest of small-leafed hardwood trees is a characteristic feature.

In the temperate zone of the Northern Hemisphere the annual amount of rainfall decreases in the secondary chains of mountains the greater their distance from the sea. Towards the centre of a continent summers become hotter and winters colder. Forests with deciduous trees—green in the summer—grow where there is sufficient rainfall and air humidity. In the drier areas treeless steppes take over and, in some parts, semi-deserts and deserts.

In the northern regions summers are moist and cool. Winters last for over six months; they are mild near the sea and cold further inland. Evergreen coniferous forests are a characteristic feature.

Only South America has a temperate zone in the Southern Hemisphere; the other continents do not extend far enough to the south.

In the temperate zone aquatic plants decline noticeably the nearer to the poles they grow. Many species are only able to exist in the wild and cannot be cultivated.

In the arctic zone a low amount of rain falls throughout the year. Most of the raindrops are frozen and fall as snow. Summers are short and cool with daylight up to 24 hours. East winds predominate. Treeless tundra vegetation is typical here. There are no aquatic plants.

On the whole, all plant species can increase their range by dispersal of seeds, spores or inner parts of the plants. At variable speed they can occupy new ground and move away further and further from their main centre of evolution. However, plants can establish themselves only if seeds or spores actually reach a new habitat, and if this offers them suitable environmental conditions. Oceans and mountains may act as insuperable barriers to dispersal. The North American *Elodea canadensis* has found favourable habitats in Europe; however, the plant was brought to Europe by Man.

Some families, which contain aquatic plants, range from the tropical-subtropical zone to the temperate latitudes, e.g. the family of Alismataceae (to which the Amazon sword plants and arrowheads belong). Within the total worldwide distribution some genera of this family grow in limited areas only. Thus the *Echinodorus* species have mainly evolved in the American tropics, but have increased their range to include temperate areas of North and South America. *Echinodorus* species do not occur in any other part of the world. The main centre of development of *Sagittaria* (also belonging to the Alismataceae family) lies in temperate North America, but a few species can be found in South America and Eurasia. Although the *Araceae* family is predominantly tropical in origin it also grows in temperate zones. The *Anubias* (of the same family) are restricted to central west Africa, and *Cryptocoryne* species occur in south-east Asia only. The Aponogetonaceae (lace plants) are purely tropical and have only one genus, *Aponogeton*; its species occur in Africa, Madagascar, south-east Asia and Australia. *Aponogeton* is not found in the tropics of South America.

The genera and species of aquatic plants may make the fullest use of an environment, or they may grow in only small parts of it. In very large areas of distribution uninhabited gaps occur widely. Very scattered occurrence of a species indicates the previous existence of a large community. In recent times Man has often disturbed the balance and brought species into new places, thus considerably extending their original area of distribution. In the secondary areas many of these plants have developed on and in the water into troublesome pests which have to be destroyed.

Habitats

Freshwater and swamps (the latter often in the vicinity of fresh water) are the habitats of most of the higher aquatic plants. The water may be running or stagnant; it may be of natural origin; or it may be artificially created (Ill. 1–6).

The largest still waters are lakes lying in depressed ground and of varying depth. Lakes owe their origin to a variety of causes and receive their water in a number of ways: from rivers flowing into them; from flood water of nearby streams and rivers; from natural springs; from underground wells; and from rainfall. The lake's water does not overflow as some of it evaporates and some is drained away either above or below ground. The depth of a lake, formation of the shore, changes of temperature and nutrients contained in the water are all of major importance for the support of plant life. The quantity of nutrients depends largely on the geological structure of the lake's bottom and the kind of eroded material deposited in it by the waters which feed it. Three basic types are distinguishable.

Most lakes of the plains and hilly country are eutrophic lakes containing plenty of nutrients, particularly nitrogen, phosphates and calcium carbonate. Thus an abundance of plant life has a chance to develop. The water is not very clear because of its high content of plankton and undissolved organic substances. The banks of eutrophic lakes are shallow and provide aquarium plants with good growth conditions. The lake bottom consists of black-brown mud full of dead plankton, decaying plants and animals—all good nutrients for aquatic plants. In the course of time the mud stratum increases in volume resulting in a state of over-nourishment. The continually working process of decay uses up much oxygen so that the depths of lakes are extremely poor in oxygen.

From the shallow shores to the middle of the lake distinctive vegetation zones may be observed, the basic scheme of which can be seen in Ill. 2. The zones are formed according to the depth of the water. The lake fills up increasingly with organic matter, vegetation advances from the shore to the open water and, finally, the lake becomes silted up.

Submerged plants grow in the innermost zone—especially the stoneworts. But other plants—higher in the morphological scale—also grow in the inner zone, e.g. *Potamogeton* and *Najas* species, *Zanichellia*, *Ceratophyllum* and *Elodea*. The *Potamogeton* species send strong runners into the substrate which can make it rather solid. The plants often form a dense growth, rather like submerged meadows, but plant shoots may tear off and drift elsewhere.

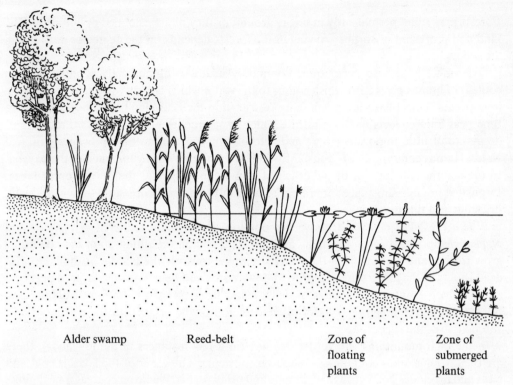

Alder swamp   Reed-belt   Zone of   Zone of
floating   submerged
plants   plants

2 Eutrophic lake, silting-up

Plants with floating leaves live in the next zone—landwards—, beginning at a water depth of 2 m. Tubers or rhizomes keep most of them firmly rooted in the mud. Various water weeds also occur in the zone, but *Nymphaea* and *Nuphar* species are especially common. Other plants which do well here are: *Nymphoides*, *Potamogeton* and *Myriophyllum*.

The third zone is the reed-belt with its most typical member, *Phragmites communis* or the common reed, having worldwide distribution. As the reed has very strong shoots and runners it develops extremely dense growth. The blades have a high cellulose content, are hard, decompose slowly and develop a kind of thatch. In parts of the reed-belt other plants may gain dominance, e.g. species of the genus *Typha*. Species of *Sagittaria*, *Alisma*, *Sparganium*, *Juncus*, *Carex*, *Cyperus* and *Lythrum* are all characteristic for the reed-belt zone. Between the second and third zone, and amongst the reeds, floating plants live. *Stratiotes aloides* is one of them; species of *Hydrocharis*, *Limnobium* and *Lemna* are others.

In the temperate zone a bog-forest community grows around the water-logged borders of the lake but beyond the reed thatch. Most of the trees are alders, many are willows. Palms, tropical trees and shrubs (Pandanaceae) grow around tropical-subtropical lakes.

Forests may stand permanently in boggy ground or they may be flooded periodically. The kind and profusion of shrubs growing in the forests depends on the degree of moisture in the soil.

Dystrophic lakes also occur quite commonly in low-lying and hilly country. A high content of humus gives a brownish colour to the water which is somewhat acid and lacking in nutrients. Thus plants are much more restricted in their development. Over a period of time peat mud collects in the substrate which is also deficient in nutrients. Processes of decay are of little importance here as micro-organisms cannot develop properly in acid water. Humus compounds are constantly laid down, thereby using up much of the oxygen. In the end the substrate of the lakes is just as poor in oxygen as that of eutrophic lakes. Deposited organic substances are rarely re-used in biological processes. Humus gradually dries out and fills in the lakes.

Where the lakes described above are not too deep, thinly scattered *Nymphaea* and *Nuphar* plants live. Peat mosses play an important part in the silting-up of the lake; they grow further and further from the water's margins towards the middle of the lake. The dead shoots of the mosses are compressed downwards and help to form a layer of peat bog (Ill. *3*) which eventually increases in density and firmness. More developed plants then often colonize the area, e.g. species of sundew and oxalic grasses. In the end moorland will take over the succession.

In the high mountains, above the tree line (in a few instances in the lowlands), there are oligotrophic lakes containing even fewer nutrients. The water of the lakes is cold and clear and precludes good growth of aquatic and other plants. Plankton content is negligible, which is one of the reasons why visibility in the water is good. The substratum is poor in decaying matter as little organic production takes place, and is almost wholly lacking in nitrogen and phosphates. Decaying processes cannot really develop so that even the depth of such lakes is rich in oxygen.

The only plants which grow in the water and on the borders of these lakes are simple and unproductive, e.g. some species of *Isoetes* and *Elatine* as well as the narrow-leafed varieties of the genus *Potamogeton*; *Eleocharis acicularis*; *Subularia aquatica*, and a few others. The lakes stay open, and silting-up is barely noticeable.

Another type of still water is found in the old beds of rivers situated in the fertile meadows adjoining large rivers. Such waters are rich in plant life. The old river beds are bends of former rivers in places where they have either separated naturally from the rivers or where the rivers have been artificially straightened. In the tropical-subtropical zone there are lakes alongside tidal stretches of rivers; the lake-water ebbs away slowly but fills up at high tide. A floating cover of vegetation is characteristic for the lakes. The vegetation develops from the shores towards the centre of the lake, a large part of which consists of *Eichhornia azurea*, *Hydrocleis nymphoides*, *Ludwigia* species and grasses. Floating plants settle within the plant cover, among them *Eichhornia crassipes*, *Pistia*, *Salvinia* and *Azolla* species. Beneath the dense vegetation cover of the water submerged plants cannot really develop.

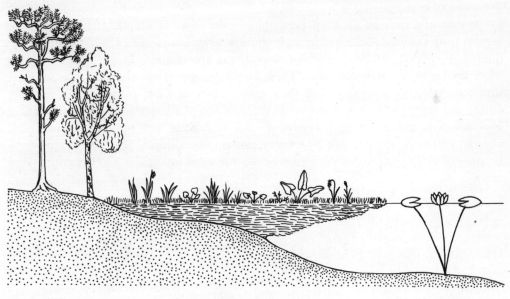

Groves of birch and pine   Mossy floating meadow   Zone of floating plants

3 Dystrophic lake, silting-up

Small and shallow ponds offer special growth conditions. In dry weather the water shrinks and may dry out completely, while in periods of cold the pond may freeze right down to the bottom. Daily temperatures fluctuate greatly. Concentration of nutrients in a pond varies according to the amount of water it holds. Decayed organic substances are either absorbed from the surrounding area or they may be flooded in. Small plants, e.g. *Limosella aquatica* which complete their life style rapidly are typical for ponds.

Many waters are artificially created. Among them are the many park and fish ponds, reservoirs and residual waters of surface mining. Rice paddies also belong to the artificial still waters.

Running water offers different life conditions from still water. The temperature of running water is more evenly balanced, and seasonal extremes are far less pronounced. Oxygen and nutrients are often more favourable in running than in still water. Plant organisms, however, have to be able to withstand the current with a minimum effort. Generally, interwoven strong roots keep them firmly embedded in the ground and the plants often develop narrow, strap-like leaves.

The names used for running waters are brooks, streams and rivers according to their size. However, no definite limits are expressed by these terms. Rivers draw their water from melting ice of glaciers or from a source in the mountains, or, in the tropical-subtropical zone, from the swamps of the plains enriched by heavy rainfall. Rivers either flow into the sea or into a lake.

The flow of a river or stream depends largely on its water supply. The latter may be derived from thawing glacier water, underground water at source and, additionally, from rainfall. In periods of irregular rainfall or thaws (particularly in the mountains) the water level is subject to fluctuations. These may be irregular, but often are in accordance with the climate of a region. Thus there may be definite times of high and low water during the year. In the lower course of the Amazon the water level has variations of as much as 10 metres in the course of a year. In regions with regular seasons of dry and rainy periods, streams and rivers may contain water during the rainy season only. In areas of extreme drought rivers may be dry for years before the water begins to flow again.

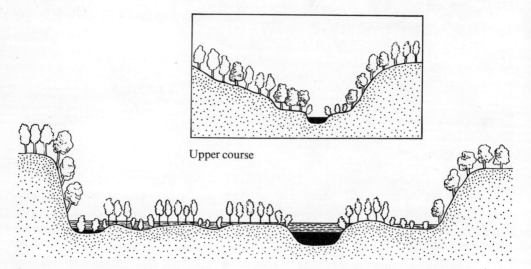

Upper course

Lower course

4 River in the temperate zone, unchanged by man (low water black, high water lineated)

The headwaters of rivers are clear and transparent as the strength of the current does not allow floating organic matter to be retained. Shallow river waters are grey-brown or ochre in colouring because they have absorbed loam and loess at source and carried it downriver with the current. Rivers with really dark water have their origins in large swamps of the plains. Humus—decomposed plant material—gives them a brown, yet clear colour.

If the source of a river is in the mountains the young river (or stream) carves deep, narrow valleys through the rock. A fast current and oxygen-rich water are characteristic features of the upper course of rivers. The current carries rocks and pebbles with it; plant growth is therefore impeded in the upper course of a river and is sparse. Willow bushes often accompany it on either side, and beyond these forests begin (Ill. *4*).

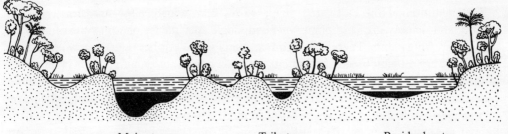

| Main stream | Tributary | Residual water |

5 River in the tropical/subtropical zone (Amazon region) (low water black, high water lineated)

The current of the river has slackened considerably by the time it reaches the lower course so that much of the suspended material the river has carried with it can be deposited. Sand and mud banks occur. Although plant growth is better in the lower than in the upper course of a river it cannot be compared with that of still waters. Abundant vegetation, however, may develop in small, shallow streams.

Lowland forest grows beyond the gravel and alluvial banks of lower river courses in uncultivated areas of the temperate zone (Ill. 4). For a brief period in the spring the river is over-full, silt collects and, thus, nutrients are added to the water. Most months of the year, however, the water level is rather low.

In the tropical-subtropical zone the flooding of the extensive swampy river plains during the rainy season is of utmost importance to the vegetation (as mentioned previously). Much of the sediment the river has carried with it is deposited in the swampy soil at such times. The river banks are often elevated and grown with rows of trees. Lakes lie in depressions beyond the banks, and dense forests occur at some distance from the lakes on higher ground (Ill. 5).

In highly cultivated areas Man's influence on a river system is considerable. Man has smoothed out bends, built up banks and erected dams across rivers. Weirs and various water-retaining basins regulate the course of a river. Canals, drainage and irrigation ditches are artificially created running waters.

All types of water are affected by organic and chemical fertilizers flooding into them. Sewage poses an additional problem.

2. Cultivation of Aquatic Plants

Aquatic plants are kept in home aquaria (Ill. 7–10), planthouses and outdoor ponds (Ill. 11, 12). Additionally, aquatic plants are cultivated in specialized nurseries, botanic gardens and park lakes. Their greatest importance they have gained as aquarium plants is by the considerable spread of aquaristics.

The condition of the cultivated plants varies enormously. One may see abundant, healthy and densely growing plants or good single specimens; one may also find poor, sparsely growing plants. There are, of course, many variations between these two extremes. It is often very difficult indeed to find out the exact causes for either good or poor growth of the plants. Interpretation of observations made should be very cautious, unless meaningful experiments have been carried out first together with investigations of the conditions of an aquarium. It should always be borne in mind that our aquatic plants in their natural habitat are conditioned by a variety of chemical, physical, and also biological factors. These factors all interact and influence each other in a complicated manner. Thus, in the wild, the composition and organic content of the substratum, the chemical constituents of the water, the light and the temperature of the water are all of major importance. Fish, lower animals, micro-organisms, even the plants themselves play a major environmental role. The conditions under which the plants are cultivated naturally differ considerably from those of their natural habitat. A naturalist who observes plants in their natural environment may find that they react very differently when they are being cultivated.

The Substratum

If aquatic and marsh plants are dug up either in still or slowly flowing water their roots are usually rather black and both the roots and the environment of the plants may well smell of hydrogen sulphide—a typical symptom of soil containing no useable oxygen. The plants are able to live under such conditions; they can make use of their inbuilt ventilation system and thus feed their roots with the essential oxygen.

Conditions on which growth depends in an aquarium appear to be different; the reasons are not yet fully known. Plants rooted in the substratum of an aquarium do not thrive if their roots turn black; or it may be said if plants with poor growth are discovered in an aquarium the condition may be caused by black roots. The roots of aquarium plants in a tank are healthy and white only if they are allowed to develop in an oxygen-rich environment. The same applies to all land plants irrespective of their habitat. Good oxygenation of an aquarium substratum is possible only if the latter is sufficiently water permeable and if the water moves a little, however slightly.

On the basis of experiences noted above opinion nowadays is that the substratum of an aquarium should consist of coarse material to fulfil the requirements of good growth conditions. The coarsest sand or fine gravel should be used; grains of 2 mm to a maximum of 5 mm are recommended. The hollow spaces always existing in gravel and coarse sand allow some slight water permeability. To further this some special methods have been developed. If a perforated intermediary stratum is inserted between the tank bottom and the substratum a shallow space is produced beneath the substratum. A filter provides this shallow space with water and creates a slight upward current. A downward current is also possible if suction is applied and water filtered off through the substratum. The method has the advantage of warming the substratum slightly which in itself is good for the plants. Many plants suffer if their roots get cold. The drop in temperature between heated tank water and substrate is mostly higher than one thinks.

The coarse sand or gravel stratum, as described above, contains some hidden dangers. Although it may take years, particularly in large aquaria, the hollow spaces between sand or gravel grains gradually fill up with waste material, such as food remnants, faeces from the fish and decaying plant matter. An assumption that micro-organisms in the gravel dispose of all the dirt has to be contradicted. The amount of decayed matter deposited reaches such a volume that any kind of biological self-purification is impossible. If one does nothing about it the substratum silts up, as a consequence becomes poor in oxygen and, thus, the roots of the plants turn black. The dirt which has settled in the substratum is actually not visible; the aquarium still looks clean. One may put up with the disadvantages and—depending on the number of fish in the tank and the amount of food they are fed—renew the substratum completely after two, three or even four years.

Alternatively, an aquarist may use washed sand for the substratum of his aquarium. If the tank is very small and needs regular, thorough cleansing the use of washed sand may well be the best solution and can be recommended. The rooting cichlids are probably best housed in a tank with a substratum of washed sand. But even in large tanks abundant plant growth has been achieved on a substratum of washed sand although it allows practically no current to pass through it. However, new warming devices have been developed in recent years. Nowadays a heated thin sheet of foil is often placed underneath the tank and its warmth provides much better conditions of temperature and aeration inside the tank. The structure of fine sand is dense so that sediment cannot penetrate and endanger a gravel substratum.

A stratum consisting of two layers has been discussed for use in large aquaria; in that case a layer of washed sand or gravel is put on top of a layer of unwashed sand mixed with some loam. The mineral substances of the bottom layer provide the roots with nutrients. The idea seems to be quite feasible. It has to be remembered, however, that plant roots can only absorb dissolved nutrients. The minerals in the substratum first have to turn into a solution before the plants can take them in as food. The bottom layer of the water can be enriched in other ways, e.g. if the substratum is sufficiently well aerated its nutrients will pass into the bottom layers of the water. In this context it should not be forgotten what concentration gradient exists in an aquarium; it is almost certain that most of the minerals are contained in the substratum; should too many of them get into the tank water this may well become over-enriched. Some aquarists claim that they have furthered the growth of single strong specimens by fertilizing the immediate area of substratum around their roots. Some of the larger *Echinodorus* species apparently react favourably to this treatment for which dried loam pellets and mineral tablets are recommended fertilizers. It should always be borne in mind, however, that submerged plants obtain most—sometimes all of their food requirements through their leaves.

The substratum should be poor in calcium salts so that no water hardening agents can penetrate into the aquarium water. Too much organic waste matter in the substratum makes the water putrid sooner or later. The addition of any earth is therefore not advisable, not even the 'special earth for aquarium plants' or similar products some-times sold in shops. The amount of dirt deposited in the substratum by snails is so little that it is of no importance.

Outdoor ponds benefit from the addition of earth. All kinds of different mixtures have been recommended. One well-proven mixture consists of seasoned compost mould to which approximately one quarter sand and a little peat have been added. The growth of water lilies is furthered if a small amount of seasoned fertilizer is added to the mixture. In large indoor basins—particularly those in which no fish are kept—mixing a little earth with the substratum may be beneficial. The earth provides the plants with nutrients. A substratum has to be renewed more often if it contains earth and not just purely sand or gravel.

The Water

As an immediate environment water has the same importance for submerged or partially submerged plants that air has for land plants. Water is a liquid which, when pure, is without odour and taste; it is also transparent. It freezes solid at 0°C and boils at 100°C when it turns into vapour. It is a poor conductor for electricity.

However, aquarium water is never pure. On the whole, tap water is used for filling a tank, but the water has been artificially treated on its way to the consumer. At the very least it has passed over sand or gravel filters and has had germicidal agents such as chlorine added to it. But even after filtering and chlorination water contains most of the substances that it has taken from underground, flowing or still waters and from the earth. These substances may vary from one region to another. Besides, tap water always contains air; the amount of air depends on the water temperature.

More air is taken in by cold water than by warm. At a temperature of 15°C one litre of water may contain up to 18 ccm of air. If temperature changes occur in an aquarium air or its components are either taken in or expelled, as the case may be. The area of water surface is also important; the larger it is the greater are the changes of air content.

The quality of water depends most of all on certain electrolytes. These are salts, acids and bases which split by dissociation in a watery solution into positively charged cations and negatively charged anions. They are significant, for instance, in all the processes which cause an acid, neutral or alkaline reaction of the water.

The water reaction is expressed in pH. The pH value is influenced by one of the air's components, carbon dioxide (CO_2); it can be taken in by the water from the air directly above it, or the breathing aquatic life forms may produce it in the water itself. Low amounts of carbon dioxide combine with water and turn into carbonic acid (H_2CO_3); the carbonic acid also dissociates. The majority of aquarium plants thrive well with a pH value of 6.2 to 7.5.

Furthermore, an extremely delicate state of balance is formed between the carbon dioxide, the calcium bicarbonate $[Ca(HCO_3)_2]$—dissolved in water, and the calcium carbonate ($CaCO_3$)—insoluble in water. This balance is affected by respiration and photo-synthesis. See page 61.

Other hydrated carbon compounds act as water-hardening agents. Temporary water hardness is usually caused by potassium carbonate (KHCO) and can be removed by boiling the water. Hydromagnesite [$Mg(HCO_3)_2$] causes permanent water hardness which can only be removed chemically. Water hardness is measured by calcium carbonate content. Water with a hardness of up to 80 mg per litre is soft; 100–200 mg per litre is medium-hard, and approximately 300 mg per litre make it hard.

The use of soft water in a tank has made it possible to breed those ornamental fishes which live in soft waters in their natural environment. At one time it was thought that the plants of the same habitat should also be kept in soft water. Experience has proved, however, that nearly all aquarium plants thrive in a tank filled with medium-hard water; actually the plants may grow badly in soft water or even stagnate. Of course, there are exceptions: a few plants are special cases and thrive only in soft water. Such plants cannot be cared for within the plant communities of an aquarium, however hard one tries.

Recently attention has been paid to another factor—the rH value. It is a measurement applied to the amount of oxydization in the water—in this particular case in the aquarium tank. Solutions of various substances exist in the water, such as sulphates, phosphates and chlorides (e.g. sodium chloride) as well as iron and nitrogen compounds. Only traces of other inorganic matter are likely to be found in the water.

The presence of organic substances in the aquarium also needs to be mentioned; they are micro-organisms resulting from decomposing plant matter and food remnants.

The aquarist will see from the above that the water of a tank—but also that of a pool in a planthouse or in a park—is composed of many different chemical and physical ingredients. All components should be evenly balanced, but, to a certain degree, they regulate them-selves. Variation of one factor usually causes change in another. Repiration and photo-synthesis may well undergo fluctuations in the course of a day; the same applies to all vital activities of animals, plants and micro-organisms living in an aquarium. The much larger seasonal changes which occur in a natural environment are eliminated in a heated aquarium. Continual attempts are being made to avoid them in planthouses and outdoor ponds as well.

An aquarist who is keen on experiments might well try to interfere with the precarious equilibrium of his aquarium. He wants to change the pH value and the hardness of the water by filtering it through charcoal, peat or other substances. He adds to the water fertilizers and ion exchange resins and throws 'water improvers' into the tank although he may not even know their composition. He may also add trace elements, vitamins and mineral salts, or weedkillers to get rid of algae. Alternatively he may put all his trust in the use of hydrogen peroxide or other agents. The water has to withstand all this interference and—luckily—it normally does.

Those aquarists who believe that exact measurements of everything are essential are advised to be careful. They should ask themselves whether they have sufficient knowledge of the fluctuating pH value which arises in the course of a day; whether they know of the many mistakes which are made when measuring the rH value. It is certain that a wrong measurement is worse than omitting measurement altogether. The best criterion of good quality tank water is the health and colouration of the fish and thriving plants.

Good aeration, water circulation and sufficient changes of water always create favourable conditions in large and medium-sized aquaria.

The Light

Unless plants are supplied with enough light they cannot grow. Some fish species also depend on light to enable them to breed.

Just like the temperature the light can be measured and regulated more easily than other environmental conditions in the aquarium, e.g. the chemical components of the water. In physical terms, light consists of electro-magnetic radiations of various wavelengths—from 380 nm to 780 nm. Within the spectrum certain wavelengths appear as colours, ranging from red to orange; from yellow and green to blue and violet. The white sunlight or daylight is composed of a mixture of all the spectral colours. However, 'white light' is needed to make the colour impression effective; colours vary in brightness according to the density and strength of certain rays that fall on them. The constituents which make up single colours are shown in Ill. 6. They are subject to variations depending on the time of day and the weather.

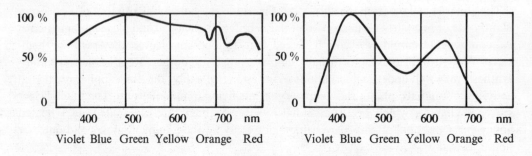

6/7 Share in radiation of the individual wave lengths in daylight (left)
Different degree of absorption in the individual ranges of wave lengths by the green plants (right)

Unlike an aquarium in a home or a planthouse, an outdoor pond has sufficient natural light. In the early days, aquarists used to keep their tanks as near a window as possible so that the maximum amount of daylight could fall on them through the window panes. At the time, a number of aquarium plants suffered badly during the short daylight hours of the winter and were classed as difficult to maintain in the winter. Such observations can still be found in present-day aquarist literature. In former times homes and even botanical gardens had no auxillary source of light for their aquaria. Eventually, artificial light came into usage and, nowadays, it has largely or entirely replaced natural light. Thus, the growth conditions in an aquarium no longer depend on a place near the window; an aquarium may be put wherever it is most decorative in a room (Ill. 8). It is essential that the spectral composition of artificial light resembles sunlight, otherwise fish and plants may develop unnatural colouration. Furthermore, if really good growth is to be promoted illumination should be provided with a similar physiological effect on plant life as sunlight.

Initially, only incandescent lamps were available. Even nowadays they are considered as useful for the illumination of very small aquaria and as an additional source of light for others. They are also effective in highlighting single groups of aquarium plants. The filament of an incandescent lamp becomes hot when a current passes through it; it glows and sends out light. The generated light is a mixture of all the colours, but their wavelengths are subject to slight variations depending on the type and capacity of the bulb. Yellows and reds are usually quite strong; blue and violet rays tend to be rather weak. A large part of the energy of an incandescent lamp is transformed into heat. Such lamps have a life of approximately 1 000 hours.

Nowadays, luminous-discharge lamps are widely used; the tubes contain gases which are induced to radiate. In the main, fluorescent tubes are used for the illumination of an indoor aquarium; they are filled with mercury vapour and their radiation is mainly ultra-violet. Luminescent substances on the inner surface of glass, or inside it, are transformed into visible light. The composition of the radiated spectrum depends on the substances which are used and varies in different types of lamps. With an equal amount of current fluorescent lamps produce three to four times more light energy than incandescent lamps; the former have an average life span of 7,500 hours. Fluorescent lamps give out some red rays; in fact, many produce a light which comes near daylight.

Plants are affected by spectral colours and they absorb these in different ways. The absorption spectrum in Ill. 7 shows that chlorophyll absorbs mainly the blue and orange-red rays of the light. The green rays, on the other hand, are largely reflected which explains the prevalent green colour in plants. With such practical considerations in mind, horticulturists have developed special fluorescent lamps with a spectrum best suited to plant functions. Such lamps are now also used by aquarists. They look darker than others to the human eye because they cut out most of the green and yellow rays; human vision is most light-sensitive to these two colours. The special lamps should only be used in conjunction with other types when illuminating an indoor aquarium.

Light plays a particularly important part in photosynthesis (see page 61) and build-up of chlorophyll. Both processes have to be very satisfactory before plants can thrive properly. Of course, all other conditions for good growth have to be met as well. Experience has proved that certain rays of the spectrum exert a specific physiological influence on plant growth; thus blue-violet rays impede the upward growth of plants whereas red rays further it.

It would not be entirely correct to say that a plant species can only thrive under specific light conditions. Advice given for the cultivation of species is therefore rather generalized. To a certain degree—although optimum growth is always reached at some stage—plants can always adapt to their environment, including light intensity. In a natural habitat strong, well-growing competitors may reduce other plants from optimim to minimum growth. It has been reported several times that Cryptocorynes have been found growing in small streams in dense woodland shade. Cryptocorynes need good light for optimum development, but they are able to adapt to poor light when necessary.

The aquarium plants themselves provide the best answer to the adequacy of lighting. If they grow well, propagate easily and show a healthy amount of green, then they prove that they are supplied with sufficient illumination. A few plants, of course, may be exceptional and not fit in. A seasoned aquarist, well versed in techniques, may wish to measure the amount of lighting in his tank; he will need a lux or an exposure meter to do this. Anyone who wants to familiarize himself with measurement methods should look up specialized literature. Many experiments and observations have been conducted; it has been ascertained that in an aquarium with a depth of 20 cm to 60 cm which is lit by daylight fluorescent tubes, the best illumination value for submerged plants lies between 600 and 2,000 lux. Thereby, the following rule of thumb is arrived at:

Lamp energy output in watt = basin content in litres $\cdot$ 0.25.

A number of factors may cause of light; light is lost when it falls on the glass-cover of a tank and is reflected and absorbed by it; with increasing water depth light is also absorbed and again some of it is lost, particularly if the water is slightly yellow after having been filtered through peat. However, the amount of light loss due to a glass-cover is insignificant and it is not necessary to do without a cover, notwithstanding many conflicting opinions. It is worthwhile to consider the advantages of a properly constructed reflector which directs the lamps' illumination as far as possible into the tank.

In any case, all lighting equipment has to be correctly mounted if the plants are to receive the maximum benefit from the illumination. Where the equipment is not adjusted properly some of the light might miss the tank altogether, or else leave it through the glass panes. Expert literature contains many notes for the construction of reflectors.

The ideas put forward above also apply to planthouses; it seems sensible to illuminate their aquaria from mid-October to end-February. However, the necessary expenditure on lighting installation is definitely higher as only fittings suited to moist-warm spaces can be used. There are a number of different types of lamps on the market.

In spring and summer the daylight is too strong and the aquarium has to be shaded from excessive light. The glass-panes are often painted with a colour for the purpose. Otherwise, dense floating plants provide a good screen from too much light, and it is quite easy to keep them in order.

Daily period of illumination and its influence on aquatic and marsh plants: see page 67.

The Temperature

Temperature requirements of aquarium plants result primarily from the conditions of their natural environment; few data relating to the latter are known, particularly as regards existing fluctuations. Tropical waters may have temperatures which are constant and fairly high throughout the year, whereas subtropical waters may be subject to considerable seasonal variations. In the mountains of the tropics and the subtropics the water temperature is decidedly lower than in the plains. Daily variations of temperature occur mainly in small and shallow still waters.

The aquarist has to work out the temperature best suited to the fish he keeps and make the choice of his plants accordingly. He will find, however, that the plants are able to withstand varying degrees of temperature. Therefore, in the notes on how to keep the various species only approximate temperatures are quoted.

The plants themselves provide the best proof as to whether the temperature suits them; of course other conditions for healthy growth must also be fulfilled. Favourable temperature can be effective only if the other conditions vital to the plants are met, e.g. the correct amounts of nutrients and light.

If the temperature is too low the growth of the plants will be stunted and leaves will disintegrate; in prolonged periods of low temperature the plants will die. The effect of too high a temperature is similar to that of having too little light. For instance, plants with attenuated shoots develop elongated internodes while the nodes themselves grow very small leaves only.

In general, it may be stated that cold-water plants of the temperate zone thrive well in summer in temperatures of 18°C to 20°C. Many North American species do well in a home aquarium with a somewhat higher temperature. Although a number of species are distributed in Europe and Asia, not many of them have been cultivated and, therefore, not much is known about them. Plants with a tropical and subtropical origin thrive best in a temperature of at least 20°C, but many are not hurt by a temporarily lower temperature. Water should be approximately 25°C for plants sensitive to cold. To go above 30°C serves little purpose.

Planting

How to plant an aquarium depends on its function or—rather—on the fish which are to be kept in it. In a breeding tank fine-leaved, feathery species like *Limnophila* and *Myriophyllum* should be planted in clumps to provide the fish with a spawning site, unless the breeder falls back on an artificial spawning medium. Some aquarium plants—not necessarily rooted in the bottom—e.g. species of *Najas* and *Elodea* grow into dense thickets and are used in breeding tanks for viviparous cyprinoids (fish akin to carp). The burrowing cichlids destroy all but the hardiest plants; therefore, the tanks in which they are kept should be planted with solitary strong specimens, perhaps species of the genus *Echinodorus* which may be put into the tank in pots and protected further by placing stones around them. In an unheated aquarium only the species which are adapted to cold water conditions can be cultivated.

Most home aquaria are meant to represent a small living community; they are also very decorative and should fit in well with the furnishings of a room. An effect often desired is achieved nowadays by the so-called 'Dutch Aquarium' (Ill. 9, 10); aquarists often try to plant their tanks in the same or, at least, a very similar way by clever grouping of a variety of species. The latter should harmonize with each other in size, growth habits, leaf characteristics and colours. Slender, tall plants fill the background and the sides, whereas medium-sized plants spread out towards the middle region of the tank. The effect is made to look more fluid by arranging a few groups of slightly taller plants amongst the medium-sized plants and—depending on the size of aquarium—one or two large single specimens are placed where they catch the eye. Short plants fill the foreground, usually they develop runners. Attractive stones and pieces of wood may be placed in the aquarium to increase its beauty.

When planting an aquarium one should have a plan in mind. It is a good idea to take pencil and paper and make an approximate sketch. Aquarist magazines and literature contain many interesting hints and ideas. Some planting designs are reproduced in Ill. 8. The planner of a design must bear in mind the characteristics and requirements of the various species. An aquarium planted according to a plan will always need adjustments later on. The weaker the growth of the plants the less attention they will need. Upwards-striving plants need more care than those that form rosette-like clusters on the bottom.

Of course, an aquarium does not have to be planted with a large variety of species. A lovely effect can be achieved by the planting of just one genus, e.g. species of *Cryptocoryne* or, even, *Ludwigia*. Alternatively, two or three different species may be used. There is not much sense in selecting plants according to their geographical habitat. Formerly aquarists recommended that an aquarium be planted with purely South American, or African, or south-east Asian varieties.

Another custom—now dated—was to put the substratum into the tank, add the technical aids and possible decorations, and then plant it. The water was to be added last of all over a piece of paper well spread out. But, however carefully the aquarist proceeded, some of the plants always floated to the surface. Therefore, the aquarium should be planted after it has been filled with water; the plants are far more likely to stay firmly attached to the substratum. Besides, water has a foreshortening optical effect and the attractiveness of plant arrangement can be gauged more accurately if the tank has first been filled with water.

Roots should be removed as far as possible before planting and no more than are needed should be left for anchorage in the ground. It has been noticed that after planting all old roots die and that they are replaced by adventitious roots. The old dead roots cause unnecessary decay. Where cuttings are used at least one node should be put into the substratum after first removing all its leaves. As a rule it is these nodes which form new roots. As experience has shown it is also advantageous to anchor the base of cuttings to the substratum

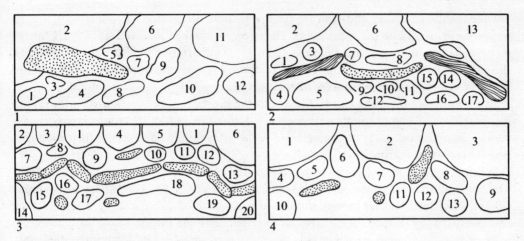

8 Schemes for planting home aquaria (1 and 2 after Schöpfel) (rockwork dotted, wood hatched)

Scheme 1

1 *Ludwigia arcuata*, 2 *Vallisneria gigantea*, 3 *Isoetes malinverniana*, 4 *Cryptocoryne nevillii*, 5 *Aponogeton ulvaceus*, 6 *Cryptocoryne blassii*, 7 *Hydrocotyle leucocephala*, 8 *Cryptocoryne petchii*, 9 *Peplis diandra*, 10 *Echinodorus latifolius*, 11 *Echinodorus major*, 12 *Myriophyllum ussuriense*

Scheme 2

1 *Myriophyllum brasiliense*, 2 *Vallisneria spiralis*, 3 *Echinodorus amazonicus*, 4 *Aponogeton crispus*, 5 *Echinodorus tenellus*, 6 *Nomaphila corymbosa*, 7 *Cryptocoryne aponogetifolia*, 8 *Hygrophila polysperma*, 9 *Cryptocoryne wendtii*, 10 *Lysimachia nummularia*, 11 *Cryptocoryne beckettii*, 12 *Cryptocoryne nevillii*, 13 *Microsorium pteropus*, 14 *Limnophila sessiliflora*, 15 *Samolus valerandi*, 16 *Eleocharis acicularis*, 17 *Aponogeton crispus*

Scheme 3

1 *Sagittaria subulata*, 2 *Hydrocotyle leucocephala*, 3 *Rotala rotundifolia*, 4 *Limnophila aquatica*, 5 *Ludwigia repens*, 6 *Hygrophila polysperma*, 7 *Bacopa amplexicaulis*, 8 *Micranthemum micranthemoides*, 9 *Alternanthera sessilis*, 10 *Anubias congensis*, 11 *Lagarosiphon madagascariensis*, 12 *Hydrocotyle verticillata*, 13 *Rotala wallichii*, 14 *Vallisneria spiralis*, 15 *Cryptocoryne petchii*, 16 *Isoetes setacea*, 17 *Marsilea crenata*, 18 *Echinodorus tenellus*, 19 *Cryptocoryne nevillii*, 20 *Heteranthera zosteraefolia*

Scheme 4

1 *Cryptocoryne retrospiralis*, 2 *C. blassii*, 3 *C. pontederiifolia*, 4 *C. legroi*, 5 *C. spiralis*, 6 *C. wendtii*, 7 *C. costata*, 8 *C. petchii*, 9 *C. lucens*, 10 *C. nevillii*, 11 *C. lingua*, 12 *C. balansae*, 13 *C. parva*

with the aid of thin glass rods. New roots can then actively penetrate into the substratum; the danger of decay caused by decomposing roots of damaged plants is thus eliminated. Rhizomes and tubers can be pushed into the ground with the fingers. Tweezers are a useful aid for planting cuttings and delicate plants; if these are gripped at the base it is easy to pull them gently into the substratum. The tweezers are then removed sideways. Contrary to earlier opinions planting depth is of no great importance. Whilst they are growing the plants themselves adjust their roots to the most favourable position. Some ferns, however, should not have the axes of their shoots covered by the substratum.

In a planthouse the basin can be filled with the substratum or, alternatively, the plants can be cultivated in appropriate pots or dishes. Decorative values are of minor importance here as the owner is usually more interested in the preservation of species or their propagation for economic reasons.

When a pond is planted it is worthwhile to study first some of the specialist literature. The scope of design is enormous; it depends, of course, on the size and shape of the pond (Ill. 11, 12). Small garden ponds should be well-sheltered from wind and should face southwards. They should not be exposed to bright sunshine for the whole day; however, trees or bushes growing on either side generally provide adequate temporary shade, although care should be taken with deciduous trees and shrubs which drop their leaves and pollute the water. Reeds and free spaces should alternate around the edges. It is also a good idea to construct the pond with a double rim (Ill. 9) in which the marsh plants have a chance to develop.

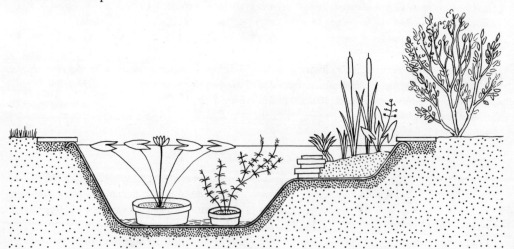

9 Profile of a garden pond

If the water is at least one metre in depth the pond will not freeze right through to the bottom, even in prolonged and severe winters. In that case it is not necessary to drain the water, provided the sides of the pond are slanted. Shallower ponds have to be emptied in autumn. A number of plants can be wintered outside as long as the pond is protected with a good layer of foliage. Other plants have to be removed and kept in water in a cool place until springtime. Appropriate advice is given in the descriptions of the various species.

1 Natural habitat of a *Limnophila* species on the Island Phuket in southern Thailand
2 Natural habitat of *Barclaya longifolia* on the Island Phuket in southern Thailand

3 Natural habitat of aquatic plants on Cuba showing a species of *Eichhornia*
4 Natural habitat of *Cryptocoryne siamensis* in southern Thailand
5 Rice paddies on Hokkaido, Japan
6 Rice cultivation in the Botanic Garden of Halle (Saale), GDR, showing *Hygrophila polysperma* as a rice field weed

7 and 8   Aquarium in a living room
9 and 10 Section of a Dutch aquarium

11 Fairly large garden pond in concrete
12 Smallish garden pond lined with synthetic material
13 *Salvinia natans* and *Hydrocharis morsus-ranae*
14 *Microsorium pteropus*

15 *Ranunculus lingua*
16 *Euryale ferox*

3. Anatomy of Aquatic Plants

Apart from the few simple mosses, aquatic plants consist of three basic organic parts: axis of the shoot, leaf and root. Axis of the shoot and leaves may be termed comprehensively as 'shoot'. Both differentiate from the shoot vegetation cone which they have in common

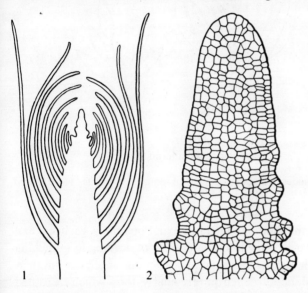

10 Vegetation cone
of *Elodea canadensis*

1 Schematic longitudinal section through tip of shoot with vegetation cone initially enclosed protectively by the young leaves, 2 longitudinal section through the tip of the vegetation cone with beginning leaf formation, cellular

(Ill. *10*). The root, on the other hand, grows from its own root vegetation cone. The great variety of our aquarium plants is mainly due to the differences in build and proportion of these three basic organs.

Shoot

The axis of the shoot develops either in the air, or in water or in the soil. Its growth is vertical to horizontal. It is composed of knobs or nodes (where the leaves spring from the stem), and interjacent knobs called internodes. It is mainly the length of the internodes which determines the habit of aquatic plants (Ill. *11*). Very elongated internodes effect attenuated growth of the plant; the latter's axis of the shoot is clearly visible and the leaves are positioned at some distance from each other. *Hygrophila polysperma* is an example of this type. If, on the other hand, the internodes are compressed, the axis of the shoot is not visible as its base is concealed by densely positioned leaves, e.g. *Echinodorus* and *Cryptocoryne* species.

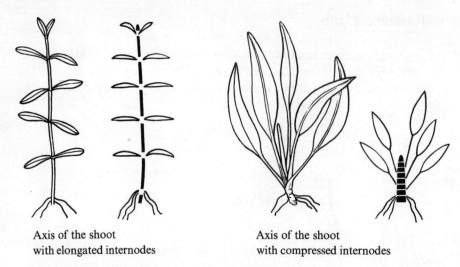

Axis of the shoot
with elongated internodes

Axis of the shoot
with compressed internodes

11 Influence shown by length of internodes on the character of aquarium plants, natural and
schematic representation

The angle between leaf and axis of the shoot is called leaf axil. Potentially, each leaf axil
is capable of producing a bud which may grow into a lateral shoot, leading to branching
of the mother shoot. The degree of branching varies greatly from one species to another.
As a rule, aquatic plants with elongated shoots branch quite regularly; those which are rooted
in the bottom develop a bushy growth while floating species grow into a dense mat. A number of cultivated aquatic plants with a compressed shoot axis rarely develop lateral shoots.
However, they often possess dormant buds—important for artificial propagation (see
page 68). It has been established that two different types of branching exist. In one type
the vegetation cone of a shoot continues its growth provided it is not disturbed; all lateral
shoots are then subordinate to the mother shoot, and flowers and inflorescences appear
at the side of the leaf axil. Flowering *Ludwigia* species serve as a good example. In the other
type, the vegetation cone of a shoot stops growing after some time; it either dies or loses
strength after producing one flower or one interflorescence. The mother shoot is replaced
and overgrown by a lateral shoot. Flowering *Cryptocoryne* species exemplify this type
of branching (Ill. *12*).

At some distance from the vegetation cone its undifferentiated divisible cells reach a state
of permanency. They take over certain functions, each of them being determined by the
position of the shoot axis, and thus their final morphological shape is attained.

All youngish shoot axes are enclosed by an epidermis consisting of one layer. The cells
of the epidermis are either united in a coherent manner, or they may be notched together
irregularly. In land plants the epidermis has the function of keeping out bacteria and
reducing loss of water vapour; in submerged plants, however, the epidermis must not hinder
an exchange of material. Thus, a so-called cuticular layer—a wax-like secretion—is deposit-

ed on top of the epidermis. In land plants the cuticular layer varies in thickness according to the habitat of the plant; in submerged plants it forms only an extremely delicate skin. The epidermis of aerial shoots is interrupted by small pores or stomata needed for regulation of water vapour and the exchange of gaseous matter. Apart from some aquatic plants, the epidermis cells contain no granules of chlorophyll.

A primary wall of fundamental tissue joins the epidermis on the inside. The fundamental tissue cells are very thin-walled; in most cases they are coated with a thin layer of protoplasm; they also possess sufficient space for the cell sap. The cells of the outer layer of coating contain granules of chlorophyll which explains the normally green colouration of young shoots. Aerial shoots most of all need pliability for bending strength; they possess varying amounts of mechanical tissue, often with noticeably thickened cell walls. Older shoots are normally enclosed by a secondary wall consisting of cork cells which replaces the epidermis. The presence of cork cells is responsible for the brownish colouration of rhizomes of the larger *Echinodorus* species.

The inner area of a shoot axis is characterised by a particular arrangement of conducting tissues; these carry the water, organic and inorganic substances. The vascular tissue cells combine to form vascular bundles. A cross-section of an aerial shoot of herbaceous, dicotyledonous plants shows that the arrangement of their vascular bundles is ring-shaped. When viewing a cross-section of an aerial shoot of a monocotyledonous plant one can see

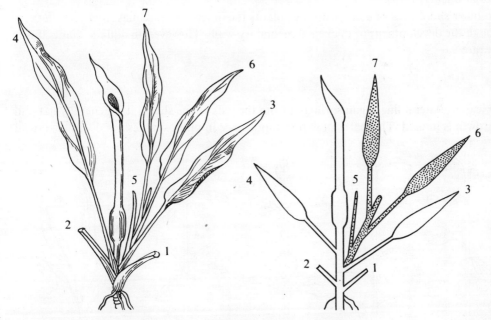

12 Formation of a terminal inflorescence and continuation of the shoot system by a lateral shoot with characteristic bract in *Cryptocoryne*. Natural representation (left); schematic representation (right) (lateral shoot dotted, leaves numbered for comparison)

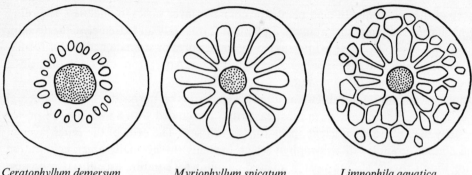

Ceratophyllum demersum   Myriophyllum spicatum   Limnophila aquatica

13 Schematic representation of the arrangement of vascular tissue (dotted) and aeration ducts shown in
   cross section of submerged shoot axes

that the vascular bundles have an uneven distribution. If the vascular bundles contain a
limited area of fundamental tissue it is referred to as pith; an occasional central cavity in
the fundamental tissue is called a pith cavity. Tensile strength is essential for shoots
growing submerged in water; their fundamental tissues unite into a central vascular strand.
In a cross-section of such shoots one can see the importance of more or less extensive
vascular ducts (Ill. 13).

   In older shoot axes of dicotyledonous plants the inner structure may alter considerably
through the development of thickened secondary walls. However, in aquatic plants this is
very rare.

Leaf

The leaf is a lateral line organ springing from the axis of the shoot; it is generally flat and
its growth is limited. The leaf is of major importance in photosynthesis and—in terrestrial

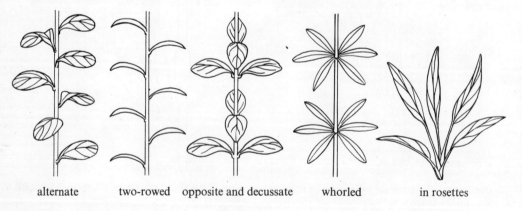

    alternate   two-rowed   opposite and decussate   whorled   in rosettes

14 Leaf arrangement

plants—it regulates loss of water vapour. It also has other functions such as food storage, and it may form reproductive cells.

Phyllotaxis is the name given to the arrangement of leaves in the nodes of the shoot (Ill. *14*). On an elongated shoot axis the leaf arrangement shows an alternate pattern. In that case each node develops one leaf and the angle between the leaves of every two nodes is always specific, often taking up two fifths of a plant's circumference. An alternate leaf arrangement is rare in aquatic plants, but it does occur in some, e.g. *Lobelia cardinalis*. A two-ranked, alternate leaf arrangement is a special phenomenon; here the angle between leaves of each two nodes is always 180°. The leaves are positioned on the shoot axis in two exactly opposite longitudinal lines as with *Potamogeton* species. Many aquatic plants

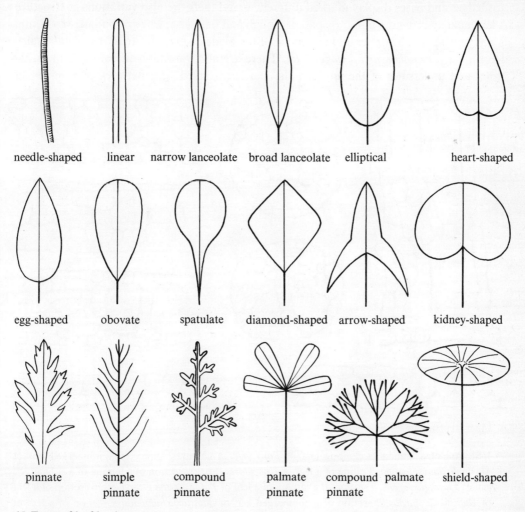

| needle-shaped | linear | narrow lanceolate | broad lanceolate | elliptical | heart-shaped |

| egg-shaped | obovate | spatulate | diamond-shaped | arrow-shaped | kidney-shaped |

| pinnate | simple pinnate | compound pinnate | palmate pinnate | compound palmate pinnate | shield-shaped |

15 Form of leaf laminae

have a decussate and opposite leaf arrangement; each node produces two leaves, opposite to each other and forming an angle of 90° with the leaves of neighbouring nodes. Examples for a decussate and opposite leaf arrangement are found in the genera *Hygrophila* and *Ludwigia*. If three or more leaves develop from one node they form a whorl, e.g. genus *Myriophyllum* and species of *Limnophila* (Ill. *40*). On a compressed shoot axis the leaves are positioned close to each other; they are arranged like rosettes.

The most common leaf—often referred to as foliage leaf—occurs in a large variety of sizes and shapes. The foliage leaf is composed of three main parts: the leaf-blade or lamina; the stalk or petiole; the leaf-base or sheath. The lamina constitutes the actual leaf area which may have many different aspects (Ill. *15*). Apart from a characteristic outline, the lamina tips, edges and bases display marked differences and there are also variations in structure. A lamina may be tender and transparent; tough and flattened; wavy or bullate. If a lamina is wavy or bullate the upper and underside of the blade displays protrusions (usually fairly dense), e.g. *Cryptocoryne aponogetifolia*. There are also variations in colouration on the upper and undersides of the lamina. The leaf is traversed by a network of veins which

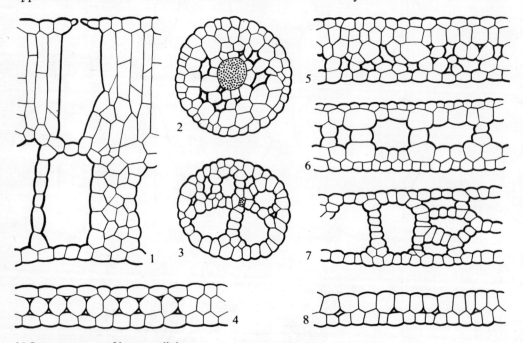

16 Inner structure of leaves, cellular

1 Section of a lamina of floating leaf of *Potamogeton natans*, 2 pinna of a submerged leaf of *Myriophyllum spicatum*, 3 pinna of a leaf of *Utricularia* spec., 4 Section of a lamina of a submerged leaf of *Ludwigia repens*, 5 section of a lamina of a leaf of *Potamogeton gramineus*, 6 section of a leaf of *Vallisneria spiralis*, 7 section of a submerged leaf of *Sagittaria subulata*, 8 section of a leaf of *Elodea canadensis*

encompass the vascular bundles. In the group of plants possessing only one cotyledon a distinct midrib is flanked by pronounced, longitudinal, parallel veins. In dicotyledonous plants transverse veins branch off from the midrib. The length of the petiole can be very variable. It may be missing altogether in the leaves of some aquatic plants or, if the leaves are elongated and tapering at the base, the petiole may be just perceptible. A leaf without a petiole is often referred to as a sessile leaf. On the other hand, the leaf-base may be of minor importance and appear as an elongation and broadening of the petiole. In some marsh and aquatic plants the leaf-base is so distinctly sheath-like in form that it is not always as discernible from the petiole as in *Cryptocoryne* species. Such sheaths also fulfil another function; they enclose and protect the succeeding young leaves for a time. The peltiphyllum is a special type of foliage leaf; its petiole is positioned approximately in the middle of the leaf underside. Examples for this type of leaf are seen in *Nelumbo* and some *Hydrocotyle* species.

Some leaves are modified and deviate from the characteristic foliage leaf, e.g. scale leaves—often found on runners; bracts positioned near inflorescences; and—finally—the flower petals which are really transformed and modified leaves.

There is a definite link between the habitat of a plant and the structure of its foliage leaves. If an environment offers stable water conditions the leaves are usually composed of an upper epidermis, palisade and spongy tissue, and a lower epidermis. Dense, longish cells constitute the palisade tissue; the spongy tissue has a loose and porous structure. The cells of the spongy tissue are irregular in shape, and the tissue contains cavities. Chlorophyll is not present in either the upper or the lower epidermis; the lower epidermis possesses some localised stomata. Some evidence of this structure is noticeable in floating leaves (although here the stomata are embedded in the upper epidermis) (Ill. *16*.1.) and the water leaves of those plants which grow primarily in marshes (Ill. *16*.4.).

Typical water leaves do not possess any stomata, but the cells of their epidermis layers contain grains of chlorophyll. The inner structure of water leaves displays two tendencies.

17 Different types of leaves
of *Sagittaria sagittifolia*

1 Tip of a submerged leaf
2 Lamina of a floating leaf
3 Lamina of an aerial leaf

One is a retrogressive metamorphosis of the palisade and sponge parenchyma which makes the leaves thinner (Ill. *16*.5.) until, finally, only the two epidermis layers are left, e.g. the water-weed family (Ill. *16*.8). The other is a distinctive development of air spaces (Ill. *16*.2, *16*.3, *16*.6. and *16*.7).

Many marsh plants adapt well to a submerged habit; it is characteristic for them that they are heterophyllous, i.e. that they are able to bear leaves of different forms dependent on how they grow. This phenomenon is unknown to many aquarists as they only cultivate their plants submerged. The heterophyllous habits of a plant show quite clearly when it develops submerged, floating, and aerial leaves in certain conditions. Thus, *Sagittaria* species often develop slender, linear submerged leaves, but their floating and aerial leaves are distinctly divided into petiole and blade (Ill. *17*). The leaves of many dicotyledons tend to become pointed and feathery when floating; *Limnophila aquatica* is a fair example. Occasionally, plants produce leaves with different blades if they grow submerged, e.g. *Echinodorus berteroi* and *Hygrophila difformis* (Ill. 98).

Root

Although the root is axial in construction it lacks the leaves of the shoot axis. Generally, roots develop in the soil, but they may also form in the water and in the air. Roots not only absorb water and minerals; they also provide the plants with firm anchorage in the soil. Occasionally the roots take over the function of a storehouse for nutrients.

When a seed germinates, the primary root or radicle (already present in the embryo) develops first. In a number of dicotyledonous plants the main root throws out subsidiary roots; these branch, become fibrous and eventually form the whole root system. Other dicotyledonous plants develop additional, adventitious roots in the axis of the shoot. Most aquarium plants belong to the latter category. The primary root often dies at a later stage. Monocotyledons always have a short-lived primary root which is replaced by adventitious roots. Ferns have adventitious roots only. For the aquarist it is invaluable that the plants have the habit of forming adventitious roots. Thus various methods of asexual propagation are possible, e.g. the use of cuttings for growing new plants. All roots growing from newly planted rhizomes or nodules develop adventitious roots. Buds form on the roots of some plants, e.g. *Microsorium* and may develop into adventitious plants.

The root grows by means of a vegetation cone protected by a special covering—the root cap (Ill. *18*.1). The younger sections of the root are enclosed by a one-layered rhizodermis (epidermis of the root). It differs from the epidermis of the shoot axis and the leaves in that it has very thin cell walls and lacks a cuticular layer as well as any stomates. Slightly behind the vegetation cone root hairs develop; they embed themselves in the soil surrounding them and support water and mineral absorption. Rhizodermis and root hairs die at a fairly early stage to be replaced by a cortical layer formed from cells which have become suberose. The cortical layer consists predominantly of fundamental tissue cells; in marsh and aquatic plants it may be crossed by ventilation ducts (Ill. *18*.2). The skin of the vertically

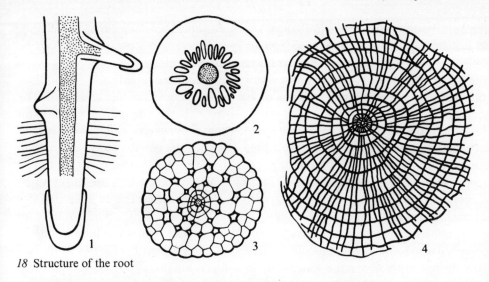

18 Structure of the root

1 Schematic diagram of longitudinal section through a young root with root cap, area of root hair and beginning lateral root formation, 2 schematic diagram of a cross section of a root of *Stratiotes aloides*, 3 cross section of root of *Vallisneria spiralis*, cellular, showing reduced central vascular strand, 4 cross section of a respiratory root of *Ludwigia adscendens*, cellular, showing highly developed aeration tissue

upwards-growing respiratory roots of many *Ludwigia* species is made up almost entirely of spongy respiratory tissue (Ill. *18*.4). A central cylinder is situated immediately below the epidermis of the root. Lateral roots form in the outermost layer of cells of the central cylinder and branch off. Thus, they develop in direct contrast to lateral shoots, lateral roots having to push their way through the epidermis of the root (Ill. *18*.1). The central cylinder is mainly composed of the vascular bundle of the root. It may be very reduced in plants with a permanently submerged habit (Ill. *18*.3). The roots of many dicotyledons develop a secondary growth in thickness which causes considerable changes in their original structure. In aquatic plants this is of little importance.

Some aquatic plants, e.g. *Ceratophyllum*, *Utricularia* and *Wolffia* are rootless.

Habit

Different lengths of internodes, specific arrangements of leaves and their shape plus the degree of dependence on water determine the habits of the various aquatic plants.

The specimens shown in the top row of Ill. *19* illustrate plants whose shoot axis grows either in the soil or just above it; they are characterised by compressed internodes and their leaves grow in sessile rosettes. It is characteristic for the habit of the specimen shown in Ill. *19*.1. that the shape of leaves is linear and that these will unfold in the air if the plants attain optimum growth: water leaves rarely occur. The specimens referred to are marsh plants, but they also thrive in shallow water. *Butomus umbellatus*, *Iris pseudacorus*, *Acorus calamus*, *Typha* as well as *Sparganium* species are marsh plants which can be planted in the shallow edges of ponds, but they are not suitable for cultivation in a home aquarium. The plant shown in Ill. *19*.2 serves as a good example of plant ecology; the plant is distinguished by growing different forms of leaves: submerged, floating and aerial. The development of different types of leaves often depends on the amount of light a plant receives during the day. This may be seen in *Sagittaria* and larger *Echinodorus* species as well as in representatives of the genus *Alisma*. Some of the marsh plants cultivated in pond margins also develop well when they are grown submerged; in that case they can be cared for equally well in a home aquarium. Ill. *19*.3 depicts a plant with water leaves which die off sooner or later; they are always succeeded by floating leaves. For an aquarium this type of plant is not very suitable as its leaves cast too much shade; in a planthouse or an outdoor pond, however, the plants have a very pleasant effect. The water lilies belong to this group but also some *Aponogeton* species. The specimens depicted in Ill. *19*.4 to Ill. *19*.6 normally do not grow above the water-level in a home aquarium nor do they develop floating leaves; however, the leaves do occur in a variety of forms. Leaves divided into a petiole and simple blade are shown in Ill. *19*.4. They occur in some medium-sized *Echinodorus* species, in some representatives of the genus *Aponogeton* and in *Ottelia alismoides*. Leaves with divided blades occur in *Ceratopteris* species as depicted in Ill. *19*.5 and in *Rorippa aquatica*. There are also slender, linear leaves as in the species of *Vallisneria*, shown in Ill. *19*.6. Some plants of this type of habit may turn into terrestrial forms if the water is removed from them. In the wild they are predominantly marsh plants which are well adapted to withstand prolonged periods of flooding. Other species have become so used to a submerged habit that they cannot re-adapt to life on land where they would die.

The examples in the middle row of Ill. *19* are characterised by shoots having elongated internodes. The leaf arrangement may be alternate, distichous, decussate or in whorls. Plants with a mode of growth as illustrated by Ill. *19*.7. to Ill. *19*.10 normally root in the soil; however, torn-off shoots may well continue growing whilst they are submerged. The specimen in Ill. *19*.11. has no roots, a habit which is typical for the genus *Utricularia*. The specimens in Ill. *19*.7 and *19*.8 have two things in common: they can both reach well beyond the water level in growth; they may also turn into terrestrial plants. They are either marsh plants, well able to withstand flooding; or they may be aquatic plants which rise above water-level when they are in blossom. The example shown in Ill. *19*.7. depicts plants whose water and aerial leaves display little or no differences; this also happens in *Ludwigia* species. The specimen in Ill. *19*.8. grows various leaf forms; as do the genera *Limnophila* and *Myriophyllum*. The mode of growth of the plants in *19*.9 and *19*.10 is closely linked to a habitat of water. The specimen in Ill. *19*.9 develops occasional floating leaves, a habit known from *Cabomba*. However, the plant in Ill. *19*.10 grows water leaves only. The latter applies to the whole family of water weeds.

The examples shown in the lowest row of Ill. *19* also have shoots with compressed internodes; they do not grow in the soil but near the surface of the water. Their leaves may

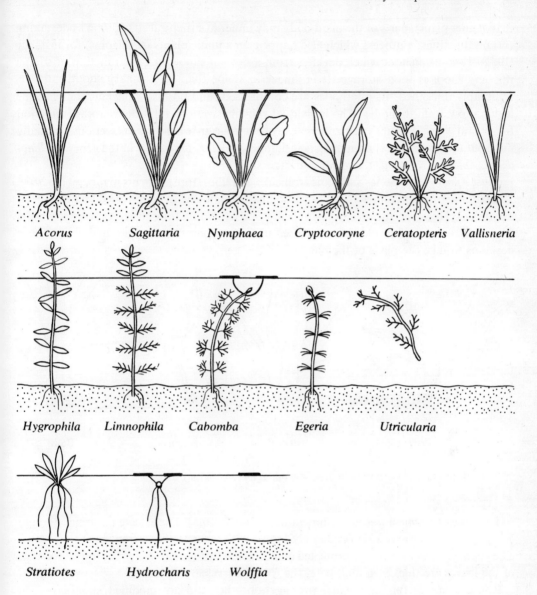

Acorus   Sagittaria   Nymphaea   Cryptocoryne   Ceratopteris   Vallisneria

Hygrophila   Limnophila   Cabomba   Egeria   Utricularia

Stratiotes   Hydrocharis   Wolffia

19 Schematic representation of different growth forms in aquarium plants

project into the air, e.g. *Pistia* and *Stratiotes*, depicted in Ill. *19*.12. Others, e.g. *Hydrocharis*, may develop floating leaves (Ill. *19*.13). Both types are normally floating plants, but if the water level sinks they may well root themselves in the soil. A few floating plants have no roots at all, as shown by *Wolffia* in Ill. *19*.14.

In higher plants, parts of the plant body may undergo structural changes on undertaking certain functions, a process which also happens in aquatic plants. A rhizome, for instance (Ill. *20*.1) emits a shoot which deviates from a normal shoot axis; the function of such a rhizome shoot is food storage. It is longer in shape than an ordinary shoot and it is noticeably thickened; its internodes are compressed; and normal foliage as well as scale leaves grow from its nodes. The individual rhizome sections fulfil their storage function for several years. The tips of rhizomes always continue growing whereas sections gradually die from the base; lateral branching is insignificant. Rhizomes occur in the genera *Echinodorus, Anubias, Nymphaea, Nuphar* and others.

Most *Aponogeton* species and some tropical water lilies store nutrients in tubers (Ill. *20*.2). The latter are rather compact and they also possess shoots with compressed and thickened internodes. However, tubers carry out their storage function for one vegetation cycle only. The food reserves of an old tuber are used up in the course of the year, and a new tuber develops to take the place of the old one.

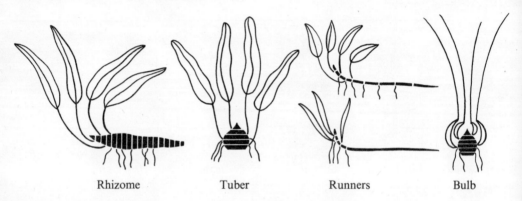

Rhizome   Tuber   Runners   Bulb

20 Special structure of vegetation bodies (schematic representation)

The genus *Crinum* stores nourishment in bulbs (Ill. *20*.5). These have a normal, though compressed, shoot axis which is densely grown with a rosette-like arrangement of leaves. The younger leaves are always protected and enclosed by the older ones. The lowest sections of the leaves are thickened and, here, the food reserves are stored.

Runners are useful for asexual propagation; they too are modified shoot axes. In contrast to other food storage organs, the internodes of runners are thin and elongated. Runners grow either in the soil or on the substratum, and scale-leaves develop in their nodes. Runners with several elongated internodes occur in the genera *Cryptocoryne* and *Potamogeton* (Ill. *20*.3). In the smaller *Echinodorus* and in *Vallisneria* species runners are always made up of only one conspicuously elongated internode (Ill. *20*.4).

In the temperate zone many plants with a submerged habit develop special winter buds for wintering. Such buds are tips of shoots with compressed internodes and densely arranged small, robust leaves. While the basal sections of the shoots wither in the autumn the winter buds sink to the ground. Winter buds occur in the genera *Ceratophyllum*, *Myriophyllum*, *Utricularia*, *Hydrocharis* and others.

Flower

A flower is a transformed shoot whose function is sexual reproduction. Flower leaves fulfil specific tasks and, therefore, deviate from the structure of typical foliage leaves. Four parts constitute the basic build of a flower: the floral axis; the perianth; the androecium; and the gynoecium (Ill. *21*). The form of the floral axis and the flower petals are subject to variations; so are the number of petals and the distribution of male and female gametes. These differences cause the rich variety in blossoms of plants.

As a rule flowers are bisexual (Ill. *22*.1); they possess stamens as well as carpels. A number of marsh and aquatic plants, however, have unisexual flowers, which possess either stamens or carpels—thus, they are either masculine or feminine. If both types of unisexual flowers exist on the same plant it is referred to as monoecious (Ill. *22*.2). Dioecious plants are those which have their unisexual flowers on separate male and female plants (Ill. *22*.3), e.g. the genus *Vallisneria*.

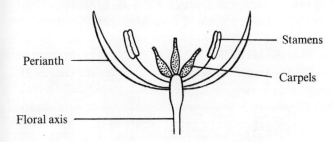

21 Construction of a flower (schematic representation)

A plant is actinomorphic if it is radially symmetrical. This means it can be divided by any arbitrary planes into exactly similar parts facing each other. If only one plane or line can divide a plant into two exactly equal parts it is mirror-symmetrical.

The floral axis carries petals, sometimes arranged in coils but more often in whorls. The floral axis may be slightly elongated or arched. It may also be hollow and then it is either tubular or cup-shaped. Examples of different forms of floral axes are depicted in Ill. *23*. On a hollow floral axis the carpels are always embedded, and often they more or less combine with it. The peduncle is the continuation of the floral axis and varies in length. In sessile flowers it is lacking.

The perianth leaves protect the flower buds' immature stamens and carpels. At the time of blossoming the colouration of stamens and carpels is one of the main attractions for the insects and birds which pollinate the flowers. A perianth may be either of simple or twofold

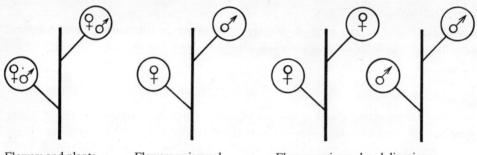

| Flowers and plants hermaphroditic | Flowers unisexual and monoecious, plants hermaphroditic | Flowers unisexual and dioecious, plants female or male |

22 Distribution of the sexes

formation. In a simple perianth all its leaves are uniform. They are either conspicuously crown-shaped as in *Zosterella dubia* or inconspicuously cup-shaped as in *Acorus*. In a twofold perianth there is a differentiation between a green calyx and a coloured corolla. It is rare that a perianth is completely lacking as in the genus *Cryptocoryne*. Perianth-leaves are either separate or combined. Separate sepals and petals occur in *Echinodorus* and *Ludwigia* species. An undivided calyx with divided tips and undivided corolla is found in the labiate flowers of *Nomaphila corymbosa*.

The stamens (androecium) come after the perianth; their function is the production of pollen. The stamens in higher plants are rather homogeneous in structure (Ill. *24*.1). Stamens are composed of filaments, which vary in length, and anthers; each anther contains four pollen sacks. The genus *Cryptocoryne* possesses stamens which deviate considerably (Ill. *24*.2). A gradual transition from stamens to petals occurs in the genus *Nymphaea* (Ill. *38*).

The gynaecium (carpels taken collectively) is the final part of the flower and the one which occurs in many variations. The carpels' function is the formation of seed. Carpels may be divided and their number may vary. Thus *Echinodorus* species possess a rather large, often indefinite number of them (Ill. *23*.1). The female flowers of *Ceratophyllum*, on the other hand, have only one single carpel (Ill. *23*.12). Although in some marsh and aquatic plants carpels may be apparently combined, this is often not so. In Nymphaeaceae and Hydrocharitaceae, for instance, the carpels are embedded in the floral axis, but spaces between them are filled by axial tissue as in Ill. *23*.5 or *23*.10. When carpels are truly undivided each directly joins the next one as shown in Ill. *23*.16 or *23*.17. The position of the carpels in a flower is superior if they are arranged above the perianth and the stamens (Ill. *23*.1 and *23*.17), but carpels are inferior if arranged below the perianth and stamens. The latter is the rule if the carpels are embedded in a hollow floral axis (Ill. *23*.5 or *23*.16).

Uncombined carpels are composed of an ovary, a stylus (of varying length), and a sticky-papillose stigma. The last collects and retains the grains of pollen. Combined carpels

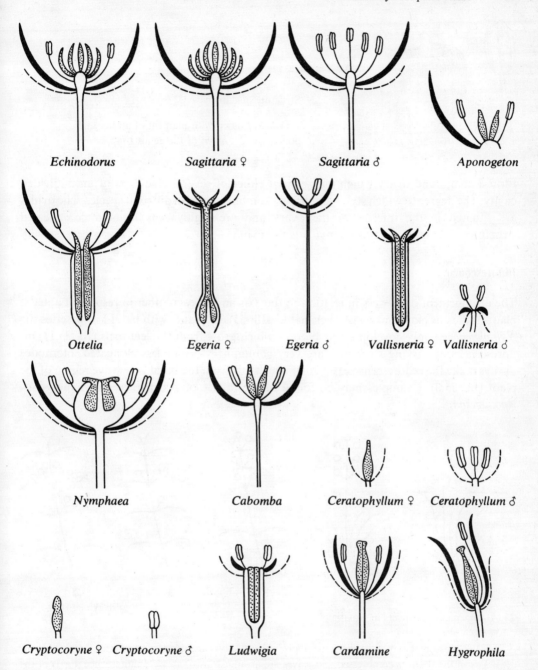

Echinodorus   *Sagittaria* ♀   *Sagittaria* ♂   *Aponogeton*

Ottelia   *Egeria* ♀   *Egeria* ♂   *Vallisneria* ♀   *Vallisneria* ♂

Nymphaea   *Cabomba*   *Ceratophyllum* ♀   *Ceratophyllum* ♂

Cryptocoryne ♀   *Cryptocoryne* ♂   *Ludwigia*   *Cardamine*   *Hygrophila*

23 Examples for structure of flowers in aquatic plants (floral axis white, calyx lineated, corolla black, carpels dotted)

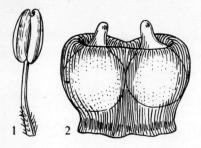

24 Structure of stamen

1 Typical stamen with filament of anther and
pollen sac, 2 stamen of the genus *Cryptocoryne*

form a compound ovary which may consist either of several chambers or an undivided
cavity. The degree to which stylus and stigma combine varies in different species. The ovules
are situated in the interior of the ovary and are highly sensitive and complicated
structures. The main part of the ovule is the ovum.

Inflorescence

The arrangement of flowers in relation to the axis and to each other in respect of aquatic
plants indicates close links with their habits (Ill. 25). In plants with basal leaf rosettes the
Nymphaeaceae only develop single blooms which grow from the leaf axils (Ill. 25.1). Inflorescences of varying structures are very common. More or less elongated internodes
always make the inflorescense easily distinguishable from the basal vegetative region of the
plant (Ill. 25.2). Examples may be found in the family of Alismataceae and the genus
Aponogeton.

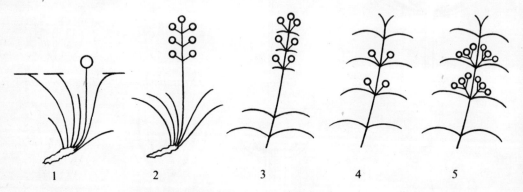

1   2   3   4   5

25 Arrangement of flowers in aquatic plants

1 Single blossom if axis of the shoot is compressed and leaves are arranged in rosettes. 2 Inflorescence
if axis of the shoot is compressed and leaves are arranged in rosettes. 3 Inflorescence if axis of the
shoot is elongated and leaves are arranged opposite and decussate. 4 Single flowers in leaf axils if
axis of the shoot is elongated and leaves are arranged opposite and decussate. 5 Flower clusters in
leaf axils if axis of the shoot is elongated and leaves are arranged opposite and decussate.

In plants with an attenuated shoot axis flower clusters often develop in the axil of normal foliage leaves, distant flower clusters in the genus *Nomaphila*, or densely positioned flower clusters in the *Alternanthera* species (Ill. 25.3). Often the number of blossoms in flower clusters decreases drastically over a period of time, and this may well be the reason why occasionally single blossoms grow from a leaf axil instead of clusters (Ill. 25.4); *Ludwigia* species provide an example here. Where bracts take the place of normal foliage leaves (bracts are smaller and of simpler build than foliage leaves) inflorescences develop again (Ill. 25.5), which complete the development of a shoot.

| Spadix | Spike | Grape, cluster | Umbel | Panicle | Thyrsus | Dichasium |

26 Examples of inflorescences

Inflorescences are either simple or branched (Ill. 26). The spike, the grape and the umbel are well-known forms of simple inflorescence. On a spike the flowers are positioned without pedicels on the main stalk (or peduncle) as in species of *Aponogeton*. The grape has a similar structure, but the flowers do have pedicels; grape-like inflorescences occur in the genus *Sagittaria*. In an umbel the peduncle is so shortened that all the pedicels spring from a common centre; some species of the genus *Hydrocotyle* have an umbellar inflorescence. Branched inflorescences often have such a complex structure that an aquarist who is sufficiently interested might like to study some botanical literature. The primary stalk in an inflorescence may be so dominant that all lateral stalks and flowers are of minor importance; the panicle is a typical example. When lateral blossoms protrude above the terminal flowers of their primary axes the inflorescence is referred to as a dichasium. Another type of inflorescence is compound and made up of controlling primary axes with branching, lateral pedicels and protruding flowers. It is referred to as a thyrsus and characteristic for *Echinodorus* species.

A correlation between size and number of blossoms is often found, i.e. the smaller the flowers the greater their number. Pollinating insects are just as easily attracted by an inflorescence composed of numerous small flowers as by the optical effect of a single large blossom. Loss of conspicuousness in flowers may be compensated by strikingly coloured bracts. Thus if a bract forms part of an inflorescence it is called a spathe. As a rule a spathe is constituted of one large bract, but it may also be composed of two or three bracts. A spathe is particularly common in the arum family; in the genus *Cryptocoryne* it either surrounds a flower cluster loosely or enfolds it closely. Alternatively, a spathe may have the function of enclosing and protecting an immature inflorescence while it develops. In that case it is inconspicuous and declining as in the *Aponogeton* species.

Fruit and Seed

After successful pollination major changes take place in the whole of the flower while it develops into the fruit. Meanwhile, the ovules situated in the interior of the ovaries, gradually turn into ripe seeds.

If a flower contains several pistils an aggregate fruit or syncarp is formed; if there is only one pistil—irrespective of whether it is constituted of one or several carpels—a simple fruit develops. The water-plantain family, for instance, bears aggregate fruit. Thus an *Echinodorus* flower or a female *Sagittaria* blossom forms a syncarp composed of a fairly large number of so-called drupelets or fruitlets. In the examples quoted the pistils have just one ovary and can therefore only develop a single seed. Accordingly, the fruitlet does not have to burst open in order to release the seed as dispersal of the whole fruitlet achieves the same result. For better protection of the fruitlet its walls become hard so that it resembles a tiny nut. When propagating species of the water-plantain family, therefore, in most cases it is not seeds which are dispersed, harvested, or 'sown', but one-seeded fruitlets.

If a flower possesses only one pistil it forms either a monospermous or polyspermous simple fruit. Preservation and distribution of species with polyspermous simple fruit is far more likely if the latter scatter each single seed separately. It happens in various ways. One of them is the development of capsules which burst open; capsules are classed as dehiscent fruits. Thus many aquatic plants, e.g. *Ammannia*, *Hygrophila*, *Ludwigia*, *Rotala* and *Iris* bear capsules. As the capsules ripen their skin becomes dry and hard; their colour generally turns brown; they also develop special bursting mechanisms such as longitudinal fissures, pores or cracking covers. The seeds are scattered by and by.

Berries are polyspermous cleistocarps; as they ripen the whole of the pericarp becomes fleshy or pulpy, also often coloured. The seeds are freed when the berries decay or if these are eaten by animals. The seeds usually pass unharmed through an animal's digestive tract. Nuts and stone-fruits are monospermous cleistocarps. In nuts the whole pericarp hardens and encloses the kernel rather in the manner of the fruitlets of aggregate fruits. In stone-fruits only the inner wall enclosing the kernel becomes hard; the part of the fruit around the stone stays fleshy or pulpy as in berries.

It is difficult to allocate a place in existing fruit classification to some of the fruits of marsh and aquatic plants. These fruits are not unlike berries which is why they are referred to as water-berries. As they ripen the pericarp stays soft and green; it disintegrates after a short time; and thus the seeds are freed. Examples for this type of berries are found amongst the water lilies and the frogbit plants.

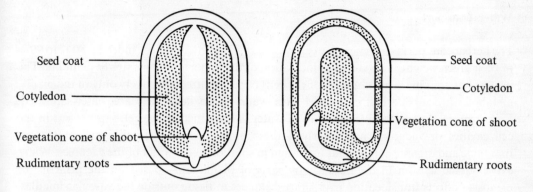

27 Structure of seeds (schematic representation)
   Left: seed of a dicotyledonous plant in which the nutrients are stored in the cotyledons. Right: seed
   of a monocotyledonous plant with nutrient tissue

A seed is a unit of reproduction and its most essential component is the embryo. The latter is the miniature plant germinating from the fertilized ovum inside the ovule. In its embryonic state within the seed the young plant is going through a resting phase. The embryo has a short shoot axis and a radicle; additionally, monocotyledons have one leaf, and dicotyledons have two leaves. The seed coat protects the rudimentary plant from environmental damage. Variable amounts of nutritive substances are deposited in the seeds; the former are essential for further development of the embryonic plant; they also cause differences in the structure of seeds. Nutrients may be stored in nutritive tissue filling the space between the embryo and the seed coat; on the other hand, they may be stored in the cotyledons of the embryo (Ill. 27).

4. Physiology of Aquatic Plants

Metabolism is a characteristic feature of every living form. All physiological processes involve intake, transformation and expulsion of organic and inorganic substances combined with energy changes. Living organisms such as all animals are dependent on existing organic combinations. Their manner of nutrition is heterotrophic. Plants, on the other hand, are autotrophic. They are able to provide themselves with food by synthesizing inorganic into organic substances. The basic raw materials they need are as follows: H_2O, CO_2 and O_2; the cations K^+, Ca^{++}, Mg^{++} and Fe^{++}, as well as the anions NO_3^-, SO_4^{--}, and PO_4^{---}. Additionally, plants need some minerals, e.g. copper, zinc, manganese and molybdenum, but the required quantities are so minute that they are referred to as trace elements. The importance of the various ingredients and the use plants make of them will be explained in the following chapters.

Water Transport

The herbaceous parts of higher plants have a very high water content indeed—80% to 90% of their green weight. This is a clear indication of the importance of water to plant life. The proteins present in the protoplasm of the cells can be utilized effectively only in the plants' metabolic processes when combined with water. Even dead cells are water-saturated. Furthermore, a considerable quantity of water is contained in the cell sap present in the cell cavities or vacuoles, particularly if these occur in fundamental tissue. Numerous inorganic and organic compounds are found in solution in the water of the vacuoles. Water causes tissue tension in the herbaceous parts of plants and—based on the principle of osmosis—effects translocation over short distances in tissue outside the vascular bundles. But water is also the agent which transports the dissolved substances contained in the vascular bundles over long distances. Moreover, water enables the plants to utilize carbohydrates and to synthesize them. A well-balanced water exchange is the prerequisite for all vital processes of plant life—absorption, transport and subsequent loss of water vapour all being important basic functions in living plants.

With the exception of epiphytes which colonize trees, all terrestrial plants, among them all marsh plants, take in most of their water through the roots. The root hairs play a major role in the process because they considerably enlarge the surface area capable of taking in water by clinging closely to moist particles of soil from which they absorb the water. Root hairs are generally lacking in marsh and aquatic plants as they have a more readily available supply of water. Water absorption by leaves and shoots of terrestrial plants is a possibility, but to what extent it occurs has not been investigated up to the present.

Initially the water is passed from cell to cell in the epidermis of the root; eventually it reaches the vascular bundles in the centre and they transport the water upwards to all parts of the plant. The mechanics of water transport in a plant are of a physical nature, interacting closely with a certain amount of root pressure, capillary action in the narrow cells and transpiration. Water-saturated surfaces of terrestrial plants exude water vapour in an atmosphere which is not water-saturated. Cuticular transpiration accounts for a considerable percentage of water loss in plants with a wet habitat, which have as one of their characteristics a very thin cuticular layer. Generally, however, stomatal transpiration causes the greatest loss of water vapour in terrestrial plants; stomata are minute pores in the intercellular system of the epidermis which shut and open according to atmospheric conditions. If water vapour loss exceeds water absorption the plant wilts.

Because they have such a delicate cuticula, submerged plants (and parts of plants) can absorb water not only through their roots but through the whole surface of the plant body. Even in submerged plants upward translocation of water has been proved. Apart from root pressure, exudation of water from apical pores and hydathodes (resembling enlarged stomata) in the leaves furthers the process. An active exudation of drops of water also occurs in some terrestrial plants. Thus drops of water can be seen at the tips and margins of leaves after a moist-warm night; these drops may be mistaken for dew.

Photosynthesis

Water is the largest ingredient in herbaceous parts of plants; carbon comes next with 5% to 10% of the green weight. Carbon is not only one of the constituents of carbohydrates such as sugar, starch and cellulose, but it is also present in most other organic compounds. Carbon dioxide (CO_2) is the source from which plants take their supply of carbon. The former is retained in the plant cells and it is assimilated by them, a process which is referred to as 'carbon dioxide assimilation'. Carbon dioxide and water build simple carbohydrates by way of synthesis, simultaneously releasing oxygen. However, the synthesis can only take place if the plant is exposed to light rays. Therefore the CO_2 assimilation in green plants is called photosynthesis; the energy of light is taken up by the plants and stored as chemical energy. At a later stage the chemical energy is re-cycled and utilized in many different processes of life. The site of photosynthesis is in the chloroplasts within the cells.

Several factors of a complex nature influence the degree of intensity in photosynthesis. These are the general health of a plant; in terrestrial plants, availability and—related to it— the degree to which stomata open; intensity of light and its spectral composition; temperature; and, lastly, the supply of CO_2. All these factors possess an optimum range. However, it is the minimum range of each factor which has to be regarded as being decisive in the whole process. If, for instance, the CO_2 supply is insufficient, favourable light and temperature cannot be fully utilized.

Land plants, also parts of land plants, utilize the CO_2 present in the air. Submerged plants live under different conditions. The latter also need carbon dioxide, but although they find a plentiful supply of inorganic substances with carbon content in the water it is far more difficult for such plants to assimilate the carbon dioxide from which they obtain the carbon.

Carbon dioxide may come in solution from dry atmospheric air; it is also formed by breathing animal and plant life. In specialist nurseries aquatic plants are often supplied with additional CO_2, a method also employed by some aquarists. Too much aeration, however, causes loss of carbon dioxide. Receptivity of water for CO_2 depends on temperature, a rise in temperature lowering it.

When CO_2 molecules dissolve in water, some of them combine with water molecules (one CO_2 to each one water molecule) and form carbonic acid:

$$CO_2 + H_2O \rightleftharpoons H_2CO_3.$$

Carbonic acid, in turn, dissociates in H^+ ions and HCO_3^- ions. An increase in H^+ ions lowers the pH value. When the pH rises above 8 the CO_2 molecules show an increasing tendency not to combine with water molecules but with OH^- ions instead:

$$CO_2 + OH^- \rightleftharpoons HCO_3^-.$$

HCO_3^- ions react with certain cations—in freshwater most of all with calcium, but also with magnesium by forming into calcium bicarbonate:

$$2\,HCO_3^- + Ca \rightleftharpoons Ca(HCO_3)_2.$$

Some of the HCO_3^- ions may dissociate further in a second stage:

$$HCO_3^- \rightleftharpoons H^+ + CO_3^{--}.$$

Thus inorganic carbon compounds occur in water as follows: CO_2, H_2CO_3, HCO_3^- and CO_3^{--}. Rising pH value in the water causes variation in quantity of these compounds in the following order. Up to pH 4 only CO_2 is present in the water; CO_3^{--} does not appear until the pH is above 7; CO_2 and H_2CO_3 are lacking if the pH rises above 10.

Initially, submerged plants make use of the CO_2 dissolved in water for carbon dioxide assimilation and the CO_2 is absorbed by the whole surface of the plant body. However, as the quantity of carbon dioxide in the water decreases with rising temperature and pH value, there is usually not enough of it for sufficient assimilation. The higher submerged plants are able to utilize instead one of the other inorganic compounds with carbon dioxide content. They obtain CO_2 for full assimilation from calcium bicarbonate. The undersides of leaves, in particular, absorb equivalent amounts of Ca^{++} ions and HCO_3^- ions so that one may say that $Ca(HCO_3)_2$ molecules are absorbed. Inside the leaves the whole of the CO_2 is extracted from the calcium bicarbonate. Ca^{++} ions together with equivalent amounts of OH^- ions come out on the uppersides of leaves. But, as the water surrounding the latter also contains HCO_3^- ions, the following reaction takes place:

$$Ca^{++} + OH^- + HCO_3^- \rightleftharpoons CaCO_3 + H_2O.$$

Thereby indissoluble calcium carbonate is deposited as a crust on leaf uppersides, a process which has been termed biogenic decalcification of water. The CO_2 contained in the air is of little value to submerged plants.

Another point is worth mentioning: carbon dioxide assimilation exerts an influence on the water and, when it takes place, the pH value in the water rises. Several hours of intensive assimilation are sufficient to cause considerable variations in pH value. The greater the mass of plants assimilating carbon dioxide in a given quantity of water the more quickly will differences in pH value occur. When there is a dense growth of submerged plants the daily pH amplitude can vary by as much as one to two degrees. It is, therefore, essential for the survival of aquatic plants that they adapt well to fluctuations of pH value.

The chemical processes of photosynthesis may be expressed in a very simplified form by the following equation of reaction:

$$6\,CO_2 + 6\,H_2O + \text{radiant energy} \rightarrow C_6H_{12}O_6 + 6\,O_2.$$

The actual processes leading to this reaction are very complicated indeed and, up to date, they are not fully understood. Intensive research, however, has clarified a number of points. It is generally recognised now that three main sub-reactions occur in photosynthesis. In one of them water evolves from OH^- ions whilst, at the same time, oxygen is liberated; the latter is therefore not derived from carbon dioxide as assumed formerly. Terrestrial plants release oxygen into the atmosphere through the stomata, but marsh and aquatic plants also diffuse some of it either into the vascular system or into the water. When observing submerged plants in the light, e.g. *Egeria densa*, small oxygen bubbles rising to the water surface may be seen. The simple sugar which is formed is entirely due to photosynthesis. Initially, the soluble sugar is converted into insoluble starch in the chloroplasts. The presence of tiny grains of starch can be proved after a plant has been exposed to light for quite a short period. It is only at a later stage that the starch turns into soluble carbohydrate: this is transported to all other areas of the plant where synthesis of organic substances takes place, e.g. organs of growth and storage; it also provides plant cells with energy.

Respiration

Not only visible efforts consume energy—for instance contraction of a muscle, but also the processes of building up and breaking down which occur in metabolism. Probably even the maintenance support of the very unstable sub-microscopic structures of the protoplasm needs a certain expenditure of energy. This energy is acquired through respiration which is a feature common to all living things. Breathing liberates chemically-bound energy thereby causing a number of complicated reactions. Thus energy-rich substances, catalyzed by enzymes, are taken apart. The complex respiratory mechanism is basically similar in most animals and plants, causing sugar to be separated into its two basic building materials, CO_2 and H_2O. This process is the exact opposite of photosynthesis as oxygen is consumed and carbon dioxide is given off. Some of the sub-reactions are comparable with processes of fermentation in that plants can survive a lack of oxygen for a short period and yet acquire some energy by continued forming of CO_2.

In contrast to photosynthesis respiration takes place in all living cells of the plant, including those which contain no chlorophyll, and irrespective of light and dark. Breathing carries on without interruption during day and night time.

The rate of respiration is subject to considerable deviations and depends on the condition of a plant as well as the circumstances of its environment. To begin with it can be said that in 24 hours a higher plant releases through respiration one fifth to one third of the amount of CO_2 which it has entrapped by photosynthesis during the day. In optimum conditions, therefore, a plant has a positive balance of substances as considerable amounts of synthesized organic compounds are left for the plant to use as building and storage materials. If it were otherwise growth would not be possible and all existing reserves would be used up completely. When plants of *Aponogeton madagascariensis* gradually become smaller and smaller the cause can probably be found in a rate of respiration which is higher than the performance of photosynthesis.

All terrestrial plants use atmospheric oxygen for respiration; sufficient and constant amounts of oxygen are always present in the air. In aquatic plants which grow higher than the water level atmospheric oxygen is taken in by the stomata and then conducted through the distinct and connected vascular system to submerged parts of the plant and right down to the roots in the substratum. For the roots this is particularly important as a muddy substratum in the water contains no free oxygen at a depth of only a few millimetres.

Submerged plants have to depend on the oxygen dissolved in water and that which they have accumulated in their vascular system by photosynthesis during the day. The oxygen content of water is decidedly lower than that of air and is subject to considerable fluctuations. Respiration by animals and higher plants, as well as bacteria, may reduce the level of oxygen in water to nil. On the other hand the level may reach saturation point where plant growth is very dense and the rate of photosynthesis is accordingly high.

Oxygen receptivity of water depends, most of all, on temperature. Almost double the amount of oxygen can be found dissolved in water at a temperature of 0°C compared with 30°C. Thus, when oxygen-consuming activities are in progress, reserves of oxygen in tropical waters are used up more quickly than in those of cooler zones. Additionally, the need for oxygen rises with the temperature as the rate of respiration increases when the temperature goes up. Furthermore, oxygen receptivity is also controlled by pressure. Plants can take in more O_2 at greater depth than they can nearer the surface of the water.

Protein Metabolism

In the process of photosynthesis building materials are synthesized and energy is stored; respiration then makes both capable of exercising many functions. Simultaneously, further important metabolic processes occur in the cells. Protein metabolism exerts a decisive influence because protein compounds form the most important constituents of protoplasm. When a plant grows new cells develop and, therefore, new protein has to be made. In respect of protein metabolism, plants possess synthesizing capabilities which far exceed those of animals. It is only plants which can make organic out of inorganic substances.

Besides the vegetation cone, further sites for active protein metabolism appear to be in other growth centres as well as in green leaves and storage tissues. In all of these protein is continually built up, partially broken up after synthesis and then translocated by the sieve cells of the vascular bundles to other parts of the plant. Germinating seeds or developing tubers also cause an active exchange of protein.

Certain amino-acids provide the most essential building block for proteins. The amino-acids are organic compounds in which a carbon atom adjacent to the COOH acid group is replaced by a hydrogen atom of the amino group NH_2:

$$NH_2 - \overset{\displaystyle H}{\underset{\displaystyle R}{C}} - COOH$$

The nitrogen, necessary for the development of amino-acids, is derived from NO_3^{--} ions. In the process the nitrate ion has to be reduced to NH_2 with the aid of hydrogen; it then combines with C compounds obtained from carbohydrate metabolism. After the synthesis of the amino-acids, peptide linkage joins them into long molecular chains. The arrangement of the different amino-acids is in definite sequences and each kind of protein has its own characteristic arrangement; various amino-acids may occur repeatedly in one chain.

Insectiverous plants, e.g. species of *Utricularia*, have access to an additional source of nitrogen for their protein metabolism because of their mode of nutrition. The animal protein is catalyzed by specific enzymes, secreted from glands, and taken apart; the resultant cleavage products are reabsorbed. The animal food is not strictly necessary if there is a good supply of mineral NO_3^-, but it often aids the development of flowers.

Ions and Trace Elements

Plants can supply their need for anions (negatively charged ions), cations (positively charged ions), and trace elements from two natural sources in which they are present: the soil and the water. Weathering of rocks and mineralizing of dead organic matter by micro-organisms continually renew the supply. Fertilizers provide an additional source, but in aquaria they are superfluous under normal conditions; their use is recommended solely to aquarium plant nurseries. In respect of ions and trace elements, it is again the minimum of each which determines plant growth. The best light, the most favourable conditions of soil and water are of no use if just one of the ions or trace elements is lacking. On the other hand, most aquarium plants suffer if they are supplied in excess. Whereas land plants take in ions and trace elements dissolved in water through their roots, submerged plants absorb them either entirely with their leaves and shoots, or with roots, leaves and shoots.

Potassium does not occur in plants in organic combination but as an ion only. It furthers adsorption in the protoplasm and activates the enzymes in protein metabolism. Tap water contains potassium minerals in varying amounts.

In contrast to potassium, calcium has a desorbent influence on protoplasm. Calcium is needed for the building of newly developing cell walls; a lack of it may cause decay of the vegetation cone. As for the importance of calcium for photosynthesis of submerged plants see page 62. An adequate amount of calcium is contained in tap water.

Magnesium is contained in chlorophyll and therefore an integral part of photosynthesis which could not proceed without this most important colour substance. Moreover, like calcium, magnesium helps to build new cell walls. It plays a certain role in breaking down carbohydrates and also activates the enzymes in energy metabolism. As a rule, tap water contains a sufficient amount of magnesium.

Iron occurs in the enzymes in respiration metabolism and it is also of some importance to photosynthesis. A lack of iron becomes apparent, typically, by chlorosis—an incomplete development of the chlorophyll. Nevertheless, the chlorophyll itself does not contain iron, but the chloroplasts do. Chlorosis is therefore a side-effect. The quantity of iron actually needed, is very small however.

Normally, the nitrate ion is the starting point in the whole process of protein metabolism in higher plants (see page 61). An abundance of nitrate is found in an aquarium, being derived from microbial decomposition of fish faeces, food remnants and dead parts of plants. The nitrate content of a tank may reach saturation point, a condition easily remedied by frequent replacement of a part of the water.

The sulphate ion is necessary for the build-up of proteins containing sulphur and is found apart from that in some enzymes. A varying amount of it is contained in tap water.

The phosphate ion is built into the proteins of the cells' nuclei, into enzymes and into organic compounds. It is also active in those substances which transmit energy for photosynthesis and respiration. A sufficient amount of it is present in an aquarium where it is derived from decomposition caused by micro-organisms.

Trace elements help in the build-up of several organic compounds, particularly those which are fermentative. A lack of any one of the trace elements will manifest itself in specific symptoms of a disease. It is likely that enough of the trace elements are contained in the water of an aquarium.

If plants are to benefit from the trace elements—even iron—present in the water these have to be loosely incorporated with certain organic compounds, the so-called ion exchange resins. Otherwise the trace elements and iron are easily lost to the plants. It is advantageous to plant growth if the aquarium water contains a few organic substances. In specialized literature additional enrichment of the water with ion exchange resins has been recommended. The author, however, considers it to be unnecessary.

Vitamins

Aquarists have occasionally experimented with adding vitamin preparations to the water of the aquarium and then claimed that they observed an obvious improvement in plant growth. However, it can be stated as a fact that a healthy plant is able to synthesize for itself all the vitamins it needs as well as other active substances.

Plant Movements

All movements which occur in aquatic plants may be classified as growth movements. Thus, in internodes of the shoot axis one side is furthered in growth, and in leaves either the base of the upper or the underside are so aided. Plants with elongated shoot axes often bend distinctly towards the light, the source which supplies the necessary stimulus. The curvature achieves an optimum gain of light. If one observes cuttings, particularly after they have just been put in, one can see how they bend. The opening and closing of quite a few blossoms depend on changes of temperature and illumination. An example is the *Nymphaea* species; some of them open their blossoms in daytime and some in the evening. It is probable that some aquatic plants do not respond to outside stimuli but depend instead on certain physiological processes within the plant body so that their 'sleep positions' occur in a 12-hourly rhythm. In *Limnophila* species, for instance, the younger leaves are flat and spread out during the day but stand upright during the night.

Photoperiodism

Photoperiodism or photoperiods refer to the dependence of plants on the daily period of illumination for the initiation of flowers. The short-day plants of the tropics and subtropics develop flowers in a daily period of light of less than 12 hours. If the daylight lasts longer growth is intensive, but only vegetative. The long-day plants of the temperate latitudes, on the other hand, flower in a daily light period of more than 12 hours. There are also indeterminate plants which initiate blossoms irrespective of duration of illumination. Our aquatic plants also react to photoperiods, but here the period of illumination not only determines flower development; it can also affect the size and shape of leaves.

Aquarium plants which have been studied most frequently, so far, in respect of photoperiodism are the *Echinodorus* species. *E. berteroi* is a typical long-day plant (Ill. *28*). The decorative, dark-green, transparent leaves form in short-day periods only. In long-day photoperiods the species produces long-stemmed, floating and aerial leaves and, eventually, inflorescences.

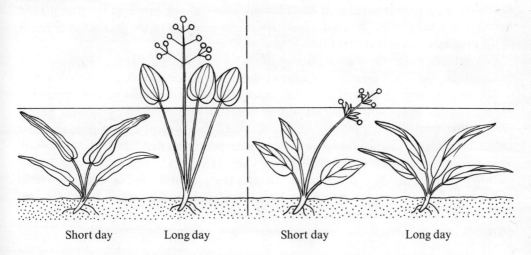

| Short day | Long day | Short day | Long day |

28 Reaction to photoperiodism in *Echinodorus berteroi* (left) and *Echinodorus parviflorus* (right)

E. parviflorus, on the other hand, is a short-day plant (Ill. *28*). In long-day periods it develops water leaves with short petioles and rather long blades. In short-day periods the leaves change considerably; petioles become longer and leaves more compact. Thus a leaf form typical of aerial leaves evolves. Nevertheless the plants do not grow higher than the

water level, even if the water is quite shallow. Inflorescences with numerous adventitious·
shoots are initiated in short-day photoperiods.

Limnophila aquatica is a further example of a short-day plant. In long-day periods it
grows submerged with finely pinnate water leaves. However, in short-day periods simple
aerial leaves develop; the plants turn into marsh plants and then flower. If the species are
made to grow as marsh plants in long-day conditions they will evolve the pinnate leaves
characteristic of the submerged form, but these are smaller and their structure is more
solid.

5. Propagation of Aquatic Plants

There is a fundamental difference between asexual vegetative and sexual generative reproduction of plants.

In vegetative propagation adult plants either divide or form new plants without involve-
ment of any sexual processes. Some forms of vegetative reproduction are quite normal
in nature. They also occur in cultivation without interference by Man, provided that
optimum growth conditions prevail. Thus vallisnerias develop slips, and adventitious
plants form in inflorescences of some *Echinodorus* species. In other plants some treatment
may be either necessary or, at least, helpful for furthering propagation. All individual
plants resulting from vegetative propagation are identical not only with the parent plant
but also with each other. Asexual, vegetative reproduction is of the greatest importance
in the propagation of aquarium plants.

As a matter of fact, there are a number of marsh and aquatic plants where vegetative
propagation is either impossible or unrewarding so that reliance has to be placed on
sexual reproduction. Moreover, in some cases of sexual reproduction, the aquarist is
given the opportunity of observing interesting biological phenomena in the flowers. Sexual
propagation means raising plants from seeds. Of course, a plant cannot produce seeds
unless it has first developed flowers which are later pollinated and fertilized. Seeds result
from the fusion of male and female gametes or sex-cells which then undergo special
maturation divisions. As a consequence, change and recombination of genetic material
within one species is always a possibility. Except in strains of plants which have been kept
pure throughout by inbreeding—a state which does not exist as yet in aquarium plants—
there is a certain, though minor genetic variability in plants raised from seeds.

Propagation by Slips

Plants are called slips when they propagate themselves vegetatively at some distance from
the parent plant. Slips are produced on runners. This process happens in nature, and good
use is made of it by aquarists. A number of plants rooted in the soil and having basal leaf
rosettes are produced on runners. Propagation by slips is characteristic of all species of the

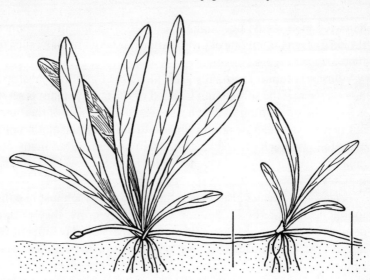

29 Propagation
by slips of a species
of *Echinodorus*
producing runners

genus *Vallisneria*; a certain group of *Echinodorus* species; nearly all cryptocorynes; and many sagittarias (Ill. *29*).

If they are provided with really favourable growth conditions, vallisnerias develop a profusion of runners from which many slips will grow after quite a short time. The single runner springs from a leaf axil and thus corresponds with a lateral shoot of the mother plant. It is formed by a basal internode with the actual bud of the lateral shoot at the apex. The runner develops through rapid horizontal growth by the internode which pushes the initially unchanged bud in front of it. The outer covering of the bud is formed by a small scale-leaf. In the interior of the bud some differentiations are already in existence. If such a bud is dissected several leaf primordia of the future slip will be found as well as the leaf rudiment of a new slip. After a time the internode ceases to grow, and activity is taken over by the bud. It raises itself to an upright position; the interior leaf primordia start to grow; and this pushes the covering scale-leaf apart. Thus, the first stage of the slip is completed, and a new plant derived from vegetative propagation is initiated.

It will be seen that the first scale-leaf is followed by others. Gradually these increase in length and are succeeded by typical foliage leaves. In the meantime the compressed internodes form the axis of the shoot which is covered with leaves initially. The first adventitious roots of the new slip grow out of the shoot axis and have to push through the covering leaf bases. As a rule, a new runner begins its growth in length at this early stage. The rapid development of successive runners explains the well-known 'chain formation' in vallisnerias; young plants in different stages of development all remain attached to each other.

The young slip can take in nutrients and accomplish photosynthesis as soon as the first leaves and roots have formed. It no longer depends for its supply on the runner of the parent plant. The slip could then be separated, but although the slip itself would not be damaged in any way, development of successive sprouting runners would be impeded. If the aim is a maximum rate of propagation it is better to allow slips to grow undisturbed for a time.

Vallisneria runners normally grow along the top of the substratum. In some conditions, however, e.g. if the substratum is raised or the mother plant is set in too deep, runners may grow in the substratum itself. The elongated internodes of the runners are fairly long-lived, but they do disintegrate after a time so that a natural isolation of the slip from the parent plant follows. Each plant forms not only one runner, but many others develop in the axils of later leaves; it is this occurrence which leads to the very high rate of vegetative reproduction in vallisnerias.

Echinodorus species also form runners and they look just like those of vallisnerias. Here too elongated internodes develop and, as they grow, they push along apical buds. But, despite this apparent conformity, the two genera display differences in their way of branching. As far as aquarium keeping is concerned, these differences are unimportant. The runners of vallisnerias are lateral shoots; in *Echinodorus* species, on the other hand, the apical vegetation cone in a leaf rosette grows into a runner, and the rosette itself carries on as a lateral shoot. Slips evolve as side shoots on the runners.

A completely different type of runner is found in the genus *Cryptocoryne*. Although the runners develop as lateral shoots in the leaf axils of parent plants, as do those of the vallisnerias, normally they grow in and not on the substratum. Furthermore, the runners possess a very different build and growth habit. Tips are not formed by temporarily dormant buds but by vegetation cones, which determine the runners' growth processes. Differentiation into internodes and nodes which carry some leaf organs occurs at the back of the vegetation cone. Runners come forth from a variable number of elongated internodes, generally not more than one to two cm in length. The scale-leaves positioned on the nodes are colourless. They enclose the internodes and also sheathe and protect the vegetation cone at the tip of the runner. These leaves are short-lived and, therefore, lacking in older sections of runners. Buds develop in leaf axils, and adventitious roots sprout from the nodes.

After a period of subterranean growth the runner tips penetrate the substratum and adopt an overground habit. Considerable changes then occur. Compressed, rather thickened internodes form which could be described as a rhizome. Moreover, the scale-leaves which contain no chlorophyll pass through intermediate stages with a slight indication of leaf-blades until they are succeeded by typical foliage leaves. In places where the compressed internodes are developing the growth of roots becomes much more active. The new plants growing as a result are slips.

If necessary, the slips can exist independently at quite an early stage; they can be separated without damage once they have developed two or three foliage leaves. Nevertheless, the runner sections from which they have been taken are preserved for quite a long time. New runners generally sprout from sections of the rhizome, but they can also develop from the buds present in the scale-leaf axils on the runners.

Some *Sagittaria* species, e.g. *S. subulata* and *S. platyphylla*, are propagated by slips. Furthermore, plants with elongated shoot axes, e.g. the genus *Potamogeton*, develop a runner, in or on the substratum. Slips form and as soon as they are sufficiently strong for cultivation they can be isolated.

Propagation by slips is typical of many floating species with a compressed shoot axis and rosette-like leaf arrangement. Such species may be rooted in the substratum in shallow water. Examples for the above are: *Eichhornia crassipes; Pistia stratiotes; Stratiotes aloides; Hydrocharis morsus-ranae;* and species of *Limnobium*. In very favourable growth conditions these plants produce a profusion of runners and slips. Mostly one elongated internode forms the runner which is short-lived so that the young plant is isolated at an early stage.

Propagation by Cuttings

All aquatic plants possessing a shoot axis composed of predominantly elongated internodes as well as a leaf arrangement, either opposite and decussate or whorled, can be propagated by cuttings; it does not matter whether the plants live submerged or emerse as marsh plants.

Propagation by cuttings plays a large role in the cultivation of aquarium plants. It is usually more productive than propagation by runners but, unlike the latter, it does need active, human intervention. Provided that some basic principles are observed propagation from cuttings is quite simple. A suitable section of a shoot which is put into the substratum for vegetative propagation is called a cutting.

What is needed, first of all, is a well-developed mother plant of the right species; it can be either branched or not branched. As an example, Ill. *30* shows a mother plant of the *Hygrophila* species which is not branched. The number of cuttings that can be obtained depends on the size of the mother plant. To begin with the top section of the shoot—therefore called head-cutting—can be used; it should be composed of the tip of the shoot and also two nodes further back on the stem. Depending on its length the remaining shoot of the mother plant can be divided into further cuttings. These may be termed shoot-cuttings and should possess at least three nodes. The number of nodes given for head and shoot-cuttings are the minimum needed to guarantee healthy development. Of course, cuttings can also be longer in which case they have more nodes.

Cuttings may be separated either with a knife or with scissors, but using one's fingers is usually adequate as most of the shoots are quite soft. Divisions should be clean and even, and care should be taken to avoid bruising and rents; otherwise there is a danger of decay. If the lowest internode rots, rooting and further development of the cutting are at risk. As a further precaution an aquarist would be well advised to remove the leaves from the bottom node or, in longer cuttings, from the two lowest nodes. Cuttings should be planted deep enough for the leafless nodes to be completely covered by the substratum. The basal nodes are the starting points from which adventitious roots sprout. Unless plants are able to form adventitious roots the method of propagation by cuttings cannot be used. If basal

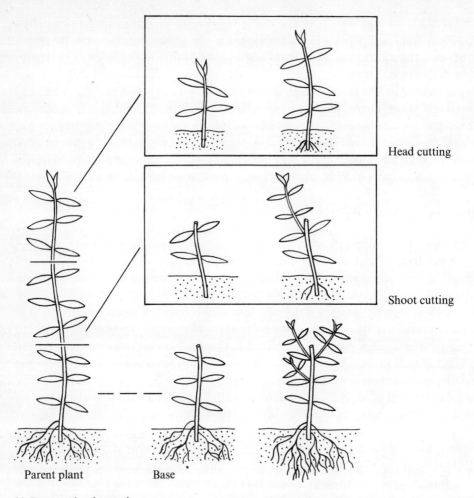

Head cutting

Shoot cutting

Parent plant   Base

30 Propagation by cuttings

leaves are left on a cutting they get into the substratum, either partially or completely. Usually they die off and may contaminate areas of the substratum. However, where larger amounts of cuttings are processed, for instance in aquarium plant nurseries, the removal of basal leaves is not necessary as growth conditions in such places differ from those of an aquarium.

In recent years a different procedure of dealing with cuttings has been recommended on a number of occasions. Cuttings should be attached to the substratum with bent glass rods instead of being planted. The new adventitious roots will penetrate the substratum and then anchor themselves in it. It is a procedure which involves greater effort, but it lessens the danger of basal internodes dying off. Leaves do not have to be removed. It might be prudent to follow this advice when valuable cuttings are handled.

Head cuttings thrive rather quickly because they have an active vegetation cone capable of functioning. Thus, new leaves and internodes are produced at the same time as new roots (Ill. *30*). Shoot cuttings take longer to become established. Apart from having to take root they also need the development of a bud in a leaf axil. It is from this bud that a lateral shoot comes forth which then continues the growth of the cutting (Ill. *30*).

If a mother plant is branched, lateral stems can be used as cuttings. They correspond to head cuttings but, if their length allows it, they can be split up into head and shoot cuttings.

Many species suitable for propagation by cuttings grow faster and branch more readily when they grow as marsh plants. Emerse cultivation of mother plants is therefore recommended if a large stock of cuttings is wanted, e.g. in aquarium plant nurseries. Of course, such cuttings should have become adapted to living submerged before they are sold in the trade. This is quite simple. Initially the cuttings should be quite short; they can either be put into the water immediately, or they can be left in very humid air and put into water after the new roots have appeared. Either way, the cuttings do well submerged in water and soon develop floating leaves.

Propagation by cuttings is used for two reasons. First, it is the sensible thing to do for someone who receives just a single shoot of a new species, as happens sometimes. Once the cutting has taken root and grown well, further cuttings suitable for cultivation can be taken from the plant. Thus it is possible to propagate a number of plants and also secure the maintenance of the species. If the shoot is long enough it can be divided into several cuttings immediately. Secondly, production of numerous cuttings may well be desired by those who either wish to give some away, or exchange or sell them. Thus all species suitable for cultivation by cuttings reach the trade not just as developed plants, but also as cuttings, although exclusively as head cuttings.

In nature, multiplication by cuttings plays an insignificant role compared with propagation by slips. Nonetheless, it does occur; sections of shoots break off, develop adventitious roots and then anchor themselves in the ground.

Propagation by Submerged Shoots

When kept submerged, the species recommended for propagation by cuttings depend, more or less, on the substratum for a part of the nutrients they need; they take them in through their roots. If shoots of such plants are left floating in the water they can survive for quite a long time. However, they are prone to look rather stunted compared with their planted counterparts.

There are, however, species which react completeley differently, e.g. those of the genera *Egeria; Elodea; Lagarosiphon; Hydrilla; Najas; Ceratophyllum*, and *Utricularia*. They take in all the nutrients they need with the whole surface of the plant body. Most of them grow a few roots and may anchor themselves in the substratum, but they are not dependent on it. They are not only well able to thrive unattached and floating, they also grow and branch out. It is therefore possible to propagate them by using submerged shoots.

Not only is this kind of propagation very simple to handle, it also produces a high yield. Longish, well-developed shoots can be split into small pieces of approximately 5 cm in length. The hindmost sections of longer shoots are rarely usable because they are often decayed. A sufficient number of leafy nodes on the other sections guarantees their further development. Tips with a functioning vegetation cone grow immediately. Sections from further back first have to form a bud in a leaf axil which has to produce a lateral shoot. The new plant develops from this shoot. The section of the mother shoot still left perishes sooner or later.

Many *Najas* species possess very brittle shoot axes; thus sections of shoots break off easily and the plants propagate themselves vegetatively from submerged shoot sections—a process which happens frequently in nature. With the other examples mentioned previously, this particular process occurs rarely. Instead, lateral shoots become isolated when the older sections of the mother shoot to which they had been attached die off.

Propagation by Rhizomes

Many marsh plants suited to being grown in margins or shallow areas of pools have rhizomes, among them: *Acorus calamus; Butomus umbellatus; Iris pseudacorus*, and the *Peltandra* species. The rhizomes of these species show a fairly marked tendency to branch out so that they form into thick clusters. They can be split into smaller sections (each possessing several shoots) either with a knife, or with a spade if the plant is very strong. Cuts on the rhizomes should be as smooth as possible to prevent decay. Protective tissue soon forms over the cuts so that they heal quickly. All the rhizome sections can then be re-planted, and they will thrive. If the aim is a maximum yield of new plants, e.g. in a nursery for aquarium plants, the rhizomes can be cut into very small pieces. Furthermore, every single lateral shoot can be detached and used, but care should be taken that at least a short segment of rhizome is left at its base.

In some species the rhizome branches out much less; in others it barely branches at all if raised in conditions of cultivation. Rhizomes with scanty branching occur in the genera *Nymphaea* and *Nuphar* as well as in *Anubias* species. Of course, lateral shoots can be taken off once they have strengthened sufficiently, but a high rate of multiplication cannot be expected from them. Medium and large *Echinodorus* species are even worse off in this respect. They very rarely send out usable lateral shoots in aquarium conditions. However, in most cases this deficiency is compensated by the plants producing adventitious buds (see page 76).

Rhizomes are rather long-lived, a fact well-known to many aquarists about species of *Echinodorus*. If an aquarium has been left with little attention for several years and is then thoroughly cleared out, older leafless sections of rhizomes are often found in the substratum after the plants have been removed. From these old rhizome sections some limited multiplication can be expected. This also applies to Nymphaeaceae and the genus *Anubias*. Aquarists often hesitate to separate the old rhizome sections. However, there is no need to worry; provided that the cut is smooth and clean the leafy front sections of the rhizomes which are to be put back into the tank will not suffer in any way. Here too, protective tissue forms quickly and heals the cut.

If the separated piece of rhizome is very long it can be cut into smaller pieces. In *Echinodorus* species a length of 3 cm is adequate. Vigorous *Nymphaea* and *Nuphar* rhizomes should be cut into pieces of at least 10 cm in length to ensure that they are left with a sufficient number of nodes. Scissors are used to cut off all root remnants neatly to prevent decay. The rhizome pieces are then put into a dish with water and left to themselves. After some time, one or more buds appear; they grow into lateral shoots which develop adventitious roots. Initially, they obtain their nourishment from the food reserves stored in the rhizome.

It may be asked why rhizome sections possess such a considerable power of regeneration. In rhizomes the shoot axes are composed of compressed and thickened internodes. Therefore, the nodes on which the leaves are positioned succeed one another closely; so do the leaf axils. Potentially, every one of the latter is capable of producing a bud. The buds stay alive long after the leaves themselves have died off. In the wild such reserve buds become active if the shoot vegetation cone perishes owing to outside environmental influences. In cultivation, cutting up of the rhizome has the same effect.

Young, lateral shoots should not be severed too early from the mother rhizome section. Although leaves develop and grow fairly soon the new shoot axis is initially very short because of its compressed growth. It is easy to be misled. If the young shoot is separated too early one may just get hold of the leaf bases, but not the shoot axis. Thus, the vegetation cone is often destroyed and the young shoot is lost. However, it is quite simple to cut off the young shoot with a knife once it has strengthened sufficiently. Cuts should be made close to the rhizome, but to ensure that mistakes are avoided the aquarist can leave a small piece of the mother rhizome attached to the shoot. When the shoots have been separated they should be planted immediately; they will grow satisfactorily.

In cryptocorynes old stolon sections as well as rhizomes are also usable for propagation. The sections should not measure less than 5 cm in length. In that case—despite elongated internodes—there should be a sufficient number of nodes capable of regeneration owing to reserve buds.

Propagation by Adventitious Shoots

An adventitious shoot is a plantlet which has formed vegetatively on any organ of the mother plant. There are two possibilities of propagating from adventitious shoots. On the one hand, they may form spontaneously and are then used for the purpose of multiplication. On the other hand, in certain species adventitious shoots are induced by human intervention.

Adventitious shoots from which plantlets grow occur in several strains of higher plants, e.g. grasses; several species related to the common onion; the dwarf water lily which is cultivated as a pot plant; and in a few terrestrial ferns. The aquarist is well aware of this phenomenon in ferns of the genus *Ceratopteris* and *Microsorium pteropus*. In the floating *Ceratopteris pteroides* as well as in submerged species numerous buds develop on leaf edges and, eventually, these grow into plantlets. The latter emit adventitious roots and sooner or later, detach themselves from the mother plant. If *Microsorium* is left undisturbed it may produce several generations, one upon another.

An aquarist will also be familiar with adventitious shoots formed by the genus *Echinodorus*. In the particular species of this genus which possess rhizomes propagation from adventitious shoots plays a very important role. Adventitious shoots develop in the region of inflorescences, but with variable intensity in different species (see page 233). Adventitious shoots also form in the region of inflorescences in *Aponogeton undulatus* and related strains (see page 298).

Adventitious shoots are known to occur in *Nymphaea* cv. Daubenyana (see page 123). The plant is a sterile hybrid and cannot be propagated from seeds. Growth of adventitious shoots is furthered by abscission of the leaves. This example serves as an introduction to those species which will only produce adventitious shoots if the process is assisted.

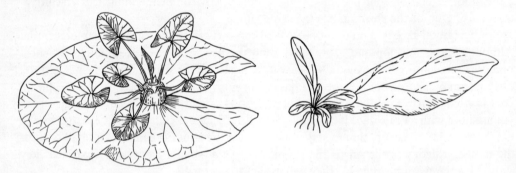

31 Development of adventitious plantlets on an isolated leaf of *Hygrophila polysperma*

In some species belonging to the Acanthus family, e.g. the genera *Hygrophila* and *Nomaphila*, single leaves can be cut off and floated on the water. After a time a bud develops owing to division of cells connected with processes of differentiation in the place of abscission, the bud producing an adventitious plantlet (Ill. *31*). A very large leaf may produce several buds. If largish leaves are cut into several pieces a new plantlet will grow from each section. Adventitious shoots develop rather slowly and need some attention. In a nursery for aquarium plants multiplication from adventitious shoots would cause too much work, particularly as the species concerned are, on the whole, easily propagated from cuttings. However, in the case of *Rorippa aquatica* propagation from adventitious shoots is recommended—indeed it is absolutely necessary; growth form of the plant is rosette-like which does not permit multiplication from cuttings.

Propagation by Tissue Culture

In recent times the possibility of asexual propagation by tissue culture has been discussed in aquarist circles. The method is being used in specialized establishments working on the propagation of cultivated plants and young trees; it has also been tried by orchid enthusiasts. In aquatic plants first successes have been recorded with cryptocorynes; small sections of their runners have been used as initial material.

Propagation by tissue culture is only feasible for plants which do not multiply readily or profusely with more orthodox methods, but which will produce a large number of individual plants if tissue culture is applied. The principle of tissue culture involves the use of certain chemicals to neutralize the blockage which discourages cells of some tissues of the plant body from dividing. Once the cells are capable of dividing again they can built up new and independent plants with all the necessary organs.

The plant sections with which one starts first have to be washed very carefully in water. They are then cut into smaller pieces, approximately one to two mm long. Afterwards these have to be sterilized in an appropriate solution. Working in completely sterile conditions is absolutely essential for success and is probably the greatest problem for the aquarist who is keen on experimenting. The slightest contamination will result in infection from bacteria or fungi. The sterilized tissue sections are put into a Petri or similar glass dish filled with certain chemical solutions in agar. The most important constituents of the chemicals are substances promoting growth. Normally the chemical medium is made up in such a way that the development of shoots only is induced. One piece of tissue may produce fifty or more shoots. These can be isolated and either re-attached or transplanted into another suitable substratum. A constant temperature and evenly fixed day/night rhythm should create favourable conditions. As soon as the young plants have become sufficiently vigorous they can be planted out in a natural environment.

Those who are really interested in the method will have to consult specialized literature dealing with the subject in greater depth.

Flower Development

If use is to be made of sexual propagation for multiplying marsh and aquatic plants one depends on their flowers. It is, therefore, necessary to know something about the flowering habits of the plants. In aquarium cultivation some plants flower readily if they are provided with very favourable growth conditions. As a rule they are species which would grow submerged permanently in the wild. Among them are many of the frogbit family (Hydrocharitaceae) often seen in an aquarium; all the species of *Aponogeton* suitable for aquarium cultivation; and a few cryptocorynes. The water lilies living permanently in water—in the wild as well as in a planthouse—flower regularly in the summer months.

Another group of aquatic plants, however, rarely flower when they are cultivated submerged, but only if they are grown emersed as marsh plants or, at least, allowed to grow out of the water. The group includes those marsh plants whose natural habitat is flooded temporarily but shallow. Examples are the species of *Echinodorus* which send out runners; many of the widely distributed cryptocorynes; and species of the genera *Bacopa*, *Hygrophila* and *Ludwigia*.

As aquarium plants are normally received in the submerged form the question arises how one can induce them to grow emersed. Older literature for aquarists often advised people to proceed very carefully and slowly, lowering the water level centimetre by centimetre. However, the circumstances which affect the plants in their natural habitat should be borne in mind; the water level may sink quite suddenly and the plants have to survive nonetheless. An area in a territory may have a few centimetres of water one day and, if the high water recedes, may be dry the next. In fact, the submerged form of an aquarium plant can become adapted to being emersed quite quickly provided it is well-rooted in the substratum for the necessary intake of extra water. Therefore, cuttings of submerged plants cannot be taken out of the water and cultivated emersed immediately. Instead, cuttings and slips should stand under water, either in flower pots or other suitable dishes. The containers should be filled with a soil mixture which is to provide the plants with sufficient nutrients once they have turned into emersed plants. As soon as roots have developed the pots can be taken out of the water and left in a very humid atmosphere to begin with; in the home it would have to be a covered aquarium tank. Some plants then lose all their leaves, but new ones soon form; these are aerial leaves adapted to the changed surroundings.

Of course, the plants cannot be expected to flower immediately after they have become emerse. In many species, for instance, flower development is subject to photoperiodism. Thus the initiation of flowers depends on a certain daily period of illumination (see page 67).

Pollination

When the flowers have formed they need to be pollinated so that they become fertile and produce seeds. Pollination is the term used for the transference of the pollen, which is contained in the anthers, to the stigma of the ovary of the flower. In the wild this happens in various ways; pollen can be carried by animals—usually insects, the wind and the water.

Entomophilous (insect-pollinated) flowers need some mechanisms to make it possible for the pollen to be brought to the stigma. The blossoms have to attract insects to pay them regular visits, to stay in or on them long enough to touch anthers as well as stigmata, and the pollen has to attach itself to certain parts of the pollinating insects for some time. Entomophilous flowers, therefore, possess certain characteristic features for luring and attracting insects, as well as sticky pollen. The lure is provided by the nourishment the insects can obtain from the sugary juice—the so-called nectar in the flower, or the surplus of pollen produced by some species. The attraction lies in the optical and chemical nature of the flowers. Often, both have a joint effect. The colouration and markings of the flowers can be regarded as the optical attraction and their smell as the chemical. The scent of flowers is normally pleasant to the human nose, but it can be repellent as for instance the smell of decay emanating from some members of the arum family.

Pollinating insects are not only attracted by single blossoms; whole inflorescences fulfil the same function. The latter applies if single blossoms are rather small, but groups of them provide a sufficiently striking optical effect. Furthermore, the flowers of some species are so inconspicuous that an additional optical lure is necessary to bring insects to them, e.g. the bracts of the arum family. Such bracts are also known to an aquarist in the form of the spathe in cryptocorynes.

Anemophily (wind-pollination) requires that the flowers scatter a large quantity of pollen; that the single pollen grains detach themselves easily once they are in the air; and that they can remain suspended for a time. Such pollen grains are therefore smooth and dry. The stigma has to be freely exposed and its surface must be large enough to allow frequent reception of pollen. A perianth would only hinder transference of pollen and, in any case, it has lost its function as a display organ. In wind-pollinated flowers, therefore, the perianth is either much reduced or completely missing. The flowers also lack the lure and attraction which would bring insects to them.

In a very small number of flowering plants the pollen is brought to the stigma by the medium of water. The pollination of some members of the frogbit family (an important one in aquarium keeping) occurs on the surface of the water. The genera *Najas* and *Ceratophyllum* are pollinated under water.

The essence of pollination does not lie in a purely random transference of pollen. What is to be achieved is a regular transference of pollen from the flowers of an individual to the stigma of flowers of another individual of the same species. This is the principle of cross-pollination and it is of great value to the maintenance and evolution of a species. Cross-pollination from a male and a female flower of the same species results in a constant recombination of hereditary factors and eliminates inbreeding.

The most effective method for achieving cross-pollination is self-sterility. It manifests itself by seeds not developing if pollen is transferred from stamens to the stigma of the same individual. In this case the styles and the stigma act as a physiological filter; by means of certain substances they hinder germination and development of the pollen tube of their own pollen as well as that of an alien species. Even in plants with a less pronounced degree of self-sterility the growth of their own pollen tubes may be delayed compared with that of other individuals so that the latter's stigma is receptive first (proterogyny).

In plants with hermaphrodite flowers self-pollination is often avoided by stamens and carpels ripening at different times. As a rule the stamens ripen first which is known as protandry. Examples are found in the genus *Myriophyllum*. However, pollination from a neighbouring blossom situated on the same plant may well occur.

In unisexual flowers stamens and carpels are in separate flowers which aids cross-pollination considerably. If the plants are monoecious (female and male unisexual flowers on the same plant) separation in time of maturing of the sexes supports cross-pollination. Thus in *Sagittaria platyphylla* the female blossoms situated in the first, or at most second, whorl of an inflorescence flower first; the blossoms have usually withered by the time the higher positioned male flowers open out. In this particular example, however, the effectiveness of the flowers' unisexuality is very limited because of their lack of self-sterility. As *S. platyphylla* also propagates itself vegetatively from runners, all the plants in the immediate neighbourhood of the mother plant are its descendants and completely identical with it genetically. Therefore, if pollination occurs in such descendants it corresponds to self-pollination. If these plants are cultivated, or others like them, and seeds are to be produced, one has to ensure that two inflorescences, each in a different phase of development, are at hand. Where the arrangement of unisexual flowers is dioecicous (male and female flowers on different plants) every pollination is a cross-pollination. Many examples can be found in the frogbit family, as with *Vallisneria*, *Egeria* and *Elodea*.

Most species of flowering plants possess varieties in which cross-pollination as well as self-pollination leads to seed development. Thus one single plant may also be able to produce seeds. In some self-pollinated plants the blossoms may no longer open out, an occurrence noted occasionally in flowers of *Barclaya longifolia*. The flowers of this plant remain submerged, but seeds form nonetheless.

There are a few cases of parthenogenesis, i.e. seeds develop although the flowers have neither been pollinated nor fertilized. However, such occurrences cannot be distinguished from self-pollination without scientific examination.

The following practical hints may be useful to those who wish to propagate plants sexually by pollination.

Very few species produce an adequate amount of seeds and not nearly every one of their flowers develops. Frequently human intervention is necessary. However, *Ludwigia* species and *Echinodorus berteroi* are known to produce flowers and seeds freely. As a rule artificial pollination needs to be used so as to obtain a really good yield of seeds. The reason is probably found in a lack of suitable pollinating insects in aquarium and planthouse conditions.

For artificial pollination a fine paint brush is normally used for the transfer of pollen. Soft bird feathers have also been recommended. One's fingers will do for large and easily accessible flowers provided sufficient care is taken. In *Echinodorus* species, for instance, one only needs to rub the pollen from the peripheral stamens gently on to the stigma in the centre of the flower. If several flowers of the same species bloom at the same time it is better to cross-pollinate.

Artificial pollination is by no means always successful. Failures can be caused by a number of factors, often difficult to discern by a plant lover, if at all. Self-sterility (mentioned previously) may play a part; the timing of pollination may be wrong as the stigma of some species is receptive at certain times of day only; or the temperature and other environmental factors may be unfavourable.

After a successful pollination the pollen grains on the stigma germinate, the pollen tubes growing through the tissue of the pistils, or certain ducts of the pistils, until they reach the ovules in the ovary. The pollen tubes penetrate the ovules and transfer sperm nuclei; subsequently each sperm nucleus fuses with a female sex-cell. This process is the actual fertilization. It initiates the changes which take place in the whole region of the flower. Eventually, the flower turns into the fruit and the seeds ripen inside the fruit.

Sowing and Germination

If marsh and aquatic plants are to be propagated from seeds some attention needs to be paid to the storage of the seeds or fruits. When to harvest and what kind of crop to expect varies with circumstances; suitable references for the different varieties are usually available. It is not really possible to generalize on the correct method of storage for seeds and fruits. The small nuts of the arum family and the seeds of dry-skinned capsules can always be stored in a dry place. As far as the seeds of water-berries are concerned, aquarists' opinions differ. Some aquarists put all their trust in storing seeds in water; others have had good results from seeds stored dry. Exact observations are not available up to date.

The life-span of seeds is very variable; in aquatic plants there is still an overall lack of experience. It is, therefore, safer to sow soon after harvesting. Seeds and fruitlets which have been kept dry are best sown in small flower pots or other suitable bowls; these can be set up either emersed or submerged. If the pots are kept submerged they have to be filled with soil so that the young seedlings are provided with sufficient nutrients. A well-proven mixture consists of two thirds of matured compost soil and one third of sand to which a little peat has been added. Finally, the soil or soil-mixture should be covered with a thin layer of fine sand; the seeds are then sprinkled on top. Larger seeds are covered with a further layer of sand. However, very small seeds—like those of the *Ludwigia* species—should not be covered as they germinate more easily if they are left exposed. The flower pots are then kept emersed in the early stages and transferred to the water later on. Very small seedlings are rather susceptible to the filamentous algae which may infest the water. On the other hand, if the flower pots are kept emersed for germination the soil may become covered with blue-green algae, and so exposing the seedlings to health hazards. If experiments are conducted in the home, and if a flower pot is set up emerse an aquarium must always be used; the tank should be filled with approximately one cm of water. The soil in the pot soaks up the water, and the latter also ensures the necessary humidity.

If seedlings are to be submerged the soil in the flower pots has to be well soaked, and it is absolutely essential that the seeds are covered with sand. Otherwise, one may be in for some sad surprises. Air bubbles will probably escape and dislodge the seeds; and the rising current of air may bring uncovered seeds to the surface of the water. In the wild the seeds float on the water for a time as they weigh so little, but eventually they tend to drift away. They never sink to the bottom until they have become saturated with water. In cultivation it is possible to counteract the seeds' tendency to rise. Pots are left emersed for a few days and put into water only after the seeds have become water-saturated.

In order to save space seeds are usually sown rather densely. But after some time the seed-lings have to be taken out, separated and transplanted in new pots. In gardening language the process is referred to as 'pricking out'.

The seeds of water-berries tend to germinate more easily; in the initial stages they develop better if one leaves them floating in the water. The seedlings can be planted once they have become sufficiently strong.

Germination temperature for tropical and subtropical plants normally lies between 20°C and 25°C, but a somewhat higher temperature will do no harm. Aquantic plants of temperate latitudes often germinate in temperatures of just over 10°C.

Every germination begins with absorption by and subsequent swelling up of the seed. The volume of the seed increases and, finally, the inner organs burst the seed-coat or, where applicable, the pericarp. At the same time, the embryo begins its growth and to

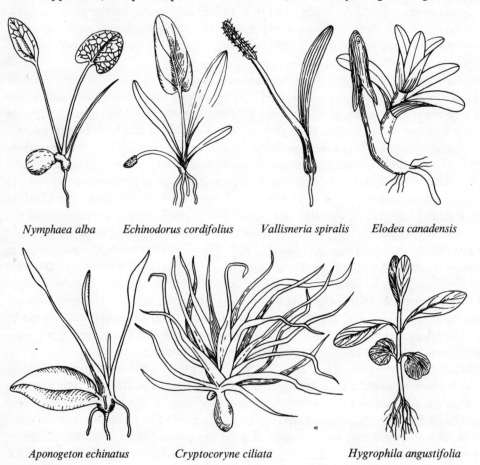

Nymphaea alba   Echinodorus cordifolius   Vallisneria spiralis   Elodea canadensis

Aponogeton echinatus   Cryptocoryne ciliata   Hygrophila angustifolia

32 Seedlings

activate the existent nutrients, decomposing and reabsorbing them. Of course, the nutrients may be stored in the embryo itself. In every germination the root appears first. Further processes of germination are very variable in the different genera. For instance, cotyledons may unfold and turn into the first assimilating organs; alternatively, the cotyledons may remain in the seed-coat, either partly or fully, and so accomplish the function of reabsorption of nutrients by taking them from the endosperm (Ill. *32*).

In our aquatic plants results from germination are very variable. Many species germinate quite easily whereas others are rather unreliable. An amateur who likes to experiment should not allow himself to be discouraged easily. A number of different factors may cause a failure, and it is often impossible to be certain of the exact reason.

Breeding

By breeding is meant the new production of valuable species of food and decorative plants as well as the support and constant improvement of their characteristics. In the course of history, man at first bred from selected species. The more active methods of cross-breeding and induced mutational changes were introduced at a much later stage.

The cultivation of aquatic plants is a very new field and—up to date— breeding has played hardly any role. The water lilies with their many species existing in the open as well as in planthouses are an exception. As a rule only imported wild plants are used for propagation. If a particularly suitable or decorative specimen is chosen an 'unconscious selection' for future breeding may well have been made; it happened often in the early days of plant cultivation. Thus, nothing is known of the origins of *Cabomba caroliniana* var. *paucipartita* which does not exist in the wild. It is known that *C. caroliniana* 'Silbergrüne' was discovered as a shoot mutant in a nursery for aquatic plants where it has been propagated.

It has been pointed out that it is quite possible to breed from selected plants in respect of the genus *Echinodorus*. Sexual propagation of imported wild plants of this genus results in a certain variability. Seedlings of some species, growing mainly as marsh plants in the wild, normally possess leaves with long stalks, but occasionally seedlings with short-stalked leaves are found among them. The latter do noticeably better in submerged conditions. It is, therefore, essential to sort out the forms with short-stalked leaves and propagate from them if they are to be kept submerged in an aquarium.

Considerable variability is also known to occur in seedlings of the *Aponogeton crispus* group and, thus, it is possible to select the most beautiful specimens and breed from them. Experienced aquarists or water-garden horticulturalists can put the method of hybridization among species to good use and breed not only particularly decorative plants but also those with special, positive qualities. In the genus *Cryptocoryne*, for example, it would be worthwhile to breed forms resistant to the so-called Cryptocoryne disease.

All those who specialize in breeding aquatic plants should, for the benefit of others, make exact notes on the nature of their experiments. If it is possible to create a new species, reliable documentation would be valuable for anyone who is interested in the subject.

6. Nomenclature

All fairly well-known plants have common names in colloquial use; to a certain degree this also applies to aquatic plants. However, common names vary from one language to another and, thus, they are not suitable for scientific nomenclature. *Egeria densa* is a plant well-known to aquarists; its German name is 'Argentinische Wasserpest'; in Dutch it is called 'Argentijnse Waterpest'; in English-speaking countries it is known as a 'Brazilian waterweed'; in the Czech language it is called 'Douška hustolistá'. Additionally, there are names invented by the trade or collectors—although rarely by aquarists—simulating scientific names by their construction and inclusion of Latin or Latinized words. But these names are not in accordance with the rules pertaining to nomenclature, and they have no scientific validity. Before the small-flowered Amazon sword plant was given its ultimate scientific name of *Echinodorus parviflorus* by the biologist Rataj it was traded under the name of 'Echinodorus peruensis' and 'Echinodorus tocantins'. In order to make a clear distinction between such imprecise names and proper scientific ones it has become common usage in aquarist circles to add the epithet 'spec.' to the generic name and then a fancy name, where correct nomenclature of a species is either in doubt or a valid scientific name has not been decided upon. Thus one finds names like *Utricularia* spec. 'Johore' or *Cryptocoryne* spec. 'Fasanenfeder' (in German).

Obligatory rules for formulation or alteration of scientific names are laid down in the "International Code of Botanical Nomenclature" which is published in three languages: English, French and German. Necessary alternations are first discussed and then decided upon by experts at an International Botanical Congress. A new edition of the code cancels the previous one.

According to the code each species has one correct scientific name, which is always the one laid down according to the rules of the last code. All other names are known as synonyms.

A valid name has to be published in a printed paper which has to be distributed either by sale, exchange, or as a gift. At the very least, the paper must be available in libraries and easily accessible to botanists. Publication in one of the popular-scientific magazines cannot be recommended.

Up to 1907 it was sufficient to submit with the name of a plant a picture showing its essential characteristics. A description or a diagnosis was demanded from 1 January 1908. A description is a detailed morphological account of the characteristics of the plant to be named, whereas a diagnosis merely includes those features which enable one to distinguish it from similar, related species. However, after 1 January 1935 a description or—at least—a diagnosis, drawn up in Latin, became obligatory. Nowadays, therefore, it is usual to find a diagnosis in Latin together with a description in a modern language.

Since 1 January 1958 the rules have specified that a scientific name has to be linked to a type of the plant. Where the latter is kept has to be mentioned at time of publication. Generally a plant is dried and kept in a herbarium folio, but preservation in alcohol is also possible.

Furthermore, a species has to be named in accordance with the binomial nomenclature founded by Linné; therefore the scientific name of a plant is composed of two parts, the first being the generic name (name of the genus) and the second the specific epithet (name of the species).

Thus, the scientific name of the Amazon sword plant is *Echinodorus amazonicus;* *Echinodorus* is the name of the genus; and *amazonicus* is the specific epithet. If a name is repeated in a text and cannot be confused with the genus of another plant, it is permissible to abbreviate the generic name to e.g. *E. amazonicus.*

To summarize the present rules: a valid, scientific name of a new species has to be in keeping with binomial nomenclature; the name has to be published together with a diagnosis in Latin; it also has to be linked to a type.

As a further mark of distinction the scientific name of a species is followed by an author's name. The latter is often printed in capital letters, but it is not used in the course of normal texts. The author is the person who published the scientific name. Thus the full name of the Amazon sword plant is *Echinodorus amazonicus* RATAJ. If an author's name appears repeatedly, it can be abbreviated in a specified manner, e.g. BUCH. (= BUCHENAU), or L. (= LINNÉ). When two authors are associated in the publication of a scientific name, both their names appear linked by the Latin word 'et', e.g. *Sagittaria montevidensis* CAMISSO et SCHLECHTENDAL. A bracket around the first name of an author expresses a change in the scientific name. The following paragraph will explain what happens in such a case.

A dwarf Amazon plant was named *Alisma tenellum* by Martius in 1830; thus the full name of the plant was *Alisma tenellum* MART. At that time the genus *Echinodorus* was unknown and it was not defined until 1848. Eventually, Buchenau recognized that the characteristics of *A. tenellum* fitted it into the genus *Echinodorus* and moved it to that genus in 1869. Thus the name of the plant was changed to *Echinodorus tenellus* (MART.) BUCH. The different genus appears in the new name.

The specific epithet is retained, but changes its ending which depends on the sex of the generic name. The name of the author who first described the species is put into brackets. Finally, the name of the author who moved the species to a different genus appears in second place, but without brackets.

The rules of nomenclature are also applied to groups of plants below the status of a species, such as sub-species and varieties.

In naturally developed species hybrids an x is put before the specific epithet. In other cases, if a new specific epithet is not required, the specific names of both parent plants are linked by an x, e.g. *Ludwigia repens x palustris.*

In plant cultivation as well as in horticulture it is customary to give names to varieties bred by crossing or selection. As far as aquarium plants are concerned, so far names of varieties have been significant only for the water lilies. How the names are to be constructed and employed is laid down in the "International Code for Nomenclature of Cultivated Plants". According to the code the name of such a variety should be a fancy name and—since 1959—it has to be taken from a living language.

The name of the variety is joined to the scientific name of the genus, a species, or a category below the status of a species; to contrast it from the scientific name it is either put into single quotes, or the abbreviation cv. (= cultivar, i.e. variety) is put between both names. Thus, it is possible to write *Nymphaea* 'James Brydon', or *Nymphaea* cv. James Brydon. The meaning is the same.

7. Classification

In general, the plant kingdom and the animal kingdom are regarded as two basically distinct and separate groups of organisms. However, nowadays, it is recognized that it is primarily the mode of nutrition which distinguishes one group from the other. Plants are able to manufacture their own food by building organic from inorganic substances, whereas animals depend on existing organic matter for their food. But there is a very profound split between anucleate organisms (Prokaryota) and organisms which possess a nucleus (Eukaryota) (Ill. *33*).

		Spermatophyta (Seed Plants) Pteridophyta (Clubmosses, Horsetails and Ferns)		Metazoa (Multicellular Animals)
	Bryophyta (Liverworts and Mosses)			
	PHYTOBIONTA	Higher Plants		ZOOBIONTA Higher Animals
SCHIZOBIONTA Fissiparous Organisms	Algae		Fungi	Unicellar Animals
		PROTOBIONTA Primitive Organisms		
Prokaryota	Eukaryota			

33 The system of the organisms

The cells of anucleate organisms are extremely small. In addition to a nucleus they also lack definable cell-spaces divided by membranes and capable of reacting. The genes which carry the hereditary characteristics are embedded in the central protoplasm; colour substances for assimilation are distributed in the outer layer of the protoplasm. The cells either exist as single units, they live in loosely-knit colonies, or in simple chains. They divide by fission; thus the blue-green algae which belong to the anucleate organisms and the bacteria are termed comprehensively fissiparous organisms (Schizobionta). The very much simpler viruses and similar groups are usually linked together with the bacteria.

Nucleate organisms include plant as well as animal organisms. They not only contain a nucleus but also cell-spaces divided by membranes in which certain metabolic processes take place, e.g. cell respiration and photosynthesis. Reproduction occurs asexually as well as sexually.

Lower orders of living beings in which a nucleus is present include the primitive organisms (Protobionta), classified as a number of independent divisions. Those capable of photosynthesis are summarized as algae. Others depending on organic nutrients are classed either as fungi or as unicellular animals (Protozoa) according to their forms and habits. In some groups there are transitions from animal to plant life or connections with both. The origin of all multicellular animals (Metazoa), which may also be classed as the higher animals (Zoobionta), can be traced to unicellular animals. The fungi, on the other hand, have not evolved into higher forms. The lichens always used to be classed as a separate group. Nowadays they are linked to the fungi; their plant bodies are really dual plants consisting of an alga and a fungus, living symbiotically.

In the group of algae there are freely moving unicellular individuals which can be distinguished as an enormous variety of forms, many with a complex metabolism. The unicellular algae are the earliest organisms in evolutionary history. Their great diversity gave rise to the different evolving groups of algae, such as green, brown, yellow-green, golden-brown and red algae. In the current system of classification they are separated into divisions. Just as in the fungi, a transition from primitive, unicellular to multicellular organisms—with cells capable of fulfilling different functions—occurred in the phyletic lines of the algae, in the course of millions of years. Algae evolved into mobile cell-colonies and attached, simple, filamentous forms. The latter diversified by developing more filaments; they became two- and three-dimensional forms, in part having a complex plant body. However, in this plant body there is no differentiation between shoot axes, leaves and roots.

Algae, which include the seaweeds and pond-scum, are aquatic plant organisms inhabiting the oceans and freshwater. With a few exceptions they have not left their wet element. The green algae are predominantly freshwater inhabitants. They are the ancestors of the first terrestrial plants. The development of new morphological and anatomical structures allowed the plant organisms to raise themselves into the air. A gradual adaptation and migration to ever drier areas of land followed.

The divisions which evolved first of all were the Bryophyta (liverworts and mosses) and the Pteridophyta (clubmosses, horsetails and ferns); further development of the latter group brought about the evolution of the large variety of Spermatophyta (seed plants). All three divisions can be classed as the higher plants (Phytobionta). By far the largest majority of them are terrestrial ones.

In the history of the higher plants, their development underwent many processes of differentiation. However, sooner or later, some species re-adapted themselves to the water as a secondary habitat. By the time they returned to the element whence they had originated their morphological, anatomical and physiological characteristics had improved greatly. Those higher plants which adopted an aquatic habit almost invariably retained the structure they had had to develop for a terrestrial existence. However, these structures became modified—rather homogenously—owing to the different conditions prevalent in the water. Sometimes whole families, sometimes only individual genera or species of otherwise terrestrial plants returned to the water as a habitat.

The Bryophyta (liverworts and mosses) comprise approx. 26,000 species. The plants are very small indeed. The plant body may be very simple, e.g. thalloid and flat with lobed edges, ribbon-like and dichotomously branched, or differentiated as tiny stems and leaves. Water and nutrients are absorbed by the whole surface of the plant body, particularly by the hair-like structures, the rhizoids, which also anchor the plant to the substratum. Reproduction and distribution are from spores.

Bryophyta are plants with an alternation of generations. But, in contrast to the ferns it is the gametophyte (sexual) generation which is superior to the sporophyte generation. First of all, a spore gives rise to the protonema which looks rather like the filament of an alga. The protonema eventually develops into the actual plant—the gametophyte. Ova and spermatozoids are produced in special containers of the plant. When the ovum has been fertilized it develops into the 'moss' capsule; the latter is stalked and, when mature, it turns brown. Spores are then produced in the inside of the capsule. Thus the spore-bearing stage, or sporophyte, presents the second, non-sexual generation. The sporophyte always remains attached to the gametophyte and takes most of its nourishment from it.

Apart from the oceans and very dry deserts there are few areas which are not colonized by the Bryophyta. They thrive best, however, in humid places—in woods, moors or shady gullies. A few species have adapted to an existence in freshwater. By far the largest variety of Bryophyta is found in the tropics.

The Bryophyta are subdivided into two very different classes:
— Hepaticae (liverworts). They comprise approximately 10,000 species. The plant body is either a flat or lobed thallus, or it consists of small stems and leaflets. The latter are one-layered and have no midrib; their arrangement is two-ranked. Species living in water occur in three families only. It is solely the family Ricciaceae which has achieved any importance for aquarists so far.
— Musci (mosses). They include approximately 16,000 species. The plant body is always differentiated by small stems and leaflets. The leaflets are one-layered, but have a midrib of several layers; leaf arrangement is alternate. Species living in water occur in approx. fifteen families. Hitherto only representatives of the families Fontinalaceae (fountain mosses) and Hypnaceae (feather mosses) have been cared for in aquaria. Thus the interested aquarist still has a large choice of plants left for experimenting. The species of the family Sphagnaceae are typical bog-forming mosses; they grow in areas with an acid and poor soil, such as moors. *Sphagnum* is one of the major components of peat, a material widely used by aquarists.

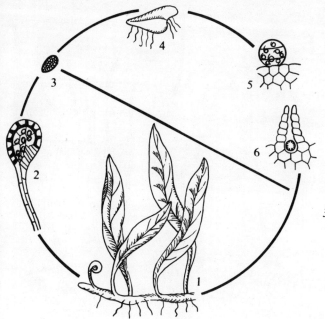

34 Alternation of generations
in ferns (top sexual,
below asexual generation)

1 Fern, 2 Spore case, 3 Spore,
4 Prothallus, 5 Archegonium,
6 Antheridium

The Pteridophyta (club mosses, horsetails and ferns) comprise approx. 12,000 species. Although they are made up of shoot axes, leaves and roots like the seed-plants, these plants reproduce from spores like the Bryophyta. But in contrast to the Bryophyta, the sporophyte (non-sexual) generation is the dominant one (Ill. *34*). When a spore has germinated it grows into an inconspicuous prothallus, representing the gametophyte (sexual) generation. Ova and spermatozoids form in special containers of the prothallus. From the fertilized ovum the actual fern-plant develops which represents the sporophyte (non-sexual) generation. When the fern-plant comes to maturity it can produce new spores. Unlike the majority of Pteridophyta, some Lycopsida (club mosses) and Hydropterides possess sexually-differentiated spores, the large ones being the megaspores, and the small ones the microspores which produce either female or male prothalli. In these groups, therefore, the life cycle, the alternation of generations, is of a very complex nature.

The Pteridophyta thrive mainly under moist conditions, although a few can be found in dry habitats. They are distributed in all climatic zones but have had their greatest evolution in the tropics where their largest representatives can be found, the tree ferns. The present-day species are remnants of correlatives which flourished in geological Medieval and, particularly, Ancient life on our earth.

The now existing Pteridophyta are divided into three different classes:
— Lycopsida (club mosses). They include approximately 1,000 species. The shoot axes are branched dichotomously. Leaves are alternate or arranged in rosettes; they are simple in form, of variable length and single-veined. The sporangia are seated singly on the base of

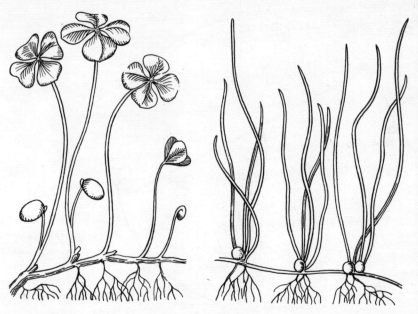

35 Sporocarps in *Marsilea*

the leaf upperside. For the culture there is only one family of interest, namely the Isoetaceae —the quillworts.

— Sphenopsida. They include approximately twenty-five species. Shoot axes are branched laterally. Leaves are arranged in whorls; they are small, scale-shaped and single-veined. Several sporangia together are seated on the underside of shield-shaped leaves. The family Equisetaceae (horsetails) is the only one which has survived into present times. Some of its species colonize a moist environment. For instance, one can find *Equisetum fluviatile* in still waters and reed-belts of the Northern hemisphere.

— Pteropsida (ferns). They include approximately 11,000 species. Their shoot axes are laterally branched. Leaves are alternate and usually arranged in rosettes, variable in size, simple to pinnate, and multi-veined. A large number of sporangia are seated on the leaf underside. Of the numerous families the following are of importance to aquarists: Polypodiaceae (Polypody Family), and Ceratopteridaceae (Pod Fern Family); also Marsileaceae (Marsilea Family), Azollaceae and Salviniaceae (Salvinia Family) (Ill. *35, 36*), the last three belonging to an independent sub-class, the Hydropterides.

The Spermatophyta (seed plants) comprise approximately 300,000 species. The plant body is made up of shoot axis, leaves and roots. Seeds are the characteristic organs for their reproduction. The Spermatophyta belong to the highest plant organisms. They represent by far the greatest part of the flora on our earth.

An alternation of generations also occurs in seed plants; however, owing to considerable modifications and the firm fusion of both generations in one plant body it is not easily recognizable as such. The gametophyte generation is extremely reduced. The embryo develops in the sporophyte—the non-sexual plant.

Spermatophyta evolved from land plants and they are, themselves, predominantly terrestrial. They have spread to the most diverse regions, from arid zones to marshes, from lowlands to high mountains. A relatively small part of them is living in marshes and in water. Many of them are cultivated by lovers of aquatic plants.

Spermatophyta are classified as two separate sub-divisions:

— Gymnospermae or Coniferophytina (plants producing naked seeds). They include approximately 1,000 species. Their seeds develop freely exposed on the carpels. All Gymnospermae are woody plants, generally bearing inconspicuous cones rather than flowers. All fir trees belong to this group. There are no aquatic plants in this sub-division.

— Angiospermae or Magnoliophytina (plants producing covered seeds). They include nearly 300,000 species. The seeds develop enclosed in the ovules formed by the carpels. Some Angiospermae are woody plants; very many are herbaceous. The majority of flowers possess a very colourful perianth. Marsh and aquatic plants occur in several families. The Angiospermae are divided into two classes:

— — Dicotyledonae or Mognoliatae (plants with two cotyledons). They comprise around 250 families with approximately 200,000 species. The seed embryos have two cotyledons. The leaves show a remarkable variety in form; they are simple to pinnate and possess a network of veins. The vascular bundles have a cambium which may cause secondary growth of thickness. The primary root is long-lived and sometimes forms the whole of a much-branched root system, but adventitious roots occur as well. Flower parts are predominantly in multiples of five. The following families are of interest to the cultivator of aquatic plants:

Ranunculaceae (Crow-Foot Family), Nymphaeaceae (Water Lily Family), Cabombaceae, Ceratophyllaceae (Hornwort Family), Saururaceae (Lizard's Tail Family), Crassulaceae

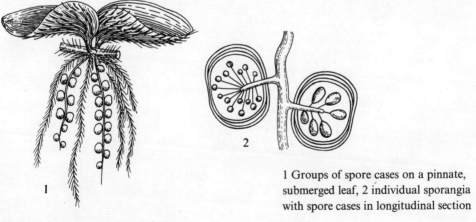

1 Groups of spore cases on a pinnate, submerged leaf, 2 individual sporangia with spore cases in longitudinal section

36 Reproduction by spores in *Salvinia*

(Orpine Family), Podostemaceae (Riverweed Family), Euphorbiaceae (Wolf's Milk Family), Lythraceae (Loosestrife Family), Onagraceae (Evening Primrose Family), Trapaceae (Water Chestnut Family), Haloragaceae (Water Milfoil Family), Hippuridaceae (Mare's Tail Family), Brassicaceae (Mustard Family), Droseraceae (Sundew Family), Elatinaceae (Waterwort Family), Apiaceae (Parsley Family), Callitrichaceae (Water Star-wort Family), Polygonaceae (Buckwheat Family), Amaranthaceae (Amaranth Family), Primulaceae (Primrose Family), Menyanthaceae, Scrophulariaceae (Figwort Family), Lentibulariaceae (Bladderwort Family), Acanthaceae (Acanthus Family), Plantaginaceae (Plantain Family), Lobeliaceae (Bluebell Family), Asteraceae (Aster Family).

—— Monocotyledonae or Liliatae (plants with one cotyledon). They include approximate-ly 50 families with about 100,000 species. Seed embryos have one cotyledon only. Leaves usually have well-developed sheaths, blades of a simple shape and striated nerves. Vascular bundles are without a cambium so that normal secondary growth in thickness does not occur. A primary root is short-lived or lacking and always replaced by adventitious roots. Flower parts in multiples of three are prevalent. Monocotyledons are mainly herbaceous plants. The following families are of interest to the cultivator of aquatic plants:

Alismataceae (Water Plantain Family), Butomaceae, Hydrocharitaceae (Frogbit Family), Aponogetonaceae (Aponogeton Family), Potamogetonaceae (Pondweed Family), Ruppia-ceae, Zannichelliaceae, Najadaceae (Najad Family), Amaryllidaceae (Narcissus Family), Iridaceae (Iris Family), Orchidaceae (Orchid Family), Pontederiaceae (Pickerelweed Family), Mayacaceae (Mayaca Family), Juncaceae (Rush Family), Cyperaceae (Sedge Family), Eriocaulaceae, Poaceae (Grass Family), Araceae (Arum Family), Lemnaceae (Duckweed Family), Sparganiaceae, Typhaceae (Cattail Family).

II. The Families, Genera and Species of Aquatic Plants

Family Ricciaceae · Liverworts

Two genera, 200 species. Distribution worldwide. Liverworts with undivided, flat, dichotomously-branched thallus. Reproduction by spores.

Next to the genus *Riccia*, the genus *Ricciocarpus* also belongs to the family. The latter is represented by just one species, the floating *R. natans*. It occurs, rather like the duckweeds, in sheltered places on the surface of still waters.

Riccia

The genus was defined by Linné in 1753. It was named after the Italian senator P. F. Ricci (about 1730).

Distribution: Almost worldwide.

Characteristics: Perennial or annual plant with a flat dichotomously-branched thallus. Sections of the thallus differ in width. Spore capsules are sunk in thallus tissue.

General Information: The species of the genus *Riccia* colonize very different habitats, being found in deserts, on fields, in a wet environment, and even in the water. The species living in the water are particularly variable. One and the same species may develop floating as well as marsh forms, usually displaying noticeable differences. Only terrestrial forms develop spores. The aquatic forms reproduce asexually. Parts of the plants may become attached to the plumage of waterfowl and, thus, be spread to distant places.

Riccia fluitans L.

The species was named by Linné in 1753.

Distribution: Almost worldwide.

Characteristics: Riccia fluitans is commonly called crystalwort. Body of the aquatic form consists of narrow sections, 0.5—1 mm in width. These are distinctly dichotomously-branched and become loosely matted.

Cultivation and Propagation: Riccia fluitans either forms cushions or spreads out loosely, in either case floating on or just below the surface of the water. It provides fish fry with good hiding places. Spawning cyprinoids (fish akin to carp) like to seek its shelter as a spawning site. Crystalworts provide a little shade. Optimal temperature between 18—25°C. Normally the plants are easy to keep, but sometimes stocks perish without any obvious reason. Propagation from picked off small pieces.

Family Fontinalaceae · Fountain Mosses

Three genera, 35 species. Predominantly plants of the northern hemisphere. Mosses with a body distinctly distinguishable as small stems and leaflets. Reproduction by spores. The three genera are all water mosses.

Fontinalis

In its present form the genus was defined by Hedwig in 1801. Fontinalis (L) = living in fountains.

Distribution: Northern hemisphere and southern Africa.

Characteristics: For the most part perennial mosses with a plant body consisting of small branched stems and leaflets, the latter being variable in shape and colour. Leaves without midrib. Spore capsule sessile or short-stalked, often hidden among the leaves.

General Information: The genus includes approximately 30 species, often difficult to define. Some grow beyond the water level, others can exist as land plants for a limited, but varying length of time.

Fontinalis antipyretica L.

The species was named by Linné in 1753.

Distribution: Temperate latitudes of the northern hemisphere; southern Africa.

Characteristics: Plant body very variable, with roundish or triangular stems. Leaves broad egg-shaped to lanceolate, up to 8 mm long, dark—either olive or black-green.

Cultivation and Propagation: A beautiful moss for an unheated aquarium receiving sufficient illumination. Temperature preferably not above 20°C. Plants best suited to being kept in an aquarium are those taken from standing waters. They should be removed with whatever they are anchored to, stones or wood, and transferred to the aquarium intact. Alternatively, the plants can be fixed to the substratum of the tank with glass rods. Propagation from small separated bunches.

Family Hypnaceae · Feather Mosses

Thirty genera, 450 species. Distributed almost everywhere in the world. Leafy mosses with a plant body divided into small stems and small leaves. Reproduction by spores. Hypnaceae generally grow on soil, on stones, and on rocks. Aquatic mosses occur in the genus *Vesicularia* only.

Vesicularia

The genus was defined by I. K. A. Müller in 1896. The name is derived from vesicularis (L) = formed like bubbles.

Distribution: Predominantly in warmer regions of the world.

Characteristics: Perennial leafy moss consisting of small stems, either creeping in or floating on the water, and egg-shaped or lanceolate small leaves. The latter either with or without midrib. Spore capsule long-stalked.

General Information: The genus includes approximately 130 species. Some south-eastern Asiatic and African species live permanently submerged.

Vesicularia dubyana (C. MUELL.) BROTH.

The species was first named *Hypnum dubyanum* by I. K. A. Müller in 1851 and later moved to the genus *Vesicularia* by Brotherus in 1925.

Distribution: Tropical south-east Asia.

Characteristics: Commonly called Java moss. Dainty moss with intensively branched small stems. Leaves up to 2 mm long, light green.

Cultivation and Propagation: An undemanding moss which has to be kept in a heated aquarium because of its tropical origin. It is at its best if it is allowed to attach itself to stones or wood and left to develop undisturbed. Propagation from small separated tufts.

Family Isoetaceae · Quillworts

Two genera, 75 species. Distribution worldwide. The quillworts are remnants of correlations which existed in a great wealth of forms in earlier periods of cosmological history. The present-day family is represented by just one genus, *Isoetes*, with the exception of a South American genus which consists of one species only.

Isoetes

The genus was defined by Linné in 1753. The name is derived from isos (Gk) = equal, and etos (Gk) = year. The name indicates that the plants' habits are equal throughout the year.

Distribution: Worldwide, but warmer regions are preferred.

Characteristics: Small to medium-sized plants with compressed, knob-like axes of the shoot and crowded leaves arranged in rosettes. Leaves are lineate, triangular or roundish, and sheathed at the base, possessing four characteristic ducts of varying length for aeration. Very complicated reproduction by spores.

General Information: Only two out of the 75 species grow in fairly dry habitats; the others live in bogs or in the water. The shoots are full of nutrients and are eaten by waterfowl and rodents. A succession of new leaves is formed every year. Every one of the first leaves bears a megasporangium, every one of the following bears a microsporangium, and the last are sterile. The sporangia are seated in a pit-like indentation of the leaf upperside near the base of the leaf. The spores are sexually differentiated and are only freed after the leaves have decayed. A much reduced female prothallus develops in the larger, female megaspore, eventually bursting the spore walls and slightly protruding from the spore. The female prothallus forms the egg-cells. Inside the smaller, male microspores male prothalli develop; they are also much reduced and consist of just a few cells. The male prothallus releases spermatozoids, the male sex cells. The spermatozoids are multi-ciliate and move to the female prothalli. A new *Isoetes* plant grows once fertilization has taken place.

Isoetes lacustris L. (Ill. 17)

The species was named by Linné in 1753.

Distribution: Europe, western Asia, North America.

Characteristics: A small quillwort with a compressed, tuberous axis of the shoot and leaves arranged in rosettes. Leaves are roundish, either straight or slightly curved, pointed, up to 20 cm long and 2 mm thick; dark-green.

Cultivation and Propagation: A rare species which does not lose its leaves in the winter and, therefore, can be recommended for an unheated aquarium. The temperature should not go above 18°C for any length of time. The plants make no particular demands on the substrate. Propagation is difficult. Division of older plants is rarely successful because pieces of the plant are likely to rot along the cuts. Propagating from spores is worth consideration. There is a lack of experience, however. References made to the propagation of the next species, *I. setacea*, may apply here as well.

Isoetes setacea LAM.

The species was named by Lamarck in 1789.

Distribution: South-west Europe.

Characteristics: Small plant with tuberous compressed axis of the shoot and a leaf arrangement in rosettes. Leaves roundish, straight or slightly curved, pointed, up to 20 cm long and 0.5 mm thick; light green.

Cultivation and Propagation: Isoetes setacea is undemanding and inconspicuous but, because of its roundish leaves, it is a useful plant to have in a lively, aquascaped aquarium. It looks best when planted in a group in the middle region of a tank. A position in good light is advisable. Temperature approximately 20°C, but it can be lower temporarily. Vegetative propagation by division is not possible. Spores are needed for multiplication. If the plants are kept in a small tank which contains neither fishes nor an appliance for suction, numerous young plants usually develop quite naturally. These can be separated when they are sufficiently strong. However, it may well take a year from the time larger plants are put into the tank until young plants are produced. Quicker results are achieved if spores are harvested and sown. This needs some experience. It should not be forgotten that megaspores as well as microspores are needed. First of all, some leaves have to be examined to see whether any sporangia are present and whether the spores are ripe enough. The spores are white when unripe, grey when half-ripe, and black when ripe. These should then be scattered on a piece of peat, positioned in the water in such a way that it can always soak up moisture from the bottom. The young plants which then grow have to be planted in the substratum when they are strong enough. Sand containing a little loam can be recommended as a substratum for such young plants.

General Information: Because practical knowledge is somewhat lacking in respect of the genus *Isoetes*, it is not certain whether the species has been correctly defined.

Isoetes malinverniana CES. et DE NOT.

The species was named by Cesati and de Notaris in 1858.

Distribution: Northern Italy.

Characteristics: Large plant with tuberous, compressed axis of the shoot and leaves arranged in rosettes. Leaves are slightly triangular and usually spirally twisted at the base; pointed; up to 1 m in length and up to 2.5 mm thick; light green.

Cultivation and Propagation: A species for the background or front corners of tall tanks. Cultivation and propagation as for *I. setacea.*

General Information: The species is only known from the rice paddies of northern Italy. However, it is assumed that it was introduced to the country together with seedcorn imported from south-east Asia and became acclimatized. Up to the present the species has rarely been cultivated.

Family Polypodiaceae · Polypody Family

Fifty genera, 1,200 species. Predominantly tropical-subtropical, although some species are found in temperate latitudes as well. Small to medium-size ferns of very variable appearance, either with rhizomes or shoots with a creeping habit; fronds may be simple or possess several pinnae. Reproduction by spores.

The Polypodiaceae are the largest family of ferns. They are represented in all kinds of different habitats. Although most of them have their roots in the ground, many of them are epiphytes. The latter grow in trees; although not parasites, they catch the water with their leaves and benefit from it. Furthermore, there are species growing on rocks and trunks of fallen trees in beds of brooks and streams, also on sandbanks, in waterfalls, and in bogs. Not only the polypody family, but other fern families as well live in such variable habitats, e.g. Aspleniaceae, Blechnaceae, and Thelypteridaceae. Plants in such habitats may be completely flooded for a time. Thus it is only to be expected that there are some species which can stand up to being constantly flooded without suffering damage and can therefore be kept in an aquarium. But only the genera *Microsorium* and *Bolbitis* have achieved a place of some significance in an aquarium so far.

In polypodies the sporangia are arranged in small groups, rarely over a large area, on the underside of fronds. In some species all fronds develop sporangia, in others only a few. Every sporangium develops numerous homosporous, sexually-undifferentiated spores which are ejected in dry weather. If these spores fall on a moist substrate, they germinate and develop into small, flat and green prothalli, not unlike the liverworts in appearance. The prothallus bears both sex organs, the one developing egg-cells and the other spermatozoids. In moist conditions the spermatozoids move towards the egg-cells and fuse with them. When fertilization has taken place, a new plant grows.

Microsorium

The genus was defined by Link in 1830. The name is derived from mikros (Gk) = small and soros (Gk) = cluster, and refers to the clusters of sporangia seated on the undersides of fronds.

Distribution: South-east Asia.

Characteristics: Small to medium-sized ferns with elongated axes of the shoot and simple, or pronounced lobate leaves.

The genus includes 40 species. Generally they colonize shady, humid habitats, such as rocks and trees in the vicinity of water. So far, only one species has been an important one in aquarium plant cultivation.

Microsorium pteropus (BL.) CHING (Ill. 14)

The species was named *Polypodium pteropus* by Blume in 1828 and moved by Ching to the genus *Microsorium* in 1933. Another name for it is *Leptochilus decurrens*.

Distribution: Tropical south-east Asia.

Characteristic: A fern (also called Java fern) well able to withstand flooding, with a thin, elongated axis of the shoot creeping closely attached to its base, and separately positioned fronds. Fronds of the submerged form short-stalked and lanceolate, up to 25 cm long and up to 3 cm wide, mid to dark-green. Aerial fronds with lanceolate to tripartite blades. Numerous adventitious plantlets form on the blades of fronds and on the roots.

Cultivation and Propagation: Undemanding fern, suitable for a light to slightly shady position in the aquarium. Optimal temperature 20—25°C. This fern must not be planted in the substratum. Instead, the shoot axis has to be fastened on pieces of wood or stones in the tank. Later on it will anchor itself by its roots. Propagation by division of larger specimens or from adventitious plantlets. These grow in several tiers, if left undisturbed while they are developing.

Bolbitis

The genus was defined by Schott in 1843.

Distribution: In all tropical zones.

Characteristics: Small to large ferns with rhizomes or elongated axes of the shoots and simple or pinnate fronds.

The genus includes 85 species. Most of them grow near water, some are temporarily flooded. Supposedly, therefore, the genus contains species which are suitable for care in an aquarium. As the species described below has been successfully cultivated, attempts have been made to do the same with *Bolbitis heteroclita* which can be seen in many botanical gardens. The rate of success has been very variable, however.

Bolbitis heudelotii (FÉE) ALSTON (Ill. 18)

The species was named *Gymnopteris heudelotii* by Fée in 1845 and moved to the genus *Bolbitis* by Alston in 1934.

Distribution: Africa.

Characteristics: A fern well able to withstand flooding with a thin, elongated axis of the shoot, creeping closely attached to its base. Each frond stands by itself. Water leaves stalked with up to 13 lobed or undulate pinnae, up to 30 cm in length, dark olive-green. Aerial fronds more solid in texture and pinnae simpler.

Cultivation and Propagation: A very decorative plant which can be used almost anywhere in an aquarium. The shoot axes must not be covered by the substratum, but like those of *Microsorium* should be initially fastened to pieces of wood or stones where they will anchor themselves with their roots later on. This species does not thrive satisfactorily in every aquarium as it needs clean water and subdued light. A place near the water outlet is supposed to help. Temperature should be near 25°C. Propagation by division of longish shoots.

Family Ceratopteridaceae · Pod Ferns

Another scientific name for the Pod Fern Family is Parkeriaceae. The sole genus belonging to it is *Ceratopteris*.

Ceratopteris

The genus was defined by Brongniart in 1821. The name is derived from keras, keratos (Gk) = horn and pteris (Gk) = fern.

Distribution: In all tropical regions.

Characteristics: Ferns of varying size, rooted in the soil or floating on the surface of the water, with a compressed, inconspicuous axis of the shoot and leaves arranged in rosettes. Leaves lobed or feathery, or having pinnate parts. Adventitious plants on leaves. Reproduction also by spore dispersal.

General Information: Four species only belong to this genus. The only species which has not been cultivated in an aquarium so far is *Ceratopteris richardii*, which occurs in South America, the Greater Antilles, Central Africa and, occasionally, on Madagascar. The possibility cannot be ruled out, however, that the species has not always been correctly identified as it bears a strong resemblance to *C. cornuta*, and may have been mistaken for it. For exact definition the spores have to be examined.

Reproduction is predominantly vegetative from the numerous adventitious plantlets that are produced. At first they appear as small buds in indentations of leaf blades, or rather pinnae. The buds grow very quickly, develop roots and detach themselves sooner or later. The spore-forming leaves are easily distinguishable from ordinary foliage leaves by having narrower pinnae with edges folded downwards. Although cultivated plants also grow such leaves in favourable conditions, spore cases have never been observed on them. Spores are all of the same type and they are not sexually differentiated. Reproduction by means of spores occurs in the same way as in the family of Polypodiaceae, described previously.

Ceratopteris pteridoides (Hook.) Hieron

The species was named *Parkeria pteridoides* by Hooker in 1825 and moved to the genus *Ceratopteris* by Hieron in 1905. Previously aquarists had usually named it *Ceratopteris cornuta* or *Ceratopteris thalictroides* forma *cornuta*.

Distribution: South America, Central America, southern North America and Greater Antilles.

Characteristics: A fern floating on the surface of the water with a dense rosette of leaves. Foliage leaves with a short petiole, the former being up to 30 cm long and 25 cm wide. Leaves of cultivated plants normally smaller. Leaf blades egg-shaped to triangular, either indented or in three to five lobes.

Cultivation and Propagation: The species thrives in good light on the water's surface. However, it must not be allowed to spread out too much as this would take away too much light from plants further down in the aquarium. In botanical gardens, aquarium plant nurseries, and also in planthouses it is a useful plant for providing natural shading. Optimal temperature approx. 25 °C, but it can be lower temporarily. Dense tufts of roots grow in the water itself and offer fish fry good hiding places. If the water level is very low, or if the species are cultivated as marsh plants, the roots penetrate the substratum. The plants are easily propagated because they form many adventitious plantlets.

General Information: In the wild, the species and *C. richardii* appear to have produced hybrids occasionally.

Ceratopteris cornuta (BEAUV.) LEPR. (Ill. 19)

The species was named *Pteris cornuta* by Beauvort in 1806 and moved to the genus *Ceratopteris* by Leprieur in 1830. Aquarists used to make no distinction between this and the species described subsequently, and referred to both as *C. thalictroides*.

Distribution: Central Africa, Madagascar, Near East, south-east Asia and northern Australia.

Characteristics: Commonly called floating fern, it roots in the soil and has rosettes with crowded leaves. Foliage leaves are petiolate and up to 1 m long and 50 cm broad. The leaves are much smaller in cultivated plants. Leaf blades simple pinnate, pinnae either indented or lobed.

Cultivation and Propagation: The plant needs a position in bright light and temperatures above 20°C. It grows quite satisfactorily in washed sand, but becomes a stronger plant if given more nutrients. In an aquarium a single plant should be used as a show specimen. Plants which become too large have to be replaced by younger ones. The plants are easily propagated by using the numerous daughter plants which form on the leaves.

Ceratopteris thalictroides (L.) BRONGN. (Ill. 20)

The species was named *Acrostichum thalictroides* by Linné in 1753, and moved by Brongniart to the genus *Ceratopteris* when this was defined in 1821.

Distribution: East and south-east Asia, northern Australia, east Africa, from central South America to south-east North America, Greater Antilles.

Characteristics: Commonly called water hornfern, it is rooted in the substratum and has leaves densely arranged in rosettes. Foliage leaves have a petiole and are up to 1 m long and up to 50 cm broad, but usually much smaller in plants cultivated in an aquarium. Leaf blades pinnate, tips of pinnae medium to very fine.

Cultivation and Propagation: As specified for *C. cornuta*.

General Information: A form with medium fine tips of the pinnae has become known under the name of Sumatra fern since 1935. But the very fine, feathery form—probably coming from Ceylon—has been known only for the last few years and is the one now best-liked for use in a tank. In aquarist literature the two previously mentioned species *C. pteridoides* and *C. cornuta* have usually been referred to under the name of *Ceratopteris thalictroides*.

Family Marsileaceae · Marsilea Family

Three genera, 80 species. Predominantly tropical and subtropical, but occurs sporadically in temperate latitudes. Small herbaceous plants with elongated horizontally growing axes of the shoot with forked branching leaves positioned singly, erect, of variable shape; young leaves spirally involuted. Complicated reproduction by spores.

The Marsileaceae colonize boggy ground, flooded at times. Species of the genera *Marsilea* and *Pilularia* have been valued as aquarium plants for a long time. One genus of the family, *Regnelidium*, has its only habitat in central South America. These plants have bipartite laminae. Occasionally they can be seen in botanical gardens.

Marsilea

The genus was defined by Linné in 1753. It was named after Count L. F. Marsigli (1658 to 1730) who made a special study of ferns and fern allies.

Distribution: Habitats in all tropical and subtropical regions with a main evolutionary centre in Australia. A few can be found in temperate latitudes.

Characteristics: Small plants with creeping axes of the shoot and erect leaves, which are positioned singly. Blades of aerial leaves quadripartite, those of water leaves in parts of one to four.

General Information: The genus includes approximately 70 species and all of them can withstand being flooded. They are found near lakes and ponds, in ditches, on flooded stretches of land and, as weeds, in rice paddies. Submerged shoots can root themselves in soil and grow, but they can also grow streaming and reach a considerable length. The quadripartite blades of aerial leaves as well as those of the floating leaves, which form when the water level is low, are thin. On the other hand, the laminae of water leaves—in parts of one to four—are of a more solid structure. *Marsilea* is the only fern-plant in which the leaves are able to take up a sleeping position (see page 67).

The genus *Marsilea* belongs to the amphibious ferns and its reproduction by spores is very complicated. Normally, the land form only develops spores. Depending on the species, between two and twenty-five oval or bean-shaped, so-called 'spore fruits' or sporocarps form at the base of the petiole. The sporocarps are ventricular receptacles with fairly solid walls, and they are composed of leaf tissue. The sporocarps contain the actual spore cases or sporangia. Groups of these, each consisting of one large megaspore case and several small microspore cases, are enclosed in the ventricles of the sporocarp and connected with each other by a ring of tissue, capable of swelling. Owing to the sporocarps many species can survive long, unfavourable and dry periods in which the mature plants die. In fact, the sporocarps maintain the capacity of being effective for many years, perhaps even decades. When ripe sporocarps are bathed by external water, further development quickly follows. The ring of tissue (mentioned previously) swells and, as a consequence, the sporangia are drawn out of the sporocarps. The spores are sexually differentiated. Each megaspore case contains one large megaspore, whereas the microspore cases contain numerous small microspores. Within a few hours the walls of the sporangia and other parts of the sporocarp turn into a gelatinous mass in which the spores are embedded. Very reduced prothalli develop inside the spores. A female prothallus with an egg-cell forms in megaspores and a male prothallus with numerous spermatozoids (male sex-cells) in microspores. The spermatozoids leave the microspores and move to the egg-cells. A new *Marsilea* plant grows after fertilization has taken place.

Because there is such a large number of species, exact definition is not easy. It is quite possible, therefore, that one or another species might have been kept in an aquarium without being detected. In aquarist literature *M. drummondii* and *M. hirsuta*, both Australian, have been mentioned repeatedly.

Marsilea quadrifolia L.

The species was named by Linné in 1753.
Distribution: Europe, Asia, North America.
Characteristics: Small fern with horizontally growing axis of the shoot and single-positioned erect leaves. No water leaves. Floating leaves of variable length depending on depth of water, may be up to 70 cm long, blades quadripartite, soft, medium-green. Aerial leaves up to 20 cm long, blades as floating leaves. Sporocarps: one to three.
Cultivation and Propagation: A hardy species which can be kept on a pond in the winter. It can be used as a border plant for a pond, but it also looks very decorative as a small floating plant in deeper water. Propagation from separated small sections of shoots.

Marsilea crenata PRESL

The species was named by Presl in 1830. In literature for aquarists it has also had the name *M. minuta*.
Distribution: South-east Asia.
Characteristics: Small fern with horizontally growing axis of the shoot and erect, single-positioned leaves. Submerged leaves up to 5 cm long, blades in parts of two to four, solid, dark-green. No floating leaves. Aerial leaves up to 10 cm long, blades always quadripartite, soft. Sporocarps: two to six.
Cultivation and Propagation: An undemanding but decorative plant, forming a dense turf after some time and suitable for planting in the foreground of a tank. Temperature not less than 18°C. Propagation by division of shoots.
General Information: As it is difficult to determine the species of *Marsilea* exactly in the absence of sufficient experience, it is uncertain whether the correct name has been used.

Pilularia

The genus was defined by Linné in 1753. The name is derived from pilula (L) = pill and refers to the form of the sporocarps.
Distribution: In limited areas of Europe, North and South America, Australia, and also New Zealand.

Characteristics: Small ferns with creeping axes of the shoot, and single-positioned, erect leaves. In contrast to the genus *Marsilea* the leaves of *Pilularia* have no laminae.

General Information: The genus includes six species, basically not very different from *Marsilea* in habit and physiology. They colonize boggy areas and can withstand being flooded.

The dark-brown, globular sporocarps contain only a few groups of sporangia; when the former are ripe they are dark-brown and their covers open up. The content of the sporocarp appears as a gelatinous drop which protrudes slightly; in it are the—now free—sporangia with female megaspores and male microspores. Sexually differentiated prothalli develop from these spores. The female prothalli turn green, but they are not as much reduced as those of *Marsilea*. The male prothalli release the actively moving male sex-cells which join the egg-cells and fuse with them. A new *Pilularia* plant grows after fertilization has taken place.

Apart from the next species, it has been reported that two other species have been cared for in aquaria, *P. americana* from North America and *P. minuta* from southern Europe.

Pilularia globulifera L.

The species was named by Linné in 1753.

Distribution: Sporadically in western and central Europe.

Characteristics: Small fern with shoot axis creeping horizontally along the bottom; leaves positioned singly and erect; when submerged up to 25 cm long, when aerial up to 10 cm long.

Cultivation and Propagation: The species has simple and inconspicuous leaves. Therefore it has enjoyed much popularity as an aquarium plant and rarely been cultivated. Thus, little is known about the kind of care it needs in a tank. *Pilularia globulifera* is a marsh and cold-water plant, but apparently it can stand temperatures of up to 25°C temporarily. Propagation by division of shoots. Those who are keen on experimenting might like to try to raise young plants from spores. In that event one should proceed as described in the section on *Isoetes setacea* (see page 97).

Family Salviniaceae · Salvinia Family

The family consists of one genus only, *Salvinia*.

Salvinia

The genus was defined by Séguier in 1754. It was named after A. M. Salvini (1633–1720), a professor who lived in Florence.

Distribution: Tropical-subtropical, predominantly in America and Africa. It has also become acclimatized in some temperate latitudes.

17 *Isoetes lacustris*
18 *Bolbitis heudelotii*

24 *Azolla caroliniana*
25 *Ranunculus lingua*, submerged form in the winter
26 *Ranunculus aquatilis*
27 *Victoria cruziana*, prominent venation on leaf underside

28 *Nymphaea* spec. 'Lotus', red form
29 *Nuphar lutea*, rhizome
30 *Crassula helmsii*
31 *Ammania senegalensis*
32 *Peplis diandra*

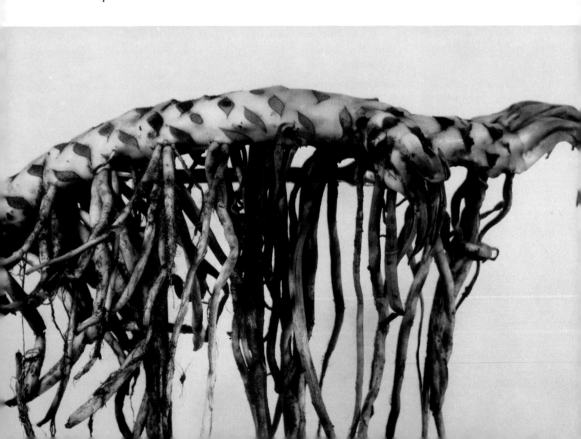

33 *Ammannia* spec., shoot with flowers growing in bog
34 *Rotala wallichii*
35 *Phyllanthus fluitans*

Characteristics: A small floating fern with a horizontally growing, much-branched axis of the shoot. Leaves in tripartite whorls of variable structure. No roots. Reproduction by spores, complicated.

General Information: Of the three leaves positioned on one node, only two develop as floating leaves. The latter have a horizontal habit and serve the function of photosynthesis. The third leaf is divided into many fine tips, reaches down into the water and undertakes the functions of the roots. It is often mistaken for a branched root. In really favourable growth conditions, sporangia form on the submerged leaves and combine as sori, enclosed in a membranous envelope. Such groups either consist of large megaspore cases or small microspore cases. A single, large megaspore develops in a megaspore case. In the microspore cases, on the other hand, 64 small male microspores develop as a general rule. There is, thus, a sexual differentiation in the spores. In the temperate latitudes, the sori detach themselves in the autumn and sink to the bottom. The old plants die. In the following spring the sori rise to the surface of the water, and prothalli develop. A female prothallus eventually bursts the spore coat, appears as a tiny, green form and protrudes slightly from the spore. The other part of the spore contains reserve nutrients for the nourishment of the prothallus. The male prothalli consist of just a few cells and remain completely enclosed by the microspore wall. The mobile, male sex-cells, of which only a moderate number develops, leave the microspores and try to reach the egg-cells in the female prothalli. When fertilization has taken place, a new *Salvinia* plant grows. Naturally, in warmer regions, the sori have no resting period in the winter.

The genus *Salvinia* includes approximately 12 species. In some areas, e.g. in East and South Africa and in South-east Asia, they have developed into undesirable water and rice paddy weeds which have to be exterminated. Occurrence of the plants in temperate latitudes is probably caused by migrating waterfowl. Apart from the species, described in detail below, *S. oblongifolia* from the Amazon region and *S. rotundifolia* from tropical South America have been cared for in aquaria. Other species of the genus have been recommended in aquarist literature for cultivation in a tank, e.g. *S. hastata* from tropical East Africa and Madagascar as well as *S. nigropunctata.* An interesting plant can be found in East and South Africa as well as in South-east Asia. The plant in question is a sterile hybrid, notable for a marked degree of vegetative multiplication. Its origins probably go back approximately 50 years when once its ancestors 'escaped' from a greenhouse and crossed with another plant. It was supposed that the plant was a *S. auriculata* which had become naturalized. It may even exist in our tanks and greenhouses, but unrecognized.

Salvinia auriculata AUBL. (Ill. 23)

The species was named by Aublet in 1775.

Distribution: Tropical America.

Characteristics: Perennial floating fern. Floating leaves very variable, round to elliptical and, depending on growth conditions, either almost flat or with slightly upturned wavy edges, medium-green, up to 3.5 cm in length. Lamina upperside with short, stiff hairs, standing in groups on small papillae and grown together at the base and towards the tips.

Cultivation and Propagation: Nowadays the species has little importance for the home aquarium as it forms a floating cover and takes away too much light from the other plants. On the other hand, it is an excellent plant for botanic gardens, aquatic plant nurseries and planthouses where it provides good, natural shade during the summer months. It is very sensitive to drip water. Multiplies freely, without needing intervention, from continual branching and isolation of lateral shoots. Spores occur rarely in cultivated plants.

Salvinia natans (L.) ALL. (Ill. 13)

The species was named *Marsilea natans* by Linné in 1753 and moved to the genus *Salvinia* by Allioni in 1785.

Distribution: Europe, Near East, central and south-east Asia.

Characteristics: Annual floating fern. Floating leaves, round to elliptical, medium-green, up to 2 cm in length. Lamina upperside with short, stiff hairs, standing in groups on small papillae and not grown together.

Cultivation and Propagation: A plant suitable for being kept in a cold aquarium or in the open air. Multiplies in the summer from branched lateral shoots which separate. The plants regularly form spores before they die in the autumn. The sporangia have to be collected and wintered in cold water. A few new plants will develop in the following spring and, in the summer, these will multiply vegetatively.

Family Azollaceae

The family includes only one genus, *Azolla*.

Azolla

The genus was defined by Lamarck in 1783. The name is probably derived from aza (Gk) = dryness and allymein (Gk) = fade.

Distribution: Almost worldwide, but particularly in warmer regions.

Characteristics: Very small floating fern with compressed axes of the shoot and much branching. Leaf arrangement dense and distichous, leaves scale-shaped. Simple roots. Complicated reproduction by spores.

General Information: The leaves of the *Azolla* species are deeply tow-lobed. The larger upper lobes are blue-green in colour, turning reddish in strong sun light; they project above the water. As these lobes are densely grown with papillae, water cannot penetrate them. The upper lobes have a pit-like indentation at the base, normally occupied by an alga *(Anabaena azollae)* capable of assimilating atmospheric nitrogen. In some rice-producing areas, therefore, *Azolla* is used as an organic compost. The smaller, lower lobes of the leaves are lighter in colour. In favourable environmental conditions, sporangia form on the smaller lobes.

The megaspore cases are brown; they are surrounded by a spore coat, and they are seated singly. Every megaspore case contains one female megaspore. When this is ripe it is enveloped by a frothy albumen substance, the upper part of which turns into a float. The microspore cases are in larger groups and enveloped by a joint spore coat. These units of microspore cases are yellow. Inside the microspore cases portions of microspores are held together by frothy albumen. Eventually, the spore portions are released by the sporangia and float on the surface of the water where they attach themselves with a barbed hook to the frothy substance enveloping the megaspores. After some time, the megaspores together with the attached microspores sink to the bottom. Within eight days approximately very reduced female and male prothalli are produced and, in turn, these form the sex cells. When fertilization has taken place a new *Azolla* plant grows.

The present genus includes approximately six species. But these are remnants of a genus, more richly represented in former geological periods. The existence of twenty-five species has been proved from fossil remains. They are now extinct. Apart from the species described below, *A. filiculoides* has been kept as an aquarium plant. The original habitat of this species was in tropical and subtropical South America, but it became naturalized in many large regions and, thus, also in parts of western and southern Europe. Other species should also be suitable for cultivation: *A. pinnata* from Australia; *A. africana* from Africa and Madagascar; and *A. nilotica* from tropical East Africa. The lastnamed is supposed to become much bigger than the other species.

Azolla caroliniana WILLD. (Ill. 24)

The species was named by Willdenow in 1810.

Distribution: Subtropical America.

Characteristics: Very small floating plant, often called fairy moss, with tiny scale-shaped leaves, generally blue-green, more rarely reddish in colour. Hair on leaves is two-cellular.

Cultivation and Propagation: Like the species of the genus *Salvinia* not much used in a modern aquarium; the plants form a floating cover which takes away too much light from the other plants in the tank. In a planthouse the fairy moss provides good natural shade in the summer months when it can also be kept out in the open. It develops particularly beautiful, dense growth in muddy soil if the water is completely withdrawn. If *Azolla caroliniana* is cultivated in daylight it becomes very sensitive if the daily period of light is much less than 12 hours. Spontaneous division by the plant makes propagation easy. Spores develop if the plants are kept out in the open, but in hot summers only.

Family Ranunculaceae · Crowfoot Family

Fifty genera, 2,000 species. Distribution worldwide, but especially well represented in the northern hemisphere and tropical and subtropical mountain ranges. Most of them are herbaceous plants with very variable habitats. Leaves alternate, either simple, or lobed, or palmate and pinnate. Flowers in inflorescences, solitary on the end of shoots, or lateral in leaf axils, hermaphroditic, actinomorphic or mirror-symmetrical, usually with a colourful corolla.

Apart from the genus *Ranunculus*, described below, the genus *Caltha* also contains aquatic forms. *Caltha* includes just ten species, distributed in temperate and cold regions and often found in a marshy habitat and shallow water.

Ranunculus

The genus was defined by Linné in 1753. Ranunculus (L) = small frog, from rana (L) = frog.

Distribution: Worldwide, but in the tropics in the cooler regions only.

Characteristics: Herbaceous plants of varying habitat, thus perennial herbs with rhizomes, tubers and runners, but also aquatic, floating annuals. Leaf arrangement alternate, leaves of variable shape, either simple or lobed to palmate and pinnate. Flowers solitary, either terminal on shoots or lateral in leaf axils, hermaphroditic, actinomorphic. Perianth double, flower parts free, as a rule in multiples of five consisting of a greenish calyx and a yellow—rarely white—corolla. Fairly large, but undetermined number of stamens. Carpels also in fairly large but undetermined numbers, hypogynous superior and free. The fruit is a syncarp composed of numerous achenes.

General Information: The genus includes approximately 400 species. Some of them are poisonous. Species are found in the most variable habitats such as woods and meadows, but also in arid fields, from the plains to the high mountains. Thirty-five species grow in water, either temporarily or permanently. Some of them are distributed across the world; their spread may well have been caused by migrating waterfowl. In some waters they exist in such profusion that they have to be kept under control. Experience is lacking concerning cultivation in aquaria and ponds. The introduction of a few species is meant to arouse enough interest in them for carrying out some experiments.

Ranunculus lingua L. (Ill. 15, 25)

The species was named by Linné in 1753.

Distribution: Central Europe, central western Asia.

Characteristics: A stoloniferous plant. Runners grow in the soil, scale-leaves forming on their nodes. Erect shoot sections with fairly short basal internodes and then very elongated ones, up to 1.50 high, little or no branching in the lower region. Submerged basal leaves stalked, with egg to heart-shaped laminae, thin, pale-green. Aerial leaves sessile, lanceolate, up to 20 cm long and 3 cm wide, medium-green. Each shoot with one to four solitary flowers. Transverse measurement of flower two to four cm. Sepals yellowy-green, petals yellow.

Cultivation and Propagation: Suitable for shallow areas in a pond or for planting among too densely growing reeds: the species can also be used in the marginal water of ponds. Slips can be transplanted in the spring as long as they are still fairly solid. This will achieve some—though limited—reproduction. Yield from sown seeds is more prolific.

General Information: Generally, the species grows in shallow water among reeds, but also in ditches and on wet meadows. Water leaves form from autumn to the spring only.

Ranunculus hederaceus L.

The species was named by Linné in 1753. Another scientific name for it is *Batrachium hederaceum.*

Distribution: Western Europe and in certain localities on the east coast of North America.

Characteristics: Perennial, herbaceous plant with elongated shoot axes. No submerged leaves. Floating and aerial leaves are stalked, laminae kidney-shaped to roundish with two to four shallow indentations, diameter 2.5 cm, medium-green. Flowers solitary in leaf axils, diameter of flowers two to five mm. Petals white, yellow at the base, divided. Five to twelve stamens.

Cultivation and Propagation: An undemanding species suitable for open-air cultivation. The small white flowers give the plants an agreeably interesting appearance if placed in a group in shallow water of a pond or along its borders. Propagation from cuttings or seeds.

General Information: This species grows in shallow water or on wet soil.

Ranunculus aquatilis L. (Ill. 26)

The species was named by Linné in 1753. Another scientific name for it is *Batrachium aquatile.*

Distribution: Temperate zones of the northern hemisphere, southern South America and the Andes, South Africa and in certain locations of Australia.

Characteristics: Perennial, but sometimes only annual, herbaceous plant with elongated shoot axes. Submerged leaves petiolate and divided into several palmate pinnae, delicate and will shrivel when out of water, pinnae very narrow. Floating leaves petiolate, their laminae in three to five lobes, these being narrow at the base, medium-green. Flowers solitary in leaf axils, diameter as a rule 1.5—2 cm, but it can be smaller or larger. Petals white with yellow base and touching each other with their edges. Stamens: generally 15—30.

Cultivation and Propagation: A plant suitable for a cold water aquarium as well as for ponds; anybody can collect it. Streaming shoots may grow to a length of up to 2 m and, usually, survive the winter, also in an aquarium if they have sufficient illumination. Propagation from cuttings or seeds.

Ranunculus trichophyllus CHAIX

The species was named by Chaix in 1786 but it is often linked with *R. aquatilis.*

Distribution: Temperate zones of the northern hemisphere, South Africa, occasional occurrences in Australia.

Characteristics: Physiology, habit and most characteristics like *R. aquatilis.* No floating leaves. Diameter of flowers not more than 1 cm. Stamens: as a rule 5—15.

Cultivation and Propagation: As *R. aquatilis.*

Ranunculus circinatus SIBTH.

The species was named by Sibthorp in 1794. *R. divaricatus* is another, but incorrect, name for it.

Distribution: Europe, northern Asia.

Characteristics: Perennial, herbaceous plant with elongated shoot axes. Submerged leaves with petiole and laminae divided into several palmate pinnae, rather solid and do not shrivel when out of water. Transverse measurement of summer leaves up to 1.5 cm, that of winter leaves up to 2.5 cm. No floating leaves. Flowers solitary in leaf axils with a diameter of up to 2 cm. Edges of petals lie one over the other, petals white with yellow base. Stamens: as a rule 20—25.

Cultivation and Propagation: As *R. aquatilis. R. circinatus* is the hardiest aquatic species of the crowfoot family.

Family Nymphaeaceae · Water Lily Family

Seven genera, 65 species. Worldwide distribution. Aquatic plants with rhizomes or tubers and leaves arranged in basal rosettes. Leaves develop as aquatic, floating and—more rarely —aerial leaves. Solitary flowers in leaf axils, hermaphroditic, usually large, actinomorphic, corolla in different colours.

The main attraction in a botanic garden is always provided by the Victoria, often called the 'Queen of Water Lilies' (Ill. 36, 37). The plant is either *Victoria cruziana,* a native from the river systems of the Parana and Paraguay with deeply folded leaf margins, up to 15 cm high, and bare sepals, or *V. amazonica* (= *V. regia*) from the Amazon region with leaf margins up to 10 cm high, and prickly sepals. The plants grow in quiet bays and old beds of large rivers. They are normally cultivated in tropical houses for aquatic plants or, in warmer regions, in heated or unheated open-air ponds. In their natural environment the plants are perennials, but it is more expedient to cultivate them like annuals in temperate latitudes. First, they suffer in seasons with poor light; besides the Victoria houses are used for other purposes during the winter months. Seeds are put into flower pots in early spring. The first leaves are small, submerged and arrow-shaped (Ill. *15*). Simple floating leaves develop shortly afterwards. At this stage the plants are transplanted to their permanent home; they should be given soil containing plenty of nutrients. Further development then quickly follows. The leaves of older plants are huge and may attain a diameter of 2 m; they possess strong veins protruding on the undersides and grown with prickles (Ill. 27). If an evenly distributed load were put upon them they could easily carry a weight of 50 kg. Water that collects on the upperside of leaves drains off through minute pores present in the laminae. Strong and healthy plants will flower in July. The *Victoria* species are night-blooming plants. The single flowers, succeeding each other closely, open their blossoms twice. In the first night their colour is a shining white, and in the second it turns into a pale pink. Then the flowers submerge, and the seeds ripen in the water.

Euryale ferox (Ill. 16) of tropical east African origin is not as well known a species. Its circular leaves are just as large as those of Victoria, but they do not have folded margins and the colour of the underside is dark violet. Flowers are rather small with violet petals, not unlike those of *Barclaya*.

The genus *Nelumbo* is characterized by shield-shaped, very water-repellent leaves, either floating on the water or growing above it. The yellow-flowering *Nelumbo lutea*, the American lotus, is a native of eastern North America, and *N. nucifera*, the Indian lotus whose blossoms are pale-red, has its habitat in east Asia (Ill. 38, 39).

The genera *Nymphaea*, *Nuphar*, *Barclaya* and *Ondinea* contain species which are being cultivated and, therefore, they are important to growers of aquatic plants and aquarists.

Nymphaea

The name was introduced by Linné in 1753. However, at the time, the present-day *Nuphar* species were included under this generic name. Smith moved the *Nuphar* species to an independent genus in 1809 and thus limited the genus *Nymphaea* in number of species *Castalia* is another generic name, often found in older scientific literature. The name *Nymphaea* is derived from nymphaia (Gk) and means 'concerning nymphs', because the plants live in the water—the domicile of the nymphs.

Distribution: Almost wordlwide, but evolved into the greatest variety of forms in the tropics.

Characteristics: Plants with rhizomes and tubers, in some cases with short runners, living in the water. Leaves arranged in basal rosettes. While the plants are young, or just after they have begun to shoot following a resting period, the submerged leaves normally perish and rarely persist. Later developed floating leaves always with long petiole; primary lateral veins curve towards leaf margins and join up before they reach the margins (Ill. *37*).

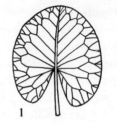
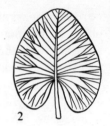

37 Venation in leaf laminae of (1) *Nymphaea*
   and (2) *Nuphar*

1   2

Flowers single, hermaphroditic, actinomorphic. Perianth polysepalous, calyx parts in multiples of four, corolla with many petals and of varying colouration. Many stamens, gradually passing into the petals (Ill. *38*). Fairly large, but indefinite number of carpels, embedded in the floral axis and partially united with it, thus forming a pistil to which the sepals and stamens in their whole length are laterally attached. The fruit is a water berry.

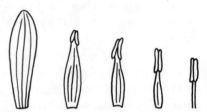

38 Gradual transition from petals to stamens
   in *Nymphaea alba*

General Information: The genus includes approximately 40 species. They grow in sheltered positions of standing or slowly flowing waters and can withstand occasional periods of drought. Several of the tropical species are cultivated in the aquatic planthouses of botanic gardens, e.g. *N. gigantea* from Australia; *N. rubra* and *N. stellata* from the east Asiatic mainland; also *N. caerulea* and *N. capensis* from the African continent. Their different colours are beautiful, white and violet being characteristic of the night-blooming species, and blue, pale pink and yellow of those which open their flowers in daytime. From these species numerous varieties have been bred and their exact ancestry is often difficult to determine. These varieties include the white *Nymphaea* 'Hofgärtner Gräbner', the red *Nymphaea* 'Emily Grant Hutchings', and the blue *Nymphaea* 'Midnight'. As more and more greenhouses for very small plants are being built, interest should increase in those exotic species and cultivated varieties remaining small in size. One variety, cultivated between 1900 and 1910 and named *N. baumii* at the time, is a small plant with star-shaped flowers; it would almost certainly be suitable. On the whole, the genus *Nymphaea* plays an insignificant role in plant cultivation for aquaria because the floating leaves cast too much shade and most species become too large for a tank. Its real importance lies in the fact that the species of the temperate latitudes can be cultivated on ponds in gardens and parks. In addition to the species, discussed in greater detail further on, *N. candida* is also suitable for cultivation; a small water lily, it grows in cool waters, lacking a good supply of nutrients, anywhere from central Europe to north-west Asia. The species is difficult to distinguish from *N. alba*, without careful investigation, and it is often not recognised as an independent one. Further rewarding species are *N. tuberosa*, the tuberous water lily from North America with tuberous, lateral shoots on the rhizome, and *N. odorata*, the fragrant water lily. In the last-named the sepals and petals are considerably broader than in *N. alba* and the floating leaves are completely round; the flowers have a pleasant scent. The species of the temperate latitudes usually have pure white flowers. Our coloured water lilies, growing in the open, can be traced back to a red-flowering variety of *N. alba* and hybridization (Ill. 42, 43, 45).

Periods of dormancy in the genus are probably not caused by a physiological rhythm in the plants; it is rather their environment which enforces them. In the temperate latitudes such periods are caused by low temperatures in the winter and, in the tropics and sub-tropics, by drying up of the waters. It is almost certain that those species which form tubers blossom more freely after periods of dormancy.

Species with long rhizomes can be propagated vegetatively by dividing backward sections of the rhizome into small pieces. If tubers are divided, on the other hand, the cut pieces often rot, and the plants may be lost. In species with short runners the slips which are produced can be used for multiplication. In wild and fertile, cultivated species, the raising of seedlings achieves a good yield but takes a great deal of time. Seeds always have to ripen under water. Germination results are good as a rule, but the young plants develop very slowly and should be re-planted into a new substratum with a good supply of nutrients fairly often.

Nymphaea spec. 'Lotus' (Ill. 28, 40)

This plant is not yet clearly defined. Some take it for a variety of *N. lotus*. In aquarist circles it is also known under the trade name 'Nymphaea brasiliensis' or referred to as 'tiger lotus'. Perhaps it is *N. zenkeri*.

Distribution: West Africa.

Characteristics: A rosette plant with short runners, living in the water. Water leaves with elliptical to roundish-wavy laminae, these indented at the base up to the point of insertion of the petiole, uppersides light to medium-green or more or less red with irregular red to brown markings, undersides pale-green, pale-violet or reddish, diameter of leaves up to 15 cm. Floating leaves dark-green with toothed margins. Flowers measure up to six cm across. Sepals green outside, white inside. Petals white.

Cultivation and Propagation: The submerged leaves are fairly persistent as a rule so that this water lily is suited to cultivation in an aquarium. In medium-sized and large tanks it can be used as a solitary specimen plant, but it also looks well if placed amongst densely growing plants. Specimens with green leaves look most decorative if the background is dark. Needs a position in good light. Temperature not less than 20°C. The substratum should not be enriched too much. If the plant is provided with many nutrients its growth will be too profuse and the whole of the substratum may be interspersed with its roots. Sooner or later all plants produce floating leaves. Removal of the latter normally causes development of more submerged leaves. Older plants from aquatic plant nurseries thrive particularly well in large aquaria. If all existing floating leaves are completely removed before the plants are put into the tank, strong submerged leaves will force through shortly afterwards.

Propagation from separated slips or seeds. The plant flowers in aquarium conditions and produces seeds which set quite easily and do not need to be handled. It is a night-blooming plant. The single blossoms open twice or three times.

General Information: A distinction is made between a form with green leaves and one with red leaves. The dividing line between these two varieties has not been clearly established so far. A plant with one-coloured reddish-brown leaves, occasionally imported under the trade name '*Nymphaea lotus* var. *japonica*', is probably not related to *N.* spec. 'Lotus'.

Nymphaea alba L. (Ill. *38*, 46)

The species was named by Linné in 1753.

Distribution: Europe, occasionally in north-west Africa.

Characteristics: Rhizome plant with basal leaf rosette. Submerged leaves occur regularly in young plants only, more rarely later on, e.g. when the plants start shooting in the spring or if the water level is very high. Floating leaves have a petiole, their laminae are elliptical to roundish, indented at the base up to the point of insertion of the petiole, leaf margins entire, diameter up to 35 cm, upperside dark-green, sometimes more or less reddish-brown, underside light-green. In the typical variety the flowers measure 10–12 cm across. Sepals as long as petals or shorter, green outside and white inside. Petals gradually pass into the stamens. Filaments of anthers of inner stamens narrow-linear, usually sulphur-yellow.

Cultivation and Propagation: A plant suitable for ponds where it thrives in a sunny position, sheltered from wind. A substratum with a good supply of nutrients, and at least 30 cm deep, is essential for good growth and production of flowers. A well-proven mixture for the substratum consists of seasoned compost soil to which some loam, sand and ground peat has been added. If the ponds remain filled with water in the winter, then the species will prove to be hardy. If the water is drained off, the rhizomes should be protected by a thick layer of leaves. Cultivation is also possible in earth-filled wire baskets or other containers which are removed from the water in the autumn and stored in a cool cellar for the winter. They have to be kept slightly moist. Propagation is fairly easy by dividing the rhizomes in the spring. Raising of seedlings is also possible. Seeds harvested in summer or autumn germinate in the following spring.

General Information: If *N. alba* grows at a depth of more than 2.50 m floating leaves and flowers do not develop, but submerged leaves endure. If the water is drained land forms might develop. Usually these have just a few short-stalked, not fully unfolded leaves and, as a rule, they do not flower.

N. alba exists in three varieties. One is the typical variety. Another is *N. alba* var. *minor*, in all parts only one half to one third of the size of the typical form and living in rather cool waters lacking nutrients. The classification of this variety is doubtful, because pygmy forms of *N. alba* can be bred artificially in cultures in which nitrogen is lacking. The third variety, *N. alba* var. *rosea*, occurs in southern Sweden and has red flowers. It has gained importance in the breeding of coloured water lilies for ponds and lakes.

Nymphaea tetragona GEORGI

The species was named by Georgi in 1775.

Distribution: Northern Europe, northern Asia, northern North America.

Characteristics: A white pygmy water lily, with rhizome and basal leaf rosette and living in the water. Only young plants have submerged leaves; at a later stage these leaves are rare and declining. Floating leaves elliptical, indented at the base up to the point of insertion of the petiole, diameter up to 15 cm, upperside dark-green and sometimes with irregular blackish spots, underside pale-green. Flowers measure 2.5—6 cm across. Sepals green outside, white inside. Petals do not pass gradually into the stamens. Filaments of anthers broad elliptical, dark-yellow.

Cultivation and Propagation: As specified for *N. alba*, but it also flowers in cooler places.

General Information: The species grows in wooded swamps and slowly flowing waters. In Finland a red-flowering species has been observed; either all or only some of its petals are coloured.

Water lilies suited to cultivation in small planthouses

Nymphaea cv. Daubenyana (Ill. 41)

Flowers of variable size, petals pale-blue. Floating leaves elliptical to roundish, size variable, upperside pale to medium-green, sometimes initially with dark-red markings, underside slightly red.

A plant which flowers freely and is ideal for a small planthouse. It used to be recommended for a home aquarium. But, although younger plants develop submerged leaves in a tank for a time, the floating leaves appearing later cast too much shade. Optimal temperature around 20°C, but can be lower temporarily.

If the substratum is unwashed sand the diameter of leaf laminae will be approximately 6 to 8 cm and flowers will measure up to 6 cm across. If the substratum consists of a nutritious soil mixture, e.g. in botanic gardens, the diameter of floating leaves might well be 30 cm and that of flowers 18 cm.

The plants do not develop seeds, but they can be propagated by using the daughter plants forming on the leaves at the point of intertion of the petiole. It is possible to expedite the process by dividing the petioles so that the leaves float freely on the water.

N. Daubenyana is a hybrid, probably bred by Daubeny in 1865 from the blue-flowering west African *N. micrantha*, which also has the habit of forming daughter plants, and *N. caerulea* from north and central Africa, likewise with blue flowers.

Nymphaea cv. Helvola (Ill. 44)

Flowers measure 3 to 5 cm across. Petals a pale-yellow creamy colour or nearly white. Laminae of floating leaves elliptical to roundish, as a rule with a diameter of 3 to 6 cm—rarely more, upperside deep green with red dots or markings, underside pale-red.

An undemanding very small variety suitable for a small planthouse and, at one time, recommended for a home aquarium. If kept in the open it endures the winter, but does not flower freely. Seeds are not produced. Propagation, therefore, is only possible by dividing the rhizomes.

The plants are hybrids bred from *N. tetragona* and the yellow-flowering *N. flava* (= *N. mexicana*) from Central America and southern North America. Formerly also called *N. pygmaea* hort. Bred by Marliac in 1890.

Water lilies suited to open-air cultivation (selection)

Cultivation and Propagation: As specified for *N. alba*. Many successful species have been bred by the Frenchman Marliac in Temple-sur-Lot at the turn of the century.

Nymphaea cv. Gladstoniana

Flowers pure-white, measure up to 28 cm across. Petals broad. Stamens very large, pale-yellow. Laminae of floating leaves a shining green, underside pale-pink, distance between basal lobes between 4 and 6 cm.

A very strong plant with large flowers. Optimal depth of water 1 m. This variety was bred by Richardson of Lordstown, who probably used *N. tuberosa* to start it off. Introduced in 1897.

Nymphaea cv. Formosa

Colour of blossom white on a pink background, measures up to 20 cm across. Petals broad-lanceolate. Stamens glowing yellow. Laminae of floating leaves shiny dark-green, underside reddish-cream coloured, very wide gaps between basal lobes.

A variety which flowers freely, has large blossoms, and is suitable for cultivation on the larger lakes. Grower unknown.

Nymphaea cv. Carnea

Flower white on a reddish background, its diameter up to 16 cm. Petals lanceolate. Stamens yellow. Laminae of floating leaves one-coloured green. Principal vein conspicuously light. Wide gap between basal lobes. Petiole reddish.

Normally flowering large variety. Also referred to as *Nymphaea* 'Rosea'. Introduced into the trade by Marliac in 1887.

Nymphaea cv. Chromatella (Ill. 43)

Flower yellow, its diameter up to 15 cm. Petals lanceolate. Stamens dark-yellow. Laminae of floating leaves slightly wavy, and folded upwards, light green with dark-red markings while young, becoming darker with fading markings later on.

Richly-flowering variety, loving bright sun and low water in the summer. Introduced into the trade by Marliac in 1886.

Nymphaea cv. Escarboucle

Flower carmine-red, its diameter up to 20 cm. Petals lanceolate. Stamens red. Laminae of floating leaves dark-green, distance between basal lobes 2 to 4 cm.

This variety should be grown at a water depth of at least 60 cm. It is difficult to propagate and is, therefore, rare. When the plants first come into blossom, the colour of the flower is rather paler. The flowers close in the evening. Introduced into the trade by Marliac in 1906.

Nymphaea cv. James Brydon

Flower carmine-red, its diameter up to 12 cm. Petals elliptical. Stamens glowing yellow. Laminae of floating leaves slightly turned upwards, dark-green with red—but later fading—markings, underside paler.

A variety which flowers freely. Also suitable for a position half in the shade, but then it produces fewer blossoms. Introduced into the trade by Dreer in 1902.

Nymphaea cv. Atropurpurea (Ill. 42)

Flower dark-red, its diameter up to 12 cm. Stamens glowing yellow to orange. Laminae of floating leaves dark-green, underside pink to wine-red, basal lobes overlap by 10—15 cm.

Richly flowering, sun-loving variety suitable for larger lakes. Probably introduced into the trade by Marliac in 1906.

Nymphaea cv. Rosennymphe

Blossom pink, fading as it gets older, its diameter up to 12 cm. Stamens yellowy-pink, more intensively coloured at the base. Young floating leaves a deep red, when older brown-green.

A rare variety and a position in the sun is absolutely essential for it; can be cultivated at a water depth of up to 70 cm. Breeder unknown.

Nymphaea cv. Ellisiana

Flower pink to purple-red, colour becoming more intense in the course of the day, its diameter up to 12 cm. Stamens yellow to orange-red. Laminae of floating leaves one-coloured green, underside reddish. Distance between basal lobes 3 to 4 cm.

Free flowering variety for deeper and larger lakes. Introduced into the trade by Marliac in 1896.

Nymphaea cv. Aurora

Flower orange to dark-pink, its diameter up to 10 cm. Petals broad-lanceolate, outermost petals with green principal veins on the undersides. Laminae of floating leaves with persistent, brown-red markings on under and upperside.

Medium-sized variety; flowers moderately well to freely. Introduced into the trade by Marliac in 1895.

Nymphaea cv. Froebelii

Flowers carmine-red, standing above the water level by a few centimetres, number of petals only moderate, diameter of flower up to 8 cm. Floating leaves dark-green with reddish borders, basal lobes wide-spread.

A very rewarding variety belonging to the group of pygmy water lilies. Introduced into the trade by Froebel in 1898.

Nymphaea cv. Laydekeri Purpurata

Flower wine to carmine-red, usually lying on the surface of the water, its diameter up to 8 cm. Young floating leaves with dark markings.

A pygmy water lily which flowers freely. Similar to the variety described previously. Brought into the trade by Marliac in 1895.

Nymphaea cv. Iga Erfurt

Colour of flower ranges from golden-yellow to intensive copper to copper-red, its diameter up to 8 cm. Petals lanceolate. Stamens yellow-copper coloured. Floating leaves green, when young with dark-red markings. Gaps between basal lobes measure several centimetres. One of the most beautiful and free flowering pygmy water lilies. Bred by Forst in 1961.

Nymphaea cv. Fabiola

Flower golden-yellow to copper-red, its diameter up to 8 cm. Petals broad-lanceolate. Floating leaves green with faded brown markings. Rather close to the previous variety. A little-known breed by Marliac.

Nymphaea cv. Graziella

Flower orange-red, its diameter up to 8 cm. Petals oval, the outermost occasionally green-striped. Floating leaves green with persistent red-brown markings.

A decorative pygmy water lily, even when it is not flowering. Brought into the trade by Marliac in 1902.

Nymphaea cv. Sioux

Flower cream-pink outside, turning an intensive yellow pink towards the inside, its diameter up to 8 cm. Tips of petals partly more intensively coloured than the rest. Floating leaves with fading red-brown markings.

A small water lily with variable flowering habits; bred by Marliac.

Nuphar

The genus was defined by Smith in 1809. The name is derived from the Arabic term for water lilies, 'nailufar'. The botanists of the Middle Ages called the water lilies 'nenuphar'.

Distribution: Temperate latitudes of the northern hemisphere and, occasionally, in the adjoining subtropical regions.

Characteristics: Rhizome plants with basal leaf rosettes and growing in the water. Submerged leaves persistent, thin and wavy. Laminae of floating leaves have primary veins branching laterally off the midrib and extending to the leaf margins (Ill. *37*). Flowers single, hermaphroditic, actinomorphic; perianth polysepalous, calyx normally in five or six parts with conspicuously large, yellow sepals, corolla multipartite with small petals. Stamens are numerous and pass into the petals, often without a definite line of demarcation between them. Carpels are present in fairly large numbers, they are embedded in the floral axis and partially fused with it, forming a hypogynous superior pistil. The fruit is a water berry, enclosed by the more or less well preserved green sepals at the base.

General Information: The genus includes approximately 15 species, but needs revision for systematic classification. The plants grow in still or slowly flowing waters, often together with species of *Nymphaea*, but they penetrate to a greater depth of water. All *Nuphar* species are suitable for cultivation on outdoor ponds, but this is rarely done because their blossoms cannot really compete with those of *Nymphaea*. However, *Nuphar* species are quite often cared for successfully in a home aquarium where the persistent green foliage of young plants, or of those raised from the more delicate rhizome sections, looks very decorative. The plants can be propagated easily by dividing rhizomes or by sowing seeds. Initially the fruits are not immersed in water. When the fruits ripen the carpels are freed and float on the water for a time; the seeds are released as soon as the carpels disintegrate. Waterfowl are fond of the seeds and eat them.

Besides the species discussed in detail below, some other species—particularly those well-known from North America—should be suited for cultivation on a pond, perhaps even in a home aquarium. *N. advena* from eastern North America has a thick, fleshy rhizome similar to *N. lutea*. The leaves of the former have blunt-edged indentations and may, at times, stand above the water level. A slender rhizome and small, roundish leaves characterize *N. microphyllum* from north-eastern North America. In *N. sagittifolium* from the south-east of the continent the submerged as well as the floating leaves have fairly narrow, longish blades. Small specimens of this species are frequently cared for in tanks.

Nuphar lutea (L.) SM. (Ill. 29, 47)

The species was named *Nymphaea lutea* by Linné in 1753. It was moved to the genus *Nuphar* when Smith defined this in 1809.

Distribution: Europe and central west Asia.

Characteristics: Yellow water lily with rhizome and basal leaf rosettes, growing in the water. Submerged leaves persistent throughout the year in any depth of water. These leaves have petioles of varying length and laminae of variable size, egg-shaped to roundish, cleft at the base up to point of insertion of the petiole, thin, wavy, pale green. Floating leaves with egg-shaped to elliptical laminae, also indented at the base up to insertion of petiole, up to 40 cm long and up to 30 cm wide, solid, medium-green. Flowers measure 4 to 5 cm across. Sepals: five, yellow. Fairly large number of petals, gradually passing into, and combining with stamens.

Cultivation and Propagation: An undemanding, though rarely seen species, suitable for garden ponds and park lakes. Its cultivation corresponds to that of *Nymphaea alba* (see page 122). If the conditions are right *Nuphar lutea* can be kept in either a cold or warm water tank for a time. A position in good light is essential, and it should not be forgotten that the plant needs a fair amount of space. A recommended method is to divide a weak rhizome into small pieces and to allow dormant buds time to shoot. The plants which then grow, initially form submerged leaves only and should be planted in a substrate, poor in nutrient content. If over-large submerged leaves and the first of the later developing floating leaves are removed, these plants can be kept in a tank for a while. The yellow water lily can also be raised from seeds, but this takes much longer. Seeds that ripen in summer or autumn germinate in the following spring.

General Information: The species colonizes still and slowly flowing, fertile waters and often grows together with *Nymphaea alba* in the zone of floating plants around a lake. Occurs rarely in acid water of ponds in moor country.

Nuphar pumilum (TIMM) DC.

The species was named *Nymphaea lutea* var. *pumilum* by Timm in 1788. After the genus *Nuphar* had been defined, *Nymphaea lutea* was moved to that genus; in 1821 De Candolle gave var. *pumilum* the status of an independent species.

Distribution: Northern Europe, occasional occurrence in central Europe, temperate latitudes of Asia.

Characteristics: Plant with rhizome and basal leaf rosette, living in the water. In the main it resembles *N. lutea* but it is noticeably smaller. Laminae of floating leaves up to 15 cm in length, only rarely up to 20 cm, up to 15 cm in width. Flowers measure 2 to 3 cm across. The fruit is often slightly curved.

Cultivation and Propagation: Like *N. lutea* suitable for ponds and home aquaria. Cultivation as described for above. However, because of its smaller size, *N. pumilum* is often easier to keep.

General Information: The species grows predominantly in cool, usually acid, infertile ponds and lakes of moors and mountains.

Nuphar japonica DC.

The species was named by De Candolle in 1821.

Distribution: Japan.

Characteristics: Plants with rhizomes and basal leaf rosettes, living in the water. Submerged leaves persistent with a petiole of varying length, laminae arrow-shaped, up to 30 cm long and up to 12 cm wide, thin wavy, pale green. Laminae of floating leaves look similar but are tougher, flat and of a darker green. Flowers measure 4 to 5 cm across. Sepals: five, yellow. A fairly large number of petals.

Cultivation and Propagation: A plant well-suited to being a show specimen in a tank. It should be given a position in good light and few nutrients in the substrate so that the development of floating leaves is delayed for as long as possible. Propagation as *N. lutea* by division of the rhizome or from seeds.

General Information: The variety *N. japonica* var. *rubrotinctum* has red-brown leaves and orange-red blossoms. It is known only as a cultivated plant.

Barclaya

The genus was defined by Wallich in 1827. The name was chosen in honour of G. W. Barclay, the English gardener and plant collector.

Distribution: Tropical south-east Asia.

Characteristics: Plants with compact rhizomes and short runners, living in deep water. Submerged leaves in basal rosettes of very variable form. No floating leaves. Flowers positioned singly in leaf axils, hermaphroditic, actinomorphic. Perianth is composed of a green calyx having four to five divided sepals, and a corolla having eight and more petals. At the base the petals are connected in the form of a tube, while at the apex they are divided; petals are green outside, violet inside. Many stamens. Up to ten carpels, embedded in the floral axis and partially fused with it. The fruit is a water berry.

General Information: The genus includes three to four species. *B. motleyi* and *B. rotundifolia* as well as the species discussed below have been imported and kept in tanks occasionally. So far, they are not widely distributed in cultivation.

Barclaya longifolia WALL. (Ill. 2, *39*)

The species was named by Wallich in 1827 when he defined the genus *Barclaya*.

Distribution: South-east Asiatic mainland.

Characteristics: Plant with rhizome, short runners and basal leaf rosette, living in the water. Petioles of submerged leaves vary in length, laminae broadly linear, narrowing

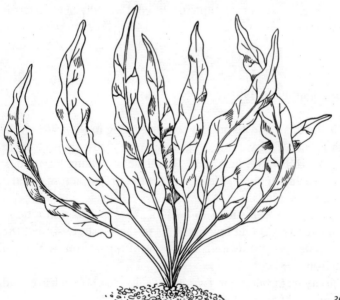

39 Barclaya longifolia

towards the apex, tip blunt, base heart-shaped, wavy, up to 50 cm long und up to 4 cm wide but usually smaller in an aquarium, upperside olive-green often with darker diagonal lines, underside reddish.

Cultivation and Propagation: A very decorative solitary specimen plant which needs a fairly large tank. If conditions in the aquarium are not right for it, it may not thrive. It is essential that the plant be given a bright to slightly shady position, a temperature of approximately 25 °C and a sufficient amount of nutrients. A substratum which is too cold has an adverse effect on the species. *Barclaya* can be propagated from separated young slips which grow close to the mother plant because the runners are short. Another possible method of multiplication is by raising seedlings. The flowers produced by strong and healthy plants either stand above the water level and open out, or they remain closed in the water. In either case seeds may develop as a result of self-pollination. Some flowers, however, are sterile and disintegrate. The ripe seeds look rather like mustard seeds, except that they are smaller. Seeds should never be stored dry. Young plants develop best if they are left to float for a time and are not planted at too early a stage.

Ondinea

The genus was defined by Hartog in 1970. Its only species is the one described below.

Ondinea purpurea HARTOG

The species was named by Hartog in 1970 when he defined the genus *Ondinea*.

Distribution: North-west Australia.

Characteristics: Plant with tubers and basal leaf rosette, living submerged in water. Submerged leaves have a long petiole, the laminae are elongated and arrow-shaped with wavy edges, up to 12 cm in length and up to 2.5 cm in width, basal lobes up to 6 cm long, uppersides yellow-green, undersides more or less brown-violet. Laminae of floating leaves longish elliptical, cleft at the base up to the point of insertion of the petiole, flat, compact, up to 4 cm in length. Flowers positioned singly in leaf axils, hermaphroditic, actinomorphic. Perianth consists solely of four violet sepals, corolla is lacking. Stamens: approximately 15; carpels: three to five, embedded in the floral axis and partially fused with it. Fruit is a water berry.

Cultivation and Propagation: Ondinea purpurea is not a well-known species, but is has been cared for in an aquarium occasionally. Nothing certain is known about its cultivation and propagation.

General Information: In relationship the species is near the genus *Barclaya*. The natural habitat of *Ondinea* is in shallow, running waters which dry out but for five to seven months of the year. The plants can withstand the periods of dryness because their tubers are deeply embedded in the soil.

Family Cabombaceae

Two genera, eight species. American. Herbaceous, aquatic plants with elongated axes of the shoot and variable leaf arrangement. Leaves submerged as well as floating. Flowers are small with a coloured perianth. Both genera, *Cabomba* and *Brasenia* are rewarding aquarium plants. Formerly they were classed together with the Nymphaeaceae.

Cabomba

The genus was defined by Aublet in 1775. The name was taken from the native language of Guyana.

Distribution: From South America to the south-east of North America.

Characteristics: Perennial aquatic plants, rooted in the substratum, having very elongated axes of the shoot that branch very little. Submerged leaves opposite-decussate or in 3-partite whorls, petiolate, their laminae divided into numerous, palmate pinnae. Floating leaves alternate, shield-shaped. Flowers positioned singly in leaf axils, hermaphroditic, actinomorphic. Perianth polysepalous composed of three coloured sepals and three coloured petals with eyelets at the base. Stamens: three to six. Carpels: two to four, free, hypogynous superior. The fruit is a nut-like syncarp.

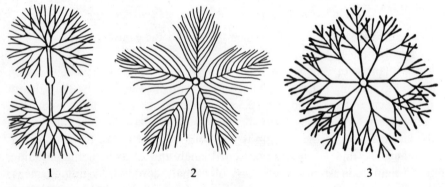

1   2   3

40 Arrangement of leaves

1 Opposite and decussate leaf arrangement of compound palmate pinnate leaves in *Cabomba*. 2 Whorled leaf arrangement of simple pinnate leaves in *Myriophyllum*. 3 Whorled leaf arrangement of multipinnate leaves in *Limnophila*

General Information: In their natural habitat the plants are rooted at the bottom of standing and slowly flowing waters, growing on elongated shoots to the water's surface. There they develop floating leaves and flowers. Branching is insignificant near the top. The upper system of shoots is short-lived; new shoots grow from the base. The coloured flowers—measuring 1 to 2 cm across—are pollinated by insects. So far it has not been possible to obtain seeds from cultivated plants.

The genus includes seven species. *C. warmingii* with delicate, transparent leaves and occurring in certain areas of central South America, and *C. palaeformis* from Central America have not been cultivated so far, but it should be rewarding to try them in aquarium conditions.

Cabomba aquatica AUBL. (Ill. 49)

When the genus *Cabomba* was defined in 1775, Aublet gave this species its name.

Distribution: In extensive regions of the Amazon estuary.

Characteristics: Aquatic plant with elongated shoots rooted at the bottom. Submerged leaves opposite-decussate. Outline of palmate and pinnate leaf laminae is roundish with a diameter of up to 5 cm, green. Tips of pinnae are not spatulate, and the midrib of pinnae is imperceptible. Laminae of floating leaves are round, their diameter 1 to 2 cm. Sepals pale-yellow.

Cultivation and Propagation: A very beautiful plant; groups of it look pleasing in the centre of a tank or in the background. *Cabomba aquatica* grows quickly to the surface and has to be cut back fairly often. It needs a well-lit position and a temperature of approximately 25°C. It does not grow satisfactorily in every aquarium. Propagation from cuttings.

Cabomba australis SPEG.

The species was named by Spegazzini in 1880.

Distribution: South-eastern South America.

Characteristics: An aquatic plant with elongated shoots, rooted at the bottom. Submerged leaves opposite-decussate; outline of palmate pinnate laminae semi-circular to kidney-shaped, diameter up to 4 cm. Tips of pinnae not spatulate, midrib usually quite distinguishable. Laminae of floating leaves lanceolate, up to 2 cm in length. Sepals pale-yellow, eyelets of petals dark-yellow.

Cultivation and Propagation: As described for *C. aquatica.*

Cabomba caroliniana GRAY (Ill. 48)

The species was named by Gray in 1837.

Distribution: South-eastern North America, has become naturalized in Cuba.

Characteristics: Aquatic plant, rooted at the bottom, with elongated shoots. Submerged leaves opposite-decussate or in 3-partite whorls. Outline of palmate-pinnate submerged laminae roundish to kidney-shaped, diameter up to 4 cm, dark-green. Tips of pinnae broadened to being spatulate, midrib distinguishable. Laminae of floating leaves lanceolate, pointed at one end, in parts of one to three at the other, up to 2 cm in length. Sepals white, eyelets of petals yellow.

Cultivation and Propagation: In the main, as described for *C. aquatica,* but the species is more robust. A period of rest during the winter in a temperature of 18–20 °C is favourable for growth in the following year; however, a resting period is unlikely in aquarium conditions.

General Information: The species is represented in our aquaria in various forms. The typical *C. caroliniana* has a round outline of its palmate pinnate laminae, many segments (120 not being an uncommon number), and very slightly broadened tips of pinnae, not more than 1 mm in width. This form has often been taken for *C. aquatica.* On the other hand, another plant has been regarded as *C. caroliniana.* This form, widely spread among European aquarists, possesses a kidney-shaped outline of palmate pinnate laminae, only 20—60 segments to each leaf, and the tips of the pinnae are noticeably spatulate and broadened to 1.8 mm. The Dutch botanists van Ramshorst and Florschütz were able to clarify the situation in 1956 and declared that this form is neither known in the homeland of *C. caroliniana* nor does it exist in any American herbarium. They assume that the plant is a variety which developed in aquarium cultivation and named it *C. caroliniana* var. *paucipartita.* The use of the name of a variety is probably more correct in this case.

The origins of a third form are certainly well-known. Thus, in the Hans Barth Aquatic Plant Nursery at Dessau, GDR, a plant with a deviation grew in the midst of a stock of typical *C. caroliniana.* In this plant one leaf on each node differed from the others; the tips of the laminae were spirally twisted so that a green upperside and a white underside could be seen in turn. The lateral shoots which grew out of the axils of the deviating leaves produced only leaves possessing this new feature. Further propagation was carried out from cuttings. As this form is a cultivated plant it should be regarded as a variety and named in accordance with the rules applied to the breeding of cultivated plants. The name of the variety is, therefore, *Cabomba caroliniana* 'Silbergrüne'. In aquarist literature the name *C. caroliniana* var. *tortifolia* has also been used for it.

Cabomba pulcherrima (Harper) Fass. (Ill. 50)

Harper interpreted this species as a variety of *C. caroliniana* and named it *C. caroliniana* var. *pulcherrima* in 1903. Fassett raised it to the status of an independent species in 1952.

Distribution: In strictly limited areas of south-eastern North America.

Characteristics: Aquatic plant with elongated shoots rooted at the bottom. Submerged leaves opposite-decussate. Outline of palmate-pinnate laminae semi-circular to kidney-shaped, their radius up to 4 cm, upperside olive-green to reddish, underside reddish. Tips of pinnae slightly spatulate, midrib noticeable. Laminae of floating leaves lanceolate, up to 4 cm in length. Sepals violet, eyelets of petals yellow.

Cultivation and Propagation: As described for *C. aquatica,* but the species suffers if the daily period of illumination is less than 12 hours.

Cabomba piauhyensis GARDN.

The species was named by Gardner in 1844.

Distribution: Northern South America, Greater Antilles.

Characteristics: Aquatic plant with elongated shoots, rooted at the bottom. Submerged leaves opposite-decussate. Outline of palmate-pinnate laminae round to kidney-shaped, their diameter up to 4 cm, upperside olive-green to reddish, underside reddish. Segments very narrow, not spatulate at the tips, midrib not distinguishable. Laminae of floating leaves lanceolate, up to 3 cm in length. Sepals violet, eyelets of petals yellow.

Cultivation and Propagation: As described for *C. aquatica*. The species suffers if the daily period of illumination is less than 12 hours.

Brasenia

The genus was defined by Schreber in 1789. So far the source for its name has not been traced. There is only one species.

Brasenia schreberi GMEL. (Ill. *41*)

The species was named by Gmelen in 1796.

Distribution: North and Central America, Greater Antilles, Africa, east Asia, Australia.

Characteristics: Aquatic plant with runners and elongated, erect shoots, rooted in the bottom. Leaf arrangement alternate, all leaves are shield-shaped and floating. Diameter of

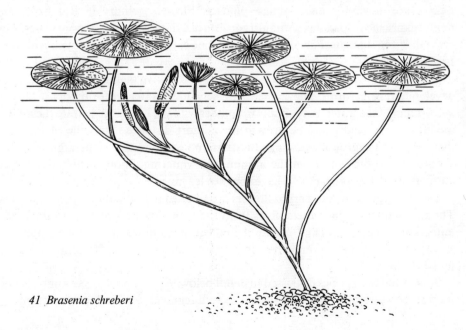

41 *Brasenia schreberi*

lamina up to 6 cm. Colour of lamina upperside dark-green, edged in brown or red, under-side reddish. Flowers positioned singly in leaf axils, hermaphroditic, actinomorphic, measuring up to 2.5 cm across. Perianth polysepalous, violet in colour, calyx and corolla both tripartite or quadripartite. Stamens: many. Carpels: 4—18, separated, hypogynous superior. Fruit a nut-like syncarp.

Cultivation and Propagation: A plant for an aquarium which is not too warm. It can be kept out in the open during the summer. It needs plenty of light and a low water level, the most favourable being 20—25 cm. Propagation from slips. These produce new runners.

General Information: Recently the species has rarely been cultivated. In earlier geological periods it was also distributed in Europe.

Family Ceratophyllaceae · Hornwort Family

Only the genus *Ceratophyllum* belongs to this family.

Ceratophyllum

The genus was defined by Linné in 1753. The name is derived from keras, keratos (Gk) = horn and phyllon (Gk) = leaf.

Distribution: Almost worldwide.

Characteristics: Submerged, rootless plants with elongated, much branched shoot axes. Leaves are in whorls and palmate-pinnate. Flowers solitary in leaf axils, unisexual, monoecious, inconspicuous. Perianth consists of a number of small green scales. Male flow-ers with 6—16 stamens. Female flowers with one carpel each which is hypogynous superior. Fruit is a nut.

General Information: The *Ceratophyllum* species thrive mainly submerged. They cannot develop terrestrial forms. They either live freely in the water, or form a dense growth on the substratum of the water. Any shoots in contact with the bottom penetrate the mud, develop modified leaves and continue growth for a short distance. Thus the plants can anchor themselves to the ground, although they have no roots. In the temperate zones all floating shoots sink to the bottom in the autumn for wintering. Shoots which develop after the autumn are more compact and have tougher leaves.

The inconspicuous, submerged flowers are adapted to pollination by the agency of water. The ripe stamens detach themselves from the male flowers and float to the surface. The anthers split lengthways and release the pollen. In calm water the pollen grains sink very slowly to the bottom and may then come into contact with the filamentous stigmas of the female flowers.

Besides the two species discussed in detail below, *C. echinatum* occurs in North America. Its fruit has several thorns. All species have a tendency to develop local forms.

Ceratophyllum submersum L.

The species was named by Linné in 1763.

Distribution: Europe, central and south-east Asia.

Characteristics: Rootless, aquatic plant with elongated but brittle shoots. Leaves tripartite, bifurcated with five to eight tips, soft, pale-green to reddish, indistinctly and sparsely finely-toothed. Fruit without thorns at the base, with short remnant of stigma at the apex.

Cultivation and Propagation: An undemanding species and hardy in the winter, suitable for ponds and cold-water tanks receiving strong illumination. It can even be put into a heated aquarium but, in that case, the south-eastern European forms, which tend to be red, should be used. Shoots can be anchored at the bottom or left to float free. They branch intensively and form dense clusters. These can be used like the waterweed family in spawning tanks for viviparous cyprinoids. Propagation by division of shoots or removal of lateral shoots.

Ceratophyllum demersum L.

The species was named by Linné in 1753.

Distribution: Almost worldwide.

Characteristics: Rootless aquatic plant with elongated shoots. Leaves are simple to bipartite bifurcated with two to four tips, tough, dark-green, distinctly toothed. Fruit has two thorns at the base and a long remnant of the stigma at the apex.

Cultivation and Propagation: An undemanding species, hardy in the winter and suitable for ponds and cold-water tanks. Propagation like *C. submersum.*

Family Saururaceae · Lizard's Tail Family

Four genera, five species. North America, east Asia. Herbaceous plants of varying sizes with runners. Leaf arrangement alternate on elongated axes of shoots or in basal rosettes. Flowers very small and inconspicuous, combined in inflorescences, some of which have coloured bracts at the base.

Of the four genera *Saururus* and *Houttuynia* colonize boggy areas and are able to withstand temporary flooding.

Saururus

The genus was defined by Linné in 1753. The name is derived from saura, sauros (Gk) = lizard and oura (Gk) = tail. The name refers to the form of the inflorescence.

Distribution: Eastern North America, east Asia.

Characteristics: Herbaceous plants with runners and erect elongated shoots. Leaf arrangement alternate. Leaves petiolate with heart-shaped, very pointed laminae, up to 15 cm long and up to 8 cm wide. The inflorescence is a slender spike which has no bracts at the base. Flowers small and inconspicuous, lacking a perianth. Stamens: four to six. Carpels: three to four, slightly fused a the base, hypogynous superior. Fruit is a nut-like syncarp.

General Information: The two species *S. cernuus* from eastern North America, and *S. chinensis* from eastern Asia (the latter occurring as a widely distributed weed in the rice paddies of its natural habitat) can be used as border plants in pond margins. The plants grow to a height of 1 m. Because of their plain appearance and inconspicuous flowers it is unlikely that they will ever be very popular.

A further disadvantage is their very rapid growth caused by the prolific runners they produce. If the plants are covered with leaves during the winter they can stand up to the cold.

Occasionally *Saururus cernuus* has been kept in an aquarium, but is has been found that here the plants are not really usable. When shoot tips of land plants were put into the tank submerged they lasted for a time under water and did not grow unduly. Generally, however, what was thought to be an *S. cernuus* was, in reality, a *Houttuynia cordata* described below.

Houttuynia

The genus was defined by Thunberg in 1874. It was named after the Dutch physician, Dr. Houttuyn who wrote a work on natural history in approximately 1870. The genus contains one species only.

Houttuynia cordata THUNB. (Ill. 51)

The species was named by Thunberg in 1874 when he defined the genus.

Distribution: East Asia.

Characteristics: Herbaceous plant with runners and erect elongated shoots. Leaf arrangement alternate. Leaves petiolate, laminae heart-shaped, up to 10 cm long and almost equally wide. The inflorescence is a sturdy spike, having four fairly large, white bracts at its base. Flowers small and inconspicuous, lacking a perianth. Stamens: three. Carpels: three, partially fused, hypogynous superior. The fruit is a capsule.

Cultivation and Propagation: A bog plant which grows to a height of 50 cm and can be used in pond margins. With its inflorescences adorned by white bracts it is certainly a more decorative plant than the related *Saururus* species. But *Houttuynia* also has prolific runners and spreads so fast that it can become a nuisance. Even if the plants are covered with a good layer of foliage in the winter, they do not always stand up to the cold. *Houttuynia* can be particularly recommended for a planthouse. Some aquarists have used it in a home aquarium where it has done better than the related *Saururus* species. Here too, it is usually tips of aerial shoots which are transferred to the tank.

Family Crassulaceae · Orpine Family

Thirty-five genera, 1,500 species. Worldwide distribution, richest evolution in southern Africa and Central America. Bushes, perennial herbs and annual plants, as a rule with leaves and also shoots containing water-storage tissue. The rather small, very regular flowers are grouped in dense clusters.

The Crassulaceae are succulent plants, predominantly found in a dry habitat. The genus *Crassula*, however, contains some marsh and aquatic plants.

Crassula

The genus was defined by Linné in 1753. The name is derived from crassus (L) = thick. It refers to the usually thick, water-storing leaves.

Distribution: Almost worldwide, but main centre of evolution in southern Africa.

Characteristics: Medium-high bushes, variable perennial herbs, and also annuals with leaf arrangement either alternate or opposite and decussate. The leaves develop water-storing tissue and, therefore, become more or less succulent and thickened. Flowers either in inflorescences of dense clusters or in leaf axils, hermaphroditic, actinomorphic. Perianth polysepalous, usually consisting of a calyx in three to nine parts, but usually five and a corolla formed likewise. Stamens: three to nine. Carpels: three to nine, free or slightly fused at the base, hypogynous superior. The fruit is a pod.

The genus includes approximately 300 species. They colonize predominantly dry habitats which is characteristic for the whole family. The plants are well adapted to life in dry places because of their capacity for water-storage. Some species, however, do occur in wet areas where they may be flooded from time to time, or even live almost permanently submerged. Among these species are the following: *C. bonariensis* from South America which has become naturalized in the rice fields of south-western Europe; *C. aquatica* occurring here and there in all temperate zones of the northern hemisphere; *C. natans*, *C. inanis* and *C. granvikii* from Africa; as well as the species described below.

Crassula helmsii KIRK (Ill. 30)

The species was named by Kirk in 1858. Further names used by aquarists are *Crassula intricata* and *Tillaea recurva*.

Distribution: New Zealand.

Characteristics: Small herbaceous plants with elongated shoots and leaves arranged opposite and decussate, living in bogs or permanently submerged. Leaves are sessile, rather thick, up to 1 cm long, pale-green. Flowers whitish, 2 to 3 mm in size, positioned in the leaf axils of aerial shoots.

Cultivation and Propagation: A dainty plant which looks most attractive in a lively tank containing a good variety of species. The most favourable position for the plant is in the middle part of the aquarium where it should be planted in a clump. Good light is advisable; temperature of approximately 18 °C is adequate. The plant makes no particular demands on the substrate. During the summer months *C. helmsii* can be kept out of doors. Propagation from cuttings.

Family Podostemaceae · Riverweed Family

Forty genera, 200 species. In all tropical areas, but particularly in South America. Plants of different sizes with modified vegetative parts resembling those of mosses and seaweeds. Flowers solitary or in diverse inflorescences, very variable.

Members of the riverweed family live attached to rocks or stones, preferably in waterfalls and river rapids, but also in fast flowing, clear, tropical waters with a periodical occurrence of a more or less fluctuating water level. In such tropical waters they are characteristic for zones washed by foam as this is rich in CO_2 content. Adaptation to these particular habitats has affected the appearance of the riverweeds to such an extent that most of them bear little resemblance to higher plants. In many species the roots are the dominant part of the plants. Roots may be long and like cords, more or less branched, formed like a strap, or attached to their base as a flat crust. The roots frequently develop special adhesive organs which allow the plants to cement themselves to a surface. Furthermore, most of the roots possess chlorophyll so that they carry on most of the photosynthesis. In these species the shoots are poorly developed and, because they originate from the roots, they are referred to as adventitious shoots. However, there are also many species possessing pronounced shoots, sometimes even lacking roots. As a rule, flowers develop during the dry seasons. Riverweeds have so far never been kept by aquarists and they have rarely been cultivated in botanical gardens. The reason is probably that it is difficult to provide them with the correct growth conditions. Perhaps, one day, sufficient interest will be taken in these rather bizarre plants so that suitable methods for their cultivation may be discovered. Until this happens our knowledge about this family will remain incomplete.

Family Euphorbiaceae · Wolf's Milk Family

300 genera, 7,000 species. Predominantly tropical-subtropical, relatively few species in the temperate latitudes. Woody plants, succulents, lianas, perennial herbs and annuals. Usually contain a milky juice. Flowers unisexual, either monoecious or dioecious, some of them very inconspicuous but, in that event, arranged in complicated inflorescences.

The species of the wolf's milk family colonize the most varied habitats. Some species live in extremely dry areas of Africa and Asia and look rather like cacti. Yet others occur in woods, in meadows, or—as weeds—in fields. A small number of species is found in wet habitats, e. g. *Euphorbia palustris* in Europe, and species of the genus *Caperonia* are found in America and Africa. A true aquatic occurs only in the genus *Phyllanthus*.

Phyllanthus

The genus was defined by Linné in 1753. The name is derived from phyllon (Gk) = leaf and anthos (Gk) = flower. This is because in some species the flowers develop on flattened shoot axes which resemble leaves.

Distribution: In all tropical and subtropical regions.

Characteristics: Trees, bushes and perennial herbs of diverse appearance with small, inconspicuous flowers. The species described below differs considerably from all others.

General Information: The genus includes approximately 600 species.

Phyllanthus fluitans MUELL. ARG. (Ill. 35)

The species was named by I. Müller.

Distribution: Northern South America

Characteristics: Small plants with delicate, elongated, horizontal shoot axes, floating on the surface of the water. Floating leaves arranged in two rows lying over each other like roofing tiles, roundish with an arched middle, their diameter up to 2 cm, pale-green to reddish. Flowers in three to fourfold inflorescences, very small, unisexual. Perianth simple, cup-shaped, laciniolated, whitish. Male flowers with three stamens. Female flowers with three carpels, these united, hypogynous superior. Fruit is a capsule.

Cultivation and Propagation: This interesting floating plant bears a certain resemblance to *Salvinia*. It forms a dense floating cover and casts too much shade which is why only a few of these plants can be kept in an aquarium. They are better suited to the conditions of a planthouse. *Phyllanthus fluitans* does not always thrive. It needs a temperature of approximately 25 °C and good light. The plant suffers if the daily period of illumination is less than 12 hours. If the water is drained completely particularly beautiful specimens develop on the wet soil.

Family Lythraceae · Loosestrife Family

Twenty-five genera, 550 species. Tropical-subtropical, particularly in America; a few species only in temperate latitudes. Rarely trees or bushes, as a rule perennial and also annual herbaceous plants. Leaves simple, of variable arrangement. Hermaphroditic flowers with a cup or tube-shaped floral axis with which the petals are united.

Members of the loosestrife family colonize many different habitats. Marsh and aquatic plants occur in seven genera. Most of the species of the genera *Cuphea* and *Nesaea* are land plants, many of them characteristic for very arid regions, but some do grow in standing or slowly flowing waters. The sole species of the genus *Decodon* occurs in waters of eastern North America. So far, the genera *Lythrum*, *Ammannia*, *Rotala*, and *Peplis* have become important for the cultivation.

Lythrum

The genus was defined by Linné in 1753. The name is derived from lythron (Gk) = being soiled by spilt blood, and it refers to the red flower colouration of many species.

Distribution: Cosmopolitan.

Characteristics: Rarely shrubs, usually perennial herbs, but also annuals. Leaves arranged alternate, opposite and decussate, or in whorls, either sessile or with a short petiole. Flowers in terminal inflorescences, but also clustered or solitary in leaf axils. Flowers hermaphroditic, actionomorphic or faintly mirror-symmetrical. Perianth polysepalous, composed of an inconspicuous calyx and a colourful corolla, both usually being in six parts. Stamens as many or double the number of the sepals. Carpels: two, united, hypogynous superior. Fruit is a capsule.

General Information: The genus includes approx. 40 species. A fair number of them grows in wet habitats, sometimes actually in the water. Some botanists have grouped these species into an independent genus, *Middendorfia*. Another reason why they are so grouped is found in the similar character of the flowers. However, the species of the genus *Peplis* are then classified with *Middendorfia*. Besides the species described below, others are also suitable for cultivation on ponds, e. g. *L. virgatum* from east and south-east Europe. A few species might be suitable plants for an aquarium. Thus the aquarist might be advised to try them out, if they are obtainable.

Lythrum salicaria L. (Ill. 52)

The species was named by Linné 1753.

Distribution: Europe, northern Asia, naturalized in some areas of North America.

Characteristics: A perennial herb with erect shoots reaching a maximum height of 2 m. Basal shoot sections which grow in the water with white, spongy aerated tissue. Leaves usually arranged opposite and decussate, but also in tripartite whorls, sessile, broad lanceolate, up to 10 cm long, dark-green. Flowers in spikes. Petals dark-red. Stamens: 12.

Cultivation and Propagation: A plant which is hardy in the winter and can be used in the marginal vegetation or shallow areas of ponds. Because of its dark-red flowers one of the most decorative of marsh plants. Propagation by division of the plant bases in autumn or early spring. Seeds can also be used for raising young plants; these usually thrive and soon produce flowers.

General Information: In *Lythrum salicaria* stamens are always arranged in two tiers. As the stamens occur in three different lengths, three different arrangements are possible: long and medium-long, long and short, medium-long and short. In the single flowers the pistils with the stigmas are also present in three different lengths. It has been established that the most favourable pollination results are achieved if the pollen of one tier of stamens is received by the stigmas of the corresponding length of pistils in the flowers.

Ammannia

The genus was defined by Linné in 1753. It was named after J. Ammann.

Distribution: In nearly all warm regions on earth.

Characteristics: Perennial or annual herbaceous plants, often with four-sided elongated shoot axes. Leaves opposite and decussate, sessile. Flowers in clusters or solitary in leaf axils, hermaphroditic, actinomorphic or faintly mirror-symmetrical. Perianth polysepalous, usually composed of an inconspicuous calyx in four parts and a coloured corolla also in four parts. The corolla may be lacking. Stamens: four or eight. Carpels: two, united, hypogynous superior. Fruit is a capsule.

General Information: The genus includes approximately 30 species. Most of them grow in a wet habitat, e. g. rice paddies. It is only in recent years that some of them have been cultivated as aquarium plants—with modest success.

Ammannia senegalensis LAM. (Ill. 31, 58)

The species was named by Lamarck in 1791.

Distribution: Tropical and subtropical Africa.

Characteristics: Herbaceous plants with erect, elongated shoot axes, growing on wet soil or submerged in water. Leaves elliptical to lanceolate, flat, up to 3 cm long, up to 1 cm wide, pale-green. Flowers in clusters in leaf axils of aerial shoots, corolla petals lacking.

Cultivation and Propagation: An inconspicuous plant which does quite well in a temperature of 20°C but needs a great deal of light. The plants may not always thrive, however. They look at their best if planted in a clump in the middle part of a tank. Propagation from cuttings. If cultivated emerse, a large amount of seeds, capable of germinating, can be harvested.

Ammannia spec. (Ill. 33, 53)

Up to the present it has not been possible to define this species properly. In aquaristic literature it is often, but erroneously, denoted as an *Ammania senegalensis*.

Distribution: Probably Africa.

Characteristics: A plant with an erect habit and elongated shoot axes, growing on wet soil or submerged in water. Submerged leaves linear, usually with margins folded downwards, up to 4 cm long and up to 1 cm wide, upperside brown in intensive light, otherwise olive-green, underside pale reddish. Flowers in clusters in leaf axils of aerial shoots, with small pale-violet corolla petals.

Cultivation and Propagation: The brown colouration provides an interesting contrast to the green of the other aquarium plants. This species should also be planted in a clump in the middle part of the tank and it should be given as much light as possible. It needs a temperature of approximately 25 °C. Propagation from cuttings.

Rotala

The genus was defined by Linné in 1771. The name is probably derived from rota (L) = wheel, and refers to the leaves being arranged in whorls resembling spokes of wheels in some of the species.

Distribution: In all warm regions on earth.

Characteristics: Perennial or annual herbaceous plants with roundish elongated shoot axes. Leaves arranged either opposite and decussate or in whorls, small, generally sessile. Flowers in terminal inflorescences, or in clusters or solitary in leaf axils, hermaphroditic, actinomorphic or faintly mirror-symmetrical. Perianth polysepalous, usually composed of an inconspicuous calyx in four parts and a coloured corolla, also in four parts. Corolla may be lacking. Stamens: normally four. Carpels: two, united, hypogynous superior. Fruit is a capsule.

General Information: The genus includes approximately 45 species. All of them grow in a wet habitat or in the water. Therefore, a number of usable aquarium plants are still to be expected from this genus.

Rotala macrandra KOEHNE (Ill. 56)

The species was named by Koehne in 1880.

Distribution: India.

Characteristics: A herbaceous plant with elongated shoot axes and leaves arranged opposite and decussate growing horizontally on wet soil, or erect under water. Submerged leaves broad egg-shaped to elliptical, wavy, up to 3 cm long and up to 1.5 cm wide, rarely larger, upperside pale-green, olive-green or reddish, underside reddish. Inflorescences are composed of several spikes, terminal. Flowers small, with pink petals of the corolla.

Cultivation and Propagation: This splendid plant is not easy to cultivate. It appears that it is easily damaged while being transported. In botanical gardens and nurseries for aquatic plants it perishes if it is cultivated in daylight, and receives less than 12 hours of light. In an aquarium it should be planted in a clump in as bright a position as possible. Temperature around 25 °C. Propagation from cuttings.

36 *Victoria cruziana*
37 *Victoria cruziana*, blossom in the second night

42 *Nymphaea* cv. Atropurpurea
43 *Nymphaea* cv. Chromatella
44 *Nymphaea* cv. Helvola
45 *Nymphaea* spec.

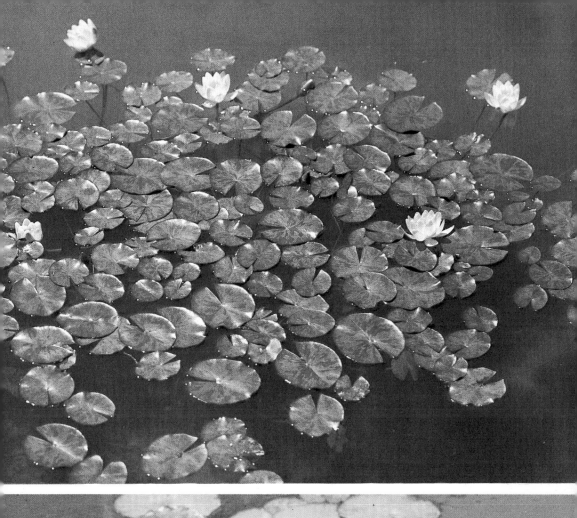

Rotala rotundifolia (ROXB.) KOEHNE (Ill. 54, 55)

The species was named *Ammannia rotundifolia* by Roxburgh in 1820. Koehne moved it to the genus *Rotala* in 1880. In aquaristic literature it is often denoted as *R. indica*, but this is an error.

Distribution: South-east Asiatic mainland.

Characteristics: A herbaceous plant with elongated shoot axes and leaves arranged opposite and decussate, creeping horizontally on wet soil and growing erect submerged. Leaves sessile. Submerged leaves very variable, linear, lanceolate, blunt, elliptical, egg-shaped or almost roundish, up to 1.5 cm long and up to 4 mm wide, upperside pale-green, underside whitish-green to reddish. Aerial leaves always round, dark-green. Inflorescence is composed of several spikes, terminal. Flowers small, with red petals of the corolla.

Cultivation and Propagation: A small-leafed, undemanding plant, to be used in a clump among larger plants in the middle part of the tank, but it also looks well in the background. It is equally suitable for being planted in the corners of the foreground. In an aquarium shoots often grow creeping along the substrate and branch intensively. This species should not be too much in the shade. Temperature just above 18 °C. Propagation from cuttings.

Rotala indica (WILLD.) KOEHNE

The species was named *Peplis indica* by Willdenow in 1799 and moved to the genus *Rotala* by Koehne in 1880.

Distribution: South-East Asia; it has become naturalized in the rice fields of northern Italy.

Characteristics: Herbaceous plants with elongated shoot axes, creeping horizontally on wet soil or growing erect when submerged. Leaves arranged opposite and decussate, sessile. Submerged leaves linear to slightly spatulate, up to 1 cm long and up to 3 mm wide, upperside pale-green, underside whitish-green. Flowers solitary in leaf axils of aerial shoots, very small with pink petals of the corolla.

Cultivation and Propagation: As described for *R. rotundifolia*. However, the species does not grow satisfactorily everywhere.

Rotala wallichii (HOOK. fil) KOEHNE (Ill. 34, 57)

The species was named *Hydrolythum wallichii* by Hooker fil. in 1867 and was moved to the genus *Rotala* by Koehne in 1880. It was introduced to aquarists under the name of '*Mayaca* spec.'.

Distribution: South-East Asian mainland.

Characteristics: Herbaceous plant with elongated shoot axes and leaves arranged in whorls, creeping on wet soil or growing erect when submerged. Up to nine submerged leaves from one whorl, leaves sessile, slender linear, rounded at the apex, up to 1.5 cm long and up to 3 mm wide, upperside olive-green, underside reddish. Flowers in terminal spikes, small, with pink petals of the corolla.

Cultivation and Propagation: At present probably the most beautiful species of the genus. The delicate leaves make it look particularly effective when planted in a clump in the middle part of a tank. The plants should be given sufficient light and temperatures of just above 20°C. Otherwise, the plant is undemanding. Propagation from cuttings.

Peplis

The genus was defined by Linné in 1753. Peplos (Gk) = upper garment.

Distribution: Europe, Asia, Australia, America.

Characteristics: Perennial or annual herbaceous plants with elongated shoot axes. Leaves opposite and decussate, small, sessile. Flowers solitary in leaf axils, inconspicuous, hermaphroditic, actinomorphic. Perianth polysepalous, consisting of a calyx in six parts, corolla lacking. Stamens: six. Carpels: two, united, hypogynous superior. Fruit is a capsule.

General Information: The genus is made up of three species only. Some botanists separate one of the species and give it the status of an independent genus, *Didiplis*. The plants grow in a wet or periodically wet habitat and can stand up to being flooded.

Peplis diandra DC. (Ill. 32)

The species was named by De Candolle in 1828. A further name for it is *Didiplis diandra*.

Distribution: Southern North America.

Characteristics: Herbaceous plants with elongated shoot axes, creeping on wet soil or growing erect when submerged. Leaves arranged opposite and decussate. Submerged leaves linear to narrow lanceolate, up to 2.5 cm long and up to 3 mm wide, pale to dark green. Even in submerged plants the inconspicuous flowers develop in the axils of the leaves.

Cultivation and Propagation: Because of its small, slender and often very crowded leaves these plants provide an interesting contrast to many of the other aquarium plants in the tank. *Peplis diandra* can be planted in a clump in the middle part of the tank and also in the foreground. Fairly frequent cutting back of the plants will bring about the development of dense bushy growth. Position should be light to slightly shady. Temperature just above 18°C. Propagation from cuttings.

Family Onagraceae · Evening Primrose Family

Twenty genera, 650 species. Rarely tropical, usually subtropical and in temperate latitudes, predominantly in America. Shrubs and herbaceous plants with simple leaves. Flowers solitary in leaf axils, hermaphroditic, actinomorphic, with a conspicuous to inconspicuous perianth.

Another scientific name for the family is Oenotheraceae, but it is not used nowadays. The evening primrose family includes several decorative species, e. g. the fuchsias and clarkias. The members of the family colonize very variable habitats, but marsh and aquatic plants occur in two genera only. Of these one is the American genus *Boisduvalia* which includes six species. So far, none of them have been cultivated. But the second genus, *Ludwigia*, has always been an important one for the aquarist.

Ludwigia

The genus was defined by Linné in 1753. The genus was enlarged considerably in volume when Hara decided do include the formerly independent genus *Jussiaea* with the genus *Ludwigia* in 1953. The name was chosen in honour of Professor C. G. Ludwig of Leipzig (1709—1773).

Distribution: Almost worldwide.

Characteristics: Shrubs or herbaceous plants with elongated horizontally growing or erect shoots. Leaves alternate or opposite and decussate, simple, sessile or with a short petiole. Flowers solitary in leaf axils, hermaphroditic, actinomorphic. Perianth polysepalous, composed of a calyx in three to seven, but usually four parts, and a yellow or white corolla in the same number of parts. The corolla may be lacking. Stamens: as many as or double the number of sepals. Carpels: two, united, inferior. Fruit is a capsule.

General Information: The genus includes 75 species. Approximately 15 species grow completely submerged, at least temporarily, The others colonize a boggy habitat or grow on banks of waters whence they send out shoots which float on the water's surface. No doubt the genus still contains more suitable species for cultivation than have been tried out so far. Some of the larger, bushy species are very suitable for emerse cultivation in a planthouse where they look very decorative, e. g. *L. peruviana* with its comparatively large, yellow flowers.

Formation of white and spongy respiratory roots, growing vertically upwards, lends an added interest to some species. These roots allow the plants a far better exchange of gases than their absorbing roots which grow in mud with little air content.

Ludwigia adscendens (L.) HARA (Ill. 59)

Linné named the species *Jussiaea repens* in 1753 and denoted it *J. adscendens* in 1767. Hara moved it to the genus *Ludwigia* in 1953; the later specific epithet had to be retained because a *Ludwigia repens* existed already.

Distribution: South-east Asia, northern Australia.

Characteristics: Herbaceous plant with horizontally growing shoot axis and alternate leaf arrangement. Leaves elliptical, tapering at the base, up to 6 cm long and up to 3 cm wide, medium to dark-green. Spongy respiratory roots growing vertically upwards. Flowers in five parts, petals of corolla yellow, diameter of flowers 5 cm.

Cultivation and Propagation: Shoots of this species grow creeping in the bog or float on the water coming from the shore. With their rather large yellow flowers the plants are among the most attractive of pond plants, but they do not always stand up to the conditions of winter in temperate latitudes. Under a dense cover of foliage some sections of the shoots usually survive and they are likely to develop in spring. However, it is safer to pot a number of shoots in the autumn and to winter them in a cool place, free of frost and as light as possible. Propagation from cuttings.

Ludwigia arcuata WALT. (Ill, *42*, 66)

The species was named by Walter in 1788.
   Distribution: South-eastern North America.
   Characteristics: Herbaceous plant with leaves arranged opposite and decussate, either creeping on wet soil or growing erect under water. Submerged leaves sessile, linear, pointed, up to 3.5 cm long and up to 2 mm wide, upperside olive-green, underside pale reddish. Aerial leaves tapering at the base, broad lanceolate, up to 2 cm long and up to 5 mm wide, dark-green. Flowers with peduncle up to 3 cm long, four sepals and four petals, these up to 12 mm in length.

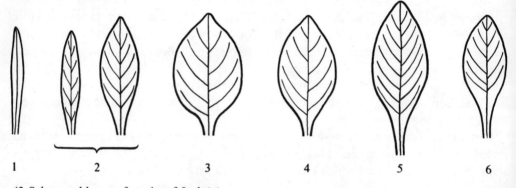

42 Submerged leaves of species of *Ludwigia*

1 *L. arcuata*, 2 short-day and long-day leaf of the narrow-leafed form of *L. repens*, 3 round-leafed reddish form of *L. repens*, 4 round-leafed greenish form of *L. repens*, 5 *Ludwigia* hybrid, 6 *L. palustris*

Cultivation and Propagation: Because of its slender leaves this undemanding species looks very attractive in a lively aquarium, containing a good variety of plants. It looks best when planted in a clump in the middle of the tank. A position in good light is needed. Temperature not less than 20°C. Propagation from cuttings.

Ludwigia brevipes (LONG) E. H. EAMES (Ill. 60, 61)

The species was named *Ludwigiantha brevipes* by Long and moved to the genus *Ludwigia* by E. H. Eames in 1933.

Distribution: South-eastern coast of North America.

Characteristics: Herbaceous plants with elongated shoots and leaves arranged opposite and decussate; creeping on wet soil or growing erect under water. Very similar to the species described previously. Submerged leaves sessile, linear to lanceolate, up to 3 cm long and up to 4 mm wide, upperside olive-green, underside pale reddish. Aerial leaves sessile or tapering at the base, up to 2.5 cm long and up to 0.8 cm wide, dark-green. Flowers with a peduncle up to 1.5 cm in length, with four sepals and four petals, these up to 0.5 cm long.

Cultivation and Propagation: As specified for *L. arcuata.*

Ludwigia repens FORST. (Ill. *42*, 67)

The species was named by Forster in 1771. Another scientific name for it is *L. natans.*

Distribution: Southern North America, Central America, Greater Antilles.

Characteristics: Herbaceous plants with elongated shoots and opposite-decussate leaf arrangement, creeping on wet soil or growing erect when submerged. Submerged leaf of variable shape and colour depending on form of species; the leaves are tough so that their horizontal positioning on the shoot axis is hardly affected when they are taken out of the water. Flowers with a pedicel of up to 0.4 cm long, four sepals and four petals.

Cultivation and Propagation: An undemanding species which comes in different forms. These display to advantage if placed in clumps in the middle or back of a tank. Good light desirable. Temperature approximately 20°C, but it can be higher. Propagation from cuttings.

General Information: At present three different forms of *L. repens* are cultivated in our aquaria. It is probable that they originate in different geographical regions. In the 'narrow-leafed form' the submerged leaves vary depending on the daily period of illumination. They are sessile and, in short-day conditions, lanceolate, up to 2.5 cm long and up to 0.5 cm wide. In long-day conditions, on the other hand, the leaves are broad lanceolate to elliptical, up to 3 cm long and up to 1.2 cm wide. The leaf upperside is olive-green in colour, the underside pale-reddish. Aerial leaves have a short petiole and rather roundish laminae. Flowers with a peduncle of 0.4 cm in length, petals approximately 0.4 cm long. The 'round-leafed-reddish form' is characterized by submerged leaves with roundish laminae, either having a short petiole or at least tapering at the base, measurement of these leaves 2.5 cm ×2 cm approximately. The leaf upperside is olive-green to reddish, the underside an intensive red. Aerial leaves can be a little larger. Flowers with a peduncle of up to 2 mm, petals approx. 2.5 mm long. The shape of the submerged leaves of the 'round-leafed-green form' is very like that of the previous form, but the leaves are rarely more than 1.5 cm in width. The leaf upperside is pale to medium-green, the underside whitish green. The red colour tones are lacking. A slight red colouration may occur in the aerial leaves. The flowers are identical with those of the second form described above. The 'round-leafed-green form' probably comes from Cuba.

Ludwigia palustris (L.) ELL. (Ill. 69)

The species was named *Isnardia palustris* by Linné in 1753 and moved to the genus *Ludwigia* by Elliot in 1817.

Distribution: Europe, central Asia, Africa, North America and also, naturalized, in New Zealand.

Characteristics: Herbaceous plant with elongated shoots and opposite and decussate leaf arrangement, either creeping on wet soil or growing erect when submerged. Submerged leaves noticeably petiolate, their laminae lanceolate to elliptical, up to 2.5 cm long and up to 1.2 cm wide, upperside pale-green, underside whitish green, soft so that leaves flop down when shoots are taken out of the water. Aerial leaves have the same shape, but they are a little smaller and tougher, dark-green, sometimes with a slight red tint. Flowers sessile with four sepals, petals lacking.

Cultivation and Propagation: In contrast to the other, related species, *Ludwigia palustris* is not suitable for a heated tank. There its internodes become too long and make the plant look unsightly. But groups of this plant can be used in a cold water tank or cultivated in the open. Propagation from cuttings.

Ludwigia repens × palustris (Ill. 68)

The plant is a hybrid produced by *Ludwigia repens* and *Ludwigia palustris*. In earlier aquarium literature it was often mistaken for *L. natans* but has also frequently been referred to as 'L. mullertii'.

Distribution: Unknown; perhaps North America where both parent species occur in some areas. Possibly the plant is a cultivated hybrid.

Characteristics: Herbaceous plant with elongated shoots and opposite and decussate leaf arrangement, either creeping horizontally on wet soil or growing erect when submerged. Submerged leaves noticeably petiolate, their laminae elliptical, up to 3 cm long and up to 15 mm wide, upperside olive-green, underside reddish, soft so that leaves flop down when shoots are taken out of the water. Aerial leaves have the same shape, but they are a little smaller and tougher. Flowers either with a very short stalk or lacking a stalk, four sepals and one to four petals, these up to 2 mm long.

Cultivation and Propagation: As specified for *L. repens*.

General Information: For many years after 1945 *Ludwigia repens × palustris* was the only *Ludwigia* species grown in aquaria in Europe. The plant is sterile and does not produce any fruit.

Family Trapaceae · Water Chestnut Family

One genus only belongs to the family—*Trapa*.

Trapa

The genus was defined by Linné in 1753. The name is derived from calcitrappa (L) = caltrop.

Distribution: Origins in Europe, Asia and Africa.

Characteristics: Annual, herbaceous plant with floating leaves arranged in dense rosettes. Leaves with spongy, inflated petioles and diamond-shaped laminae. Flowers solitary in leaf axils, hermaphroditic, actinomorphic. Perianth polysepalous, composed of a calyx in four parts and an inconspicuous, usually whitish, corolla also in four parts. Four stamens, two carpels, united, perigynous. Complicated nut-like fruit with horn-shaped appendages which develop from the sepals.

General Information: Systematic evaluation of the different varieties is still a matter of debate among botanists so that the number of species given varies from one to thirty. The genus has become naturalized in Australia and North America. The fruits contain starch and fat and are therefore often collected and eaten. They are still considered a major source of nourishment, particularly in Asia where they are being cultivated in rather extensive areas. The plants do especially well in standing waters which become warm during the summer and contain a good supply of nutrients.

Trapa natans (Ill. 72)

The species was named by Linné in 1753.

Distribution: Europe, Asia.

Characteristics: As specified for the whole genus. Diameter of rosettes up to 50 cm.

Cultivation and Propagation: This species is an adornment on any pond. The plants are undemanding. Fruits should be collected in the autumn and stored in cold water during the winter.

Family Haloragaceae · Water Milfoil Family

Eight genera, 160 species. Distribution almost worldwide. A large number of species are found in Australia. Most of the plants are perenniel shrubs or herbs, rarely annuals. Leaves simple, lobed or pinnate. Flowers hermaphroditic or unisexual, monoecious or dioecious, inconspicuous and united in varying inflorescences.

Earlier scientific names for the family were Haloragidaceae or Halorrhagaceae. The members of the family are predominantly marsh and aquatic plants. Very few of them colonize dry habitats. The genus *Haloragis* includes approximately 60 species widely distributed in east Asia and Australia. Most of the species of this genus grow submerged, *Haloragis brownii* being one of them; some live in marshy areas. The four species of the genus *Laurenbergia* are marsh plants distributed in south-east Asia, Africa and South America. So far only the genera *Myriophyllum* and *Proserpinaca* have become important for cultivation. One member of the water milfoil family, however, can often be admired in botanical gardens. This is the gunnera with leaves resembling those of rhubarb. Inconspicuous flowers, often combined in impressive inflorescences, are typical of this family of plants and a characteristics of predominantly wind-pollinated species.

Myriophyllum

The genus was defined by Linné in 1753. The name is derived from myrios (Gk) = innumerable; and phyllon (Gk) = leaf. It designates the large number of feathery submerged leaves.

Distribution: Almost cosmopolitan, absent only in very cold regions and rare in Africa.

Characteristics: Perennial or annual, herbaceous plants with elongated shoots either creeping on wet soil or growing erect in water. Leaves usually arranged in whorls (Ill. *40*) but they can be opposite or alternate. Leaves sessile, simple, more or less dentate or finely feathered. Flowers usually terminal in spike-like inflorescences or solitary in leaf axils, hermaphroditic or unisexual, normally monoecious, actinomorphic, inconspicuous. Perianth polysepalous, calyx in four parts or lacking, two to four scale-shaped petals of corolla, or corolla may be lacking. Hermaphroditic and male flowers with four to eight stamens. Hermaphroditic and female flowers with two carpels, these united, hypogynous. Loculicidal fruit resembling a nut.

General Information: Myriophyllum species are usually rooted in the bottom of the waters and their shoots grow up to the surface. The main branching occurs in basal shoot sections. But torn-off streaming shoots also continue developing even though they do not attain optimum growth. Whereas the vegetation of the plants endures in warmer regions, they develop winter buds in the temperate latitudes. At present, aquarists are familiar only with the species whose leaves are arranged in whorls. But leaf arrangement in some species is alternate, e.g. *M. humile* in North America and *M. dicoccum* in south-east Asia and Australia. In *M. amphibium* occurring in Australia and in some other species leaves are arranged opposite and decussate. When submerged shoots reach the water's surface they normally develop spikelike inflorescences which raise themselves into the air. Other species develop solitary flowers in the leaf axils of aerial shoots, yet some species have well-developed aerial shoots producing no flowers. In unisexual flowers the females are present on the base of the inflorescence but frequently are without petals of the corolla.

The genus includes approximately 40 species and probably most of them could be cultivated either in aquaria or on ponds. However, the submerged shoots of most species tend to look very alike so that interest in obtaining new species is somewhat limited. Owing to the size of the genus and insufficient knowledge on some of the species, it is not certain whether all the plants in cultivation have been correctly defined.

Myriophyllum spicatum L.

The species was named by Linné in 1753.
   Distribution: Europe, Asia, North America, Africa.
   Characteristics: An aquatic with elongated, more or less branched shoot axes, and rooted in the bottom. Submerged leaves usually in whorls of four—more rarely three or five—up to 3 cm long, dark-green. The fine pinnae slightly incurved, the lower being shorter than those in the middle. Flowers in spikelike inflorescences, the lower female, the upper male.
   Cultivation and Propagation: A species widely used in cold water aquaria and on ponds. It fades away during the winter but remains vegetative nevertheless. The plant does not form winter buds. Propagation from cuttings.

Myriophyllum verticillatum L.

The species was named by Linné in 1753.
   Distribution: Europe, Asia, North Africa, North America.
   Characteristics: Herbaceous plant with moderately branched shoot axes, growing as marsh plant or submerged. Leaves in whorls of five, more rarely in whorls of three or four, up to 4.5 cm long, dark-green. Fine pinnae slightly incurved, the lower being approximately the same length as those in the middle. Flowers in a long spike with variable bracts, lower female, upper male.
   Cultivation and Propagation: Like the previous species usable in cold water aquaria and on ponds. But the foliage of this species does not persist; nevertheless it endures the winter by forming winter buds. Propagation from cuttings.

Myriophyllum heterophyllum MICHX.

The species was named by Michaux in 1808.
   Distribution: North America, naturalized in some parts of Europe.
   Characteristics: An aquatic with elongated, moderately branched shoot axes. Submerged leaves in whorls of four to six, maximum length 5 cm, but shorter in a higher temperature. The fine lower pinnae as long as those in the middle. Flowers in spikelike inflorescences, at the bottom hermaphroditic and female, at the top male.
   Cultivation and Propagation: As specified for *M. spicatum.*

Myriophyllum brasiliense CAMBESS. (Ill. 62)

The species was named by Cambessedes in 1829. *M. proserpinacoides* is a further scientific name for it. In more recent years it has also been denoted *M. aquaticum*.

Distribution: South America, naturalized in some parts of North America, east and south-east Asia, northern Australia.

Characteristics: Herbaceous plants with intensively branched, elongated shoot axes, growing as marsh plants or submerged. Submerged leaves in whorls of four to six, up to 4 cm long, pale-green, sometimes with pale reddish tips. Aerial leaves tougher, medium-green to bluish-green. Fine pinnae almost straight, the lower ones being shorter than those in the middle. Flowers are produced rarely, but if they are they appear in the leaf axils of aerial leaves.

Cultivation and Propagation: A robust, undemanding, but light-loving species which is suitable for a heated as well as an unheated aquarium. The plants can also be cultivated out in the open where they will last through the winter provided that they are in a sheltered position and well covered with a thick layer of foliage. The Brazilian water milfoil also does very well if cultivated emersed as a land plant. Propagation from cuttings.

Myriophyllum scabratum MICHX.

The species was named by Michaux in 1803. *M. pinnatum* is another scientific name for it.

Distribution: Eastern North America, Central America, Greater Antilles.

Characteristics: An aquatic rooted in the bottom, with elongated shoot axes, usually intensively branched. Submerged leaves in whorls of three to five, but between whorls some single and alternate leaves, up to 3 cm long, dark-green, Aerial leaves smaller and tougher, bearing in their axils the normally hermaphroditic flowers.

Cultivation and Propagation: The species is suitable for heated as well as unheated tanks. Temperature up to 25 °C approximately. Should be given a place in good light. Otherwise these plants are undemanding, although they are easily damaged if dirt is deposited on their leaves. The best effect is achieved if three to five shoots are planted in a small clump. Suitable for the middle and the back of the aquarium. Once the shoots have grown upwards to the surface of the water they have to be cut back. Propagation from cuttings.

Myriophyllum ussuriense (REGEL) MAXIM.

In 1861 the plant was named by Regel as *Myriophyllum verticillatum* var. *ussuriense*, but it was given the status of an independent species by Maximowicz in 1874.

Distribution: Eastern Asia.

Characteristics: An aquatic rooted at the bottom with little-branched, elongated shoot axes. Submerged leaves in whorls of three to four, up to 2.5 cm long, straight, dark-green. Pinnae either straight or slightly curved outwards, the lower and the middle ones almost equal in length. Aerial leaves smaller and more compact, bearing the hermaphroditic or unisexual flowers in their axils.

Cultivation and Propagation: As specified for *M. scabratum.*

Myriophyllum hippuroides TORR. et GRAY (Ill. 71)

The species was named by Torrey and Gray in 1848.

Distribution: North and Central America.

Characteristics: Aquatic with elongated, reddish, slightly branched shoot axes, rooted at the bottom. Submerged leaves in whorls of four to six, up to 5 cm long, olive-green to reddish depending on illumination. Pinnae slightly incurved, not positioned evenly, lower and middle ones approximately the same length. Margins of aerial leaves entire, sometimes dentate, up to 2 cm long. Flowers axillary, unisexual.

Cultivation and Propagation: As specified for *M. scabratum.*

Proserpinaca

The genus was defined by Linné in 1753. The name is assumed to be derived from proserpere (L) = creep forth and to refer to the plants' habit of growing out of the water.

Distribution: Eastern North America, Central America.

Characteristics: Perennial, herbaceous plants either creeping on boggy ground or growing erect when submerged, with elongated slightly branched shoots and an alternate leaf arrangement. Leaves are very variable. Flowers solitary in leaf axils, hermaphroditic, inconspicuous. Perianth polysepalous, calyx in three parts, corolla lacking. Stamens: four. Carpels: three, united, hypogynous. Loculicidal fruit resembling a nut.

General Information: The genus includes just two, perhaps three species living in marshes or standing waters. Submerged and aerial leaves of *P. pectinata* are pinnate. The species described below is occasionally cultivated in an aquarium.

Proserpinaca palustris L. (Ill. 70, 95)

The species was named by Linné in 1753 when he defined the genus.

Distribution: Eastern North America, Central America.

Characteristics: A marsh or aquatic plant with elongated shoot axes. Submerged leaves depend on the amount of light they receive and are, thus, very variable, ranging from simple and entire to dentate and feathery, up to 4 cm long, dark-green. Aerial leaves always simple.

Cultivation and Propagation: An undemanding and beautiful plant which can be kept in temperatures of above 18 °C. The daily period of illumination should be more than 12 hours. The plants look at their most effective if they are planted in small clumps in the middle of a tank. Propagation from cuttings.

Family Hippuridaceae · Mare's Tail Family

Only the genus *Hippuris* belongs to this family.

Hippuris

The species was defined by Linné in 1753. The sole species it contains is the one described below. The name is derived from hippos (Gk) = horse and oura (Gk) = tail.

Hippuris vulgaris L. (Ill. 63)

The species was named by Linné in 1753 when he defined the genus *Hippuris*.
Distribution: Temperate and cold zones of the northern hemisphere.
Characteristics: Perennial herbaceous marsh and aquatic plants with runners growing in the soil and erect, elongated shoots with leaves arranged in whorls. Every whorl contains up to 15 leaves, these narrow linear. Submerged leaves soft, up to 5 cm long and up to 3 mm wide, pale-green. Aerial leaves smaller, tougher and darker in colouration. Flowers solitary or in small clusters in axils of aerial leaves, hermaphroditic, unisexual or sterile, inconspicuous. Floral envelope reduced to a narrow strip. One stamen, one hypogynous carpel. Fruit nut-like.
Cultivation and Propagation: The plant can be used in many ways, nevertheless it is rarely cultivated. It looks its best when grown submerged, but is also attractive emerse. The species is hardy during the winter and, therefore, can be planted in ponds. Alternatively it may be put into a cold or slightly warmed tank. Sufficient light is essential for good growth. If mare's tail is cultivated in an aquarium a little loam should be added to the substratum; it helps to produce particularly strong specimens. Plants kept in the open die back during the winter, but their runners survive. In warmer cultivation, however, the shoots remain vegetative. Propagation by division of runners or from cuttings.

Family Brassicaceae · Mustard Family

350 genera, 3,000 species. Predominantly in temperate and cooler regions of the northern hemisphere; in the tropics and subtropics in the mountains only. The plants display great differences; they can have rhizomes, tubers or turnip-shaped roots; they may be simple perennial herbs but also annual herbaceous plants. Leaves simple to pinnate. The hermaphroditic flowers have a coloured corolla, and they are combined in inflorescences of variable size.

Another scientific name for the family is Cruciferae, but it is not used any more. The family includes numerous cultivated plants such as radishes and various kinds of cabbages. The representatives of the family colonize many different habitats ranging from plains to high mountains. However, aquatic and marsh plants occur in the genera *Rorippa*, *Cardamine* and *Subularia* only. All three genera have become important in cultivation.

Rorippa

The genus was defined by Scoparius in 1760. The origin of the name is not clear. It may be derived from ros, roris (L) = dew; and ripa (L) = shore. Nowadays, many botanists set apart a number of the species and group them together as an independent genus under the name of *Nasturtium*.

Distribution: In all temperate zones and in tropical mountain regions.

Characteristics: Perennial or annual herbaceous plants with shoots either creeping or growing erect. Leaf arrangement on young shoots often in rosettes, on older ones alternate, leaves simple to pinnate. Flowers in small inflorescences, hermaphroditic, actinomorphic. Perianth polysepalous, composed of a calyx in four parts and a yellow, white or bluish corolla also in four parts. Stamens: six. Carpels: two, united, hypogynous superior. The fruit is a pod.

General Information: The genus includes approximately 70 species some of which grow in marshy areas, and even submerged. *Rorippa nasturtium-aquaticum* and *R. microphylla* as well as a hybrid produced by both species are water cresses. They are often eaten in salads and, in some areas, they are specially cultivated. *R. amphibia*, distributed in Europe and northern Asia, has not yet been used in aquarium plant cultivation. It would be worth a trial, however. Yet so far, the species described below is the only one in cultivation.

Rorippa aquatica (EAT.) PALM. et STEYERM. (Ill. 73)

The species was named *Cochlearia aquatica* by Eaton in 1829 and moved to the genus *Rorippa* by Palmer and Steyermark in 1935. A later scientific name for the species is *Armoracia aquatica*, and the plant was introduced to aquarists under this name. The cultivated horse-radish belongs to the genus *Armoracia*.

Distribution: Eastern and North America.

Characteristics: Small perennial rosette plant growing in boggy areas and submerged. Submerged leaves up to 10 cm long, very variable, either petiolate or tapering at the base, their laminae with irregularly toothed margins, pinnate parts coarsely or finely divided, solid yet brittle, dark-green. Aerial leaves softer and paler in colour. Flowers very small with white petals.

Cultivation and Propagation: A very decorative, but slow-growing plant suitable for being planted in the front part of a heated tank. Most probably it can also be used in a cold water aquarium. As a rule the rosette growth lasts for a long time but, occasionally, the plants develop ascending shoots carrying very finely pinnate leaves. Temperature optimum is 18-25 °C, position in the tank should be light to shady; otherwise the plants are undemanding. The best propagation results are obtained from cut-off lower leaves allowed to float on the surface of the water. Adventitious plants form on the petioles after quite a short time, something well-known from the family of Acanthaceae. Such adventitious plants can be taken off as soon as they are sufficiently strong and have formed their own roots.

Cardamine

The genus was defined by Linné in 1753. The name is derived from kardamon (Gk = cress).
  Distribution: In nearly all temperate zones and tropical mountain regions.
  Characteristics: Perennial or annual herbaceous plants with creeping or erect growing shoots. Leaves alternate, simple to pinnate. Flowers in small inflorescences, usually in clusters, hermaphroditic, actinomorphic. Perianth polysepalous with a calyx in four parts and white, yellow, pink or pale violet corolla also in four parts. Stamens: six. Carpels: two, united, hypogynous superior. The fruit is a pod.

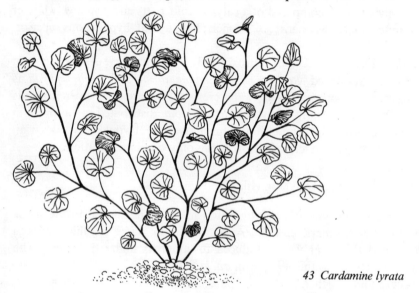

43 *Cardamine lyrata*

  General Information: The genus includes approximately 160 species of which many are bog plants. Besides the species discussed below *C. prorepens* and *C. variabilis* also grow submerged for lengthy periods.

Cardamine lyrata BUNGE (Ill. *43*)

The species was named by Bunge in 1835.
  Distribution: Eastern Asia.
  Characteristics: Dainty herbaceous plant living in marshes and also submerged. In the water the shoot axes are erect. Leaf arrangement is alternate. Submerged leaves are always

petiolate, up to 5 cm long, their laminae are roundish or slightly kidney-shaped, often with crenate margins, pale-green. Some submerged leaves near the surface of the water and all aerial leaves are pinnipartite or pinnate with large terminal lobes. Flowers small with white petals.

Cultivation and Propagation: These pretty plants feel happiest in temperatures of 15 °C to 20 °C and are thus best suited to cold water tanks. In too high a temperature the plants may wilt. They need good light, but otherwise undemanding. Propagation from cuttings.

Subularia

The genus was defined by Linné in 1753. The name is derived from subula (L) = awl and refers to the shape of the leaves.

Distribution: Europe, central Asia, Africa, North America.

Characteristics: Small plants with simple leaves arranged in rosettes, these up to 5 cm in height, rarely up to 10 cm. Inflorescences are very small and in 2 to 15 flower parts. Flowers hermaphroditic, very small. Perianth polysepalous composed of a calyx in four parts and a white corolla, also in four parts. Stamens: six. Carpels: two, united, hypogynous superior. The fruit is a pod.

General Information: The genus consists only of the two species described below. These live submerged but also in boggy habitats which may become dry periodically. In literature the plants are normally described as annuals but, if they live submerged, they may last longer. Flowers also develop if growth is submerged but, in that case, the flowers remain closed and seeds develop as a result of self-pollination.

Subularia aquatica L.

The species was named by Linné in 1753.

Distribution: Europe, central Asia, North America.

Characteristics: Small rosette plant living submerged or in marshes. Leaves awl-shaped, pointed.

Cultivation and Propagation: Nowadays a rarely cultivated plant which, in earlier aquarium literature, was recommended for the foreground of a tank. Propagation only from seeds. Young plants will develop even in an aquarium if they are left undisturbed.

Subularia monticula SCHWEINF.

The species was nemd by Schweinfurth.

Distribution: In the mountains of central Africa.

Characteristics: Small rosette plant living submerged and in bogs. Leaves are divided into petioles and small lanceolate laminae.

Cultivation and Propagation: As specified for *S. aquatica.*

Family Droseraceae · Sundew Family

Four genera, 90 species. From tropical to temperate latitudes. Small herbaceous plants of different sizes and diverse appearance with hermaphroditic flowers. Insectivorous plants.

The representatives of the sundew family produce proteolytic enzymes which enable them to digest small insects, very small crustaceans etc. This provides them with an additional source of nitrogen for nourishment. However, all species can exist without animal protein. The plants hold on to their prey and digest it with the aid of special glands present on the laminae. Sensitive hairs may be distributed on the latter; they release a mechanism for clasping and trapping if prey alights on them. The Droseraceae normally colonize sandy or marshy habitats in common with the species of the well-known genus *Drosera*. The aquarist might well be interested in the genus *Aldrovanda*.

Aldrovanda

The genus was defined by Linné in 1753. He named it after the Italian naturalist U. Aldrovandi (1522—1605). Its only species is the one described below.

Aldrovanda vesiculosa L. (Ill. *44*)

The species was named by Linné in 1753 when he defined the genus.
   Distribution: Europe, east and south-east Asia, north Africa, north-east Australia.

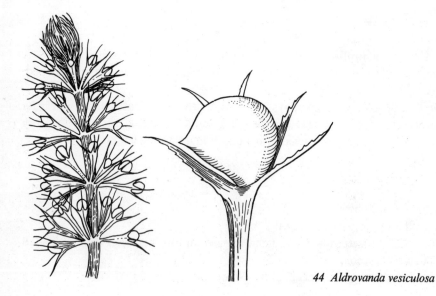

44 *Aldrovanda vesiculosa*

Characteristics: Rootless, streaming, insectivorous plant with elongated shoots. Leaves in whorls of six to nine, petioles wedge-shaped with some bristles at the apex where lamina begins. Laminae roundish kidney-shaped, up to 7 mm long and up to 10 mm wide, thickened in the centre. Laminae halves either side of midrib fold easily; their margins bear small teeth and hairs and their uppersides glands. Flowers solitary in leaf axils on the surface of the water, hermaphroditic, actinomorphic, small. Perianth polysepalous, composed of a calyx in five parts and a corolla, also in five parts. Stamens: five. Carpels: five, united, hypogynous superior. The fruit is a capsule.

Cultivation and Propagation: A plant which has very rarely been cultivated so that nothing definite is known about it. However, an aquarist with biological interests might well find it a rewarding species to look after.

General Information: Aldrovanda vesiculosa, although a rare plant, may be met in soft and acid, still waters of the lowland, particularly among reeds in shallow places where the water temperature may rise to 30 °C. In temperate zones it occurs occasionally, although the plants can form winter buds. It is probable that migrating waterfowl are responsible for a continuous re-introduction of the plants in these latitudes. Stimulation of the hairs on the leaf margins triggers off the catching mechanism. The folding-up of the leaf lamina halves takes 0.2 seconds. Every leaf lamina is capable of functioning several times.

Family Elatinaceae · Waterwort Family

Two genera, 35 species. Distributed from the tropical to the temperate latitudes. Predominantly small herbaceous plants of different appearance with simple leaves. Flowers small and inconspicuous.

Besides the genus described below, *Bergia* also contains numerous species of marsh and aquatic plants. *Bergia* enjoys a worldwide distribution in all warm regions, but its species have not yet been tested for their suitability as aquarium plants.

Elatine

The genus was defined by Linné in 1753. The name is derived from elate (Gk) = fir tree.

Distribution: Cosmopolitan.

Characteristics: Annual or rather short-lived perennial, herbaceous plants with creeping or erect, elongated shoot axes. The small, simple leaves are opposite and decussate, only rarely arranged in whorls. Flowers usually solitary in leaf axils, hermaphroditic, inconspicuous. Perianth polysepalous, composed of a calyx in two to four parts, and a corolla with petals like scales in the same number of parts. Stamens: two to eight. Carpels: two to four, united, hypogynous superior. The fruit is a capsule.

General Information: The genus includes approximately 15 species, all adapted to a habitat with a fluctuating water level. Thus they usually grow in wet areas flooded at

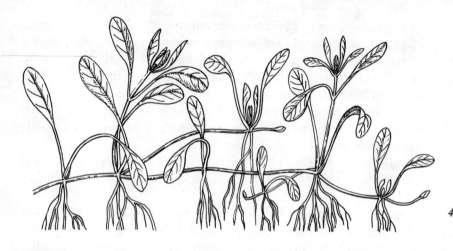

45 *Elatine*
macropoda

certain times or dried out completely at others. The seeds of the species are often distributed by waterfowl so that many species colonize large areas.

To quote a few examples of the genus: *E. americana* with opposite and decussate leaves and *E. alsinastrum*, the European *Elatine*, with its leaves arranged in whorls. These have hardly ever been tried in an aquarium so that experience is lacking. *E. macropoda* is mentioned in older aquarium literature. The species is found in southern Europe and north Africa and was recommended as a suitable plant for the front part of a tank where it is supposed to form a good turf (Ill. *45*).

Family Apiaceae · Parsley Family

300 genera, 3,000 species. Distribution almost worldwide, although the main centre of evolution lies noticeably in the temperate latitudes. Normally shrub-like plants with rhizomes, tubers or turnip-shaped roots, but the family also contains stoloniferous as well as other annual or perennial, herbaceous plants. Leaves are predominantly pinnate to multi-pinnate. The small flowers are generally white and, as a rule, combined in umbelliform inflorescences. All the plant organs contain ethereal oil (or resin).

An older scientific name for the family is Umbelliferae. The family contains a number of cultivated plants, e.g. vegetables like the carrot but also herbs such as parsley and dill. The Apiaceae colonize most habitats, from the coast to the high mountains. Species of 15 genera occur in marshes and in the water. This figure indicates that the family is likely to contain plants suited to the conditions of ponds and tanks. Nevertheless, although many of the plants are quite decorative because of their divided, pinnate leaves, the genus *Hydrocotyle* seems to be the only one which has really attracted the aquarist's attention. In recent years species of the genus *Lilaeopsis* have been cared for in tanks occasionally. The genus *Sium* also contains attractive plants for outdoor cultivation. No doubt, it would be rewarding to try cultivation of various representatives of the family in the future. The genus *Apium*, to which the celery belongs, embraces seven species which grow in the water or on wet soil. The same applies to the two species of the genus *Berula*. Of the genus *Carum* the species *C. verticillatum* has its home in western Europe and grows submerged during the winter months. The south-eastern Asiatic genus *Centella* includes a species which thrives in water but does not possess pinnate leaves. The European genus *Oenanthe* contains a number of aquatic plants. The genera *Oxypolis* and *Phillinium* from North America might well be interesting as aquarium plants. Attention should be drawn to the fact that the poison hemlock of the genus *Cicuta* grows in the vicinity of European waters.

Sium

The genus was defined by Linné in 1753. The name is derived from sion, a Greek plant name.

Distribution: Spread nearly everywhere with the exception of South America.

Characteristics: The species of *Sium* (water parsnip) are perennial herbs or persistent herbaceous plants of varied appearance; they have runners and either horizontally growing or erect shoots. Leaves are pinnate, either arranged in rosettes or alternate. Flowers are formed as an umbel; they are hermaphroditic, actinomorphic and rather small. Perianth polysepalous, calyx either in five parts or lacking, corolla white and in five parts. Stamens: five. Carpels: two, united, hypogynous. The fruit is a schizocarp.

General Information: The genus includes approximately 15 species; most of them live in periodically flooded wet habitats or grow permanently in shallow water.

Sium latifolium L.

The species was named by Linné when he defined the genus in 1753.

Distribution: Europe, western Asia.

Characteristics: A plant of bogs and shallow water with short runners. Leaves initially arranged in rosettes and, at a later stage, alternate on an elongated axis. Water leaves petiolate, divided into several pinnae, up to 30 cm in length. Aerial leaves smaller and simple pinnate.

Cultivation and Propagation: These plants reach a height of 1.20 m and are well worth caring for on ponds where they look very interesting. They should be planted at a water depth of 20-30 cm if their varied leaves are to show off to best advantage. The early water leaves growing in the spring are divided into several pinnae. The succeeding leaves have fewer pinnae, but each single pinna is noticeably wider. Finally, simple pinnate aerial leaves are positioned on elongated shoots. The white flower umbels are also quite attractive. As the species is sufficiently hardy the plants do not need to be covered with foliage in the winter. Propagation by division of the plants at the base in early spring, separating slips or by sowing the fruits which develop abundantly.

Hydrocotyle

The genus was defined by Linné in 1753. The name is derived from hydor (Gk) = water and kotyle (Gk) = umbilicus.

Distribution: Worldwide.

Characteristics: Small, herbaceous plants with elongated shoots, either creeping or floating on the surface of the water, with an alternate leaf arrangement. Commonly called pennywort. The leaves have a petiole and a roundish to kidney-shaped lamina; margins more or less deeply indented or only undulate. Some leaves are peltate. The form of the inflorescences is varied. Flowers hermaphroditic, actinomorphic, small. Perianth polysepalous with an inconspicuous calyx in five parts and a whitish, yellow or green corolla, also in five parts. Stamens: five. Carpels: two, united, hypogynous. The fruit is a schizocarp.

General Information: Many botanists regard this genus as an independent family, Hydrocotylaceae. It includes approximately 100 species of which many live in periodically or permanently wet habitats, but also grow in the water. Probably a number of untried species would be interesting as aquarium plants, e.g. the European *H. vulgaris* or the American *H. americana.*

Hydrocotyle leucocephala CHAM. et SCHLECHT. (Ill. 64, 65)

The species was named by Chamisso and Schlechtendal in 1826.

Distribution: Tropical South America.

Characteristics: Small herbaceous plants with elongated shoot axes and alternate leaf arrangement, either creeping on bog or floating on the water. Rooting profusely at the nodes. Leaves petiolate, their laminae roundish to kidney-shaped with a diameter of 2 to 4 cm, dependent on the amount of light, flat or slightly wavy, pale green. Leaf margins irregularly crenate. Flowers white, in long-stemmed small umbels.

Cultivation and Propagation: An attractive plant suitable for decoration of the back or the corners at the front of a tank. However, it does need some attention. When clumps of shoots are planted they look very decorative with tufts of their fine roots appearing in the water, but the shoots tend to grow to the surface very quickly. There they continue growth and develop floating leaves, just as they would in their natural environment. It is therefore necessary to re-attach the tips of shoots to the substrate rather frequently to achieve a tidy-looking bushy growth. The plants need a temperature of above 20 °C, and they thrive even if they are slightly in the shade. Propagation from cuttings.

Hydrocotyle verticillata THUNB. (Ill. 53, 75)

The species was named by Thunberg in 1798.

Distribution: South-eastern North America, Central America.

Characteristics: Herbaceous plants with elongated shoot axes rooted in boggy soil or at the bottom of the water. Arrangement of shield-shaped leaves is alternate and they are borne on erect stems, up to 10 cm in length. Diameter of laminae up to 3 cm, colour pale to medium-green. Leaf margins irregularly crenate. Floating leaves tougher than aerial leaves. Flowers greenish and arranged in whorled inflorescences.

Cultivation and Propagation: The species looks highly decorative in the front part of a medium-high or high aquarium, but it can also be used in the middle of a tank, particularly against a darker background. A well-lit position is essential, else the petioles become over-long and the laminae remain too small. Temperature above 20 °C. Propagation from separated, small sections of shoots on which at least three leaves have been left.

Lilaeopsis

The genus was defined by E. C. Greene in 1821. It has not been possible to find an explanation for the origin of the name.

Distribution: North and South America, Australia, New Zealand.

Characteristics: Small, herbaceous plants with a creeping habit or shoots floating on the surface of the water. Leaves arranged alternate, simple, awl-shaped, linear or slightly spatulate. Inflorescences umbellate. Flowers hermaphroditic, actinomorphic, small. Perianth polysepalous, with an inconspicuous calyx in five parts and a corolla in the same number of parts. Stamens: five. Carpels: two, united, hypogynous. The fruit is a schizocarp.

General Information: The genus includes approximately 20 species usually growing in bogs or submerged, and occurring often in fairly deep water. A few can be found in brackish water. Some species should be suitable for the front part of an aquarium as the plants form a good turf. A species occasionally offered for sale is probably *L. attenuata* from South America.

Family Callitrichaceae · Water Starwort Family

The family embraces just one genus, *Callitriche*.

Callitriche

The genus was defined by Linné in 1753.

Distribution: Almost worldwide, but rare in some areas.

Characteristics: Small, perennial or annual, herbaceous plants living either in boggy soil where they form a turf, or growing submerged in branched tufts with ascending shoots. The latter are loosely foliated with opposite leaves, except near the surface of the water where the leaves are often crowded in dense rosettes. Leaves linear to spatulate, rounded, crenate to bipartite, pale green. Flowers solitary or in pairs in leaf axils, unisexual, monoecious, inconspicuous. Perianth lacking. Male flowers with one stamen. Female flowers with two carpels, these united, hypogynous superior. The fruit is a schizocarp.

General Information: All species of the genus *Callitriche* are marsh and aquatic plants. In the temperate latitudes those growing on land usually perish in the winter, whereas the submerged forms are likely to survive and may even withstand very low temperatures. The species are apt to be very variable and difficult to define. The native species might be usable in a cold water aquarium. As the plants are really rather attractive it would be worthwhile to try them out in higher temperatures as well.

Two species are widely distributed. One of them is *C. vernalis*, the land as well as the submerged form possessing leaves in densely crowded, rosettes; the other is *C. autumnalis* which has no leaf rosettes. Both are to be found in the northern hemisphere.

Family Polygonaceae · Buckwheat Family

Forty genera, 800 species. Distributed in all parts of the world, especially in the northern temperate latitudes. Rarely trees or bushes, in the main perennial herbs or other persistent and also annual, herbaceous plants. Leaves often have a stem-clasping sheath at the base. The hermaphroditic or unisexual, rather small flowers normally occur in fairly large inflorescences. One of the food plants belonging to the Polygonaceae is the rhubarb. The members of the family colonize very diverse habitats. Proper marsh and aquatic plants, however, occur only in the genera *Rumex* and *Polygonum*. Of these it is purely the latter which has achieved some importance in cultivation.

Polygonum

The species was defined by Linné in 1753.

Distribution: Almost worldwide.

Characteristics: Perennial herbs or other persistent and annual plants, with shoots creeping, erect or floating on the surface of the water. Leaves alternate with characteristic stem-clasping sheath. Flowers always in inflorescences, hermaphroditic or unisexual, mirror-symmetrical. Perianth polysepalous or united at the base, composed of two to six uniform segments which more or less enclose the ripening fruit. Stamens: three to nine. Carpels: generally three, united, hypogynous superior. The fruit is a nut.

General Information: The genus includes approximately 150 species. Many of them grow in wet or periodically flooded locations. Approximately 15 species are notable for having shoots floating on the surface of the water. These are predominantly tropical species, e.g. *P. acuminatum*, *P. barbatum*, *P. celebium*, *P. javanum*, *P. lanigerum*, and *P. limbatum;* they have developed into weeds in rice paddies and canals. *P. amphibium* is distributed in the temperate latitudes of the northern hemisphere and is a pleasing plant for ponds. The plants are characterized by lanceolate to longish egg-shaped floating leaves with dark markings and by reddish flowers. On wet meadows and moist fields containing a good supply of nutrients the species may occur as a land form.

Family Amaranthaceae · Amaranth Family

Sixty genera, 900 species. From the tropics to the temperate latitudes, particularly in America and Africa. Rarely small trees or bushes, usually perennial and annual herbaceous plants. The very small flowers are massed in dense and diverse inflorescences or they grow in small clusters in the leaf axils.

Several species of the Amaranthaceae have become popular, ornamental plants because of their conspicuously shaped or coloured inflorescences or colourful foliage. The family avoids very dry areas on the one hand, but on the other it includes very few species which colonize a wet habitat or the water. *Centrostachys aquatica* is a marsh plant of tropical Africa and south-east Asia. All other marsh and aquatic plants of the family belong to the genus *Alternanthera*.

Alternanthera

The genus was defined by Forskål in 1775. The name is derived from alterno (L) = alternate and anthera (Gk) = stamen. *Telanthera* is another name for the genus.

Distribution: In all rather warm regions, particularly in tropical South America.

Characteristics: Persistent or annual, herbaceous plants with shoots erect, creeping or floating on the surface of the water. Leaves arranged opposite and decussate. Leaves simple, petiolate or sessile, partly coloured or spotted. Small, dense inflorescences, either terminal or axillary, or small groups of flowers may be positioned in leaf axils. Flowers hermaphroditic, inconspicuous. Perianth polysepalous, in five parts, dry-skinned like a husk. Stamens: two to five. Carpels: two to three, united, hypogynous superior. The fruit is a nut.

General Information: The genus includes approximately 170 species and, because there are so many, the single species are often difficult to define. The species and their cultivated varieties with their variegated foliage have played a considerable part as carpet-bed and border plants in gardens, particularly at the turn of the century. They help in the creation of imaginatively patterned flower-beds. But in aquarium plant cultivation the genus made a belated entry. Not until fairly recently have several coloured species from the group of marsh and aquatic plants been tried in aquaria. Rate of success has been varied. Occasionally a plant is offered for sale under the name of 'A. sessilis', with blood-red shoots and leaves. It is a very beautiful marsh plant but does not grow submerged. Possibly *A. tetramera* and *A. aquatica* from South America might be suitable for aquarium cultivation. For the time being the three following species can be recommended to the aquarist.

Alternanthera sessilis (L) DC. (Ill. 82, 83)

The species was named *Gomphrena sessilis* by Linné in 1753 and moved to the genus *Alternanthera* by De Candolla in 1813.

Distribution: In all tropical regions.

Characteristics: Small, herbaceous plants growing in marshes and submerged with erect, elongated shoots and leaves arranged opposite and decussate. Leaves lanceolate, narrowed like a stalk or with a very short petiole, up to 8 cm long, and up to 15 mm wide, upperside olive-green to pale brownish, underside dark-red. The inconspicuous flowers are arranged in dense clusters in the leaf axils of aerial shoots.

Cultivation and Propagation: The best thriving and probably the most beautiful *Alternanthera* species at present kept in aquaria. It needs a bright to slightly shady position in a tank and a temperature of above 20 °C; otherwise the plants are undemanding. They are suitable for being planted in clumps in the middle or back of a tank together with pale-green species, e.g. from the genus *Hygrophila.* An aquarium planted with colourful and varied species cannot really do without the species. Propagation from cuttings.

Alternanthera reineckii BRIQ. (Ill. 74, 83, 84)

The species was named by Briquet in 1899. In the trade the plant was introduced under the name of 'Telanthera osiris'.

Distribution: Tropical South America.

Characteristics: Small, herbaceous plants with elongated shoot axes and opposite and decussate leaf arrangement, either creeping on boggy soil or growing submerged and erect. Leaves broad-lanceolate to elliptical, narrowed like a stalk or with a short petiole, up to 4 cm long and up to 15 mm wide, upperside light to olive-green, in a bright position sometimes pale-red around the edges, underside pale-green to slightly reddish. The very small flowers densely clustered in leaf axils of aerial shoots.

Cultivation and Propagation: The species does not thrive as well as *A. sessilis* but is to be cultivated and propagated in the same way.

Alternanthera spec. 'Lilacina' (Ill. 83, 94)

As yet the species has not been defined properly. In aquarist circles it was introduced under the trade name 'Telanthera lilacina'.

Distribution: Tropical South America.

Characteristics: Small, herbaceous plants growing in marshes and submerged, with erect, elongated shoots and leaves arranged opposite and decussate. Leaves broad-lanceolate to longish ovate, narrowed like a stalk or with a short petiole, up to 6 cm long and 20 mm wide, upperside dark-green, dark olive-green or reddish-green, often with red portions, underside pale to dark-red. The inconspicuous flowers are positioned in dense clusters in leaf axils of aerial shoots.

Cultivation and Propagation: As specified for *A. sessilis.* However, the plant takes longer to become established and even later on grows very slowly.

Family Primulaceae · Primrose Family

Forty genera, 800 species. Mainly in northern, temperate latitudes with a few representatives only in the tropics and subtropics. Generally perennial herbs or other persistent or annual, herbaceous plants. Flowers hermaphroditic, usually with a colourful corolla.

The primula family includes a number of ornamental plants such as the coloured garden primulas and the cyclamens. Many members of this family can stand up to very low temperatures and are able to live in arctic regions and high mountains. Marsh and aquatic plants occur in four genera only. One of these, *Anagallis*, has never been cultivated so far. The other three, *Hottonia*, *Lysimachia* and *Samolus*, however, are well-known to growers of aquatic plants.

Hottonia

The genus was defined by Linné in 1753. The name was chosen in honour of the Dutch botanist P. Hotton (1648—1709).

Distribution: Temperate latitudes of the northern hemisphere.

Characteristics: Small, herbaceous plants with elongated shoots and leaf arrangement in rosettes or alternate, generally growing submerged either rooted at the bottom or floating on the surface. Leaves with a short petiole or sessile, their laminae simple pinnate. Inflorescences above the water surface.

Flowers hermaphroditic, actinomorphic. Perianth gamopetalous, composed of a calyx in five parts and a corolla in the same number of parts. Stamens: five. Carpels: five, united, hypogynous superior. The fruit is a capsule.

General Information: The genus contains only the two species described below. They colonize quiet, still waters. Sometimes they develop land forms, rather compact in shape, but then they are not at their best and they do not flower. Inflorescences submerge after they have finished flowering so that the ripening of seeds takes place under water. Winter buds develop on the ends of shoots in the autumn.

Hottonia palustris L.

The species was named by Linné in 1753 when he defined the genus.

Distribution: Europe, northern Asia.

Characteristics: Small, herbaceous plants with elongated shoot axes, usually growing submerged. Their simple pinnate leaves up to 12 cm long and up to 8 cm wide, pale-green. Floral axes very thin. Corolla white or pale-pink.

Cultivation and Propagation: A beautiful species for a cold water aquarium or the open air. However, it does not always thrive. The plants probably prefer soft and acid water. Propagation from cuttings.

Hottonia inflata ELL. (Ill. 77)

The species was named by Elliot in 1817.
Distribution: South-eastern North America.
Characteristics: Like *H. palustris*, but floral axes are spongy and thickened, and the flowers are inconspicuous.
Cultivation and Propagation: Experience on cultivation does not exist.

Lysimachia

The genus was defined by Linné in 1753. The genus was named after the Greek general, Lysimachos, the guardian of Alexander the Great and later king of Thrace and Macedonia.
Distribution: Almost worldwide.
Characteristics: Perennial herbs with erect, elongated shoots or—rarely—herbaceous plants with creeping, intensively branched shoots. Leaves arranged in whorls or opposite and decussate. Leaves simple, sessile or with short petioles. Flowers in terminal or axillary inflorescences or solitary in leaf axils, hermaphroditic, actinomorphic.
Perianth gamopetalous, composed of a calyx in five parts and a yellow or orange corolla, also in five parts. Stamens: five. Carpels: five, united, hypogynous superior. Fruit is a capsule.
General Information: The genus includes approximately 200 species: many of them grow in marshes. The species described below is a very adaptable one. It has frequently been grown, especially in the early days of aquarium plant cultivation.

Lysimachia nummularia L.

The species was named by Linné in 1753.
Distribution: Europe.
Characteristics: Small plant with shoots creeping on wet soil, but also adapted to living submerged. Submerged shoots erect, elongated. Leaves arranged opposite and decussate, usually with a very short petiole, their laminae roundish, elliptical or egg-shaped, up to 2.5 cm long and up to 2 cm wide, pale-green. Laminae delicate and wavy. The glowing yellow flowers positioned solitary in leaf axils of aerial shoots.
Cultivation and Propagation: A cold-water plant which needs a well-lit position but is otherwise undemanding. The land form, living in nature along ditches and on wet meadows, can easily be adapted to submerged cultivation. Propagation from cuttings.

Samolus

The genus was defined by Linné in 1753. The name is a Roman plant name.
Distribution: Almost worldwide, but particularly in the southern hemisphere.

Characteristics: Persistent, herbaceous plants with rosettes or creeping shoots. Flowers hermaphroditic, actinomorphic, small. Perianth gamopetalous with a calyx in five parts and white or pink corolla, also in five parts. Stamens: five. Carpels: five, united, hypogynous superior. Fruit is a capsule.

General Information: The genus includes approx. ten species living in wet locations or in shallow water. A few species occur in brackish water. Apart from the species described below. *S. floribundus*, a native of America, is mentioned in literature for aquarists. It is not certain whether the plants are correctly defined.

Samolus valerandi L. (Ill. 78)

The species was named by Linné in 1753.
   Distribution: Europe, northern Africa.
   Characteristics: A rosette plant growing in bogs and shallow water. Leaves spatulate, up to 8 cm in length, pale-green.
   Cultivation and Propagation: The rosettes being offered for sale by the trade can be used to decorate the front of a heated or an unheated tank. Normally these are young marsh plants which have been adapted to submerged cultivation. Their rosette growth lasts for some time but, sooner or later, they develop an elongated shoot which makes them look unsightly. The growth of the elongated shoot initiates the flowering phase. Propagation from seeds only.

Family Menyanthaceae

Five genera, forty species. Worldwide distribution. Small, perennial herbs or other persistent, herbaceous plants with simple or pinnate leaves. Gaily coloured hermaphroditic flowers. Tissues often contain bitter substances.
   The family is related to the gentian family (Gentianaceae) and formerly was often classed with it. All members of the family are marsh and aquatic plants. Whereas the genera *Menyanthes* and *Nymphoides* are generally well-known to cultivators of aquatic plants they are not at all familiar with *Villarsia*, *Liparophyllum* and *Nephrophyllidium* so far.

Menyanthes

The genus was defined by Linné in 1753. The generic name is a Greek plant name. There is only the one species described below.

Menyanthes trifoliata L. (Ill. 85)

The species was named by Linné in 1753.
   Distribution: In all temperate regions of the northern hemisphere.

Characteristics: Thick shoots like those of a rhizome either creeping on boggy soil or floating on the surface of the water, with leaves arranged alternate and always reaching above the water into the air. Leaves with a long petiole and trifoliate like those of clover. Racemose inflorescences. Flowers hermaphroditic, actinomorphic. Perianth gamopetalous, composed of a calyx in five parts and white or pale-pink corolla, also in five parts; tips of corolla fringed. Stamens: five. Carpels: two, united, hypogynous superior. The fruit is a capsule.

Cultivation and Propagation: A beautifully flowering hardy plant suitable for cultivation in pond margins. Propagation by division of rhizomes.

Nymphoides

The genus was defined by Hill in 1757. The name is derived from the genus *Nymphaea* and eidos (Gk) = form. Another, but incorrect name for the genus is *Limnanthemum*.

Distribution: Almost worldwide, but particularly in the tropics and subtropics.

Characteristics: Perennial, aquatic plants with runners growing on the soil and erect, elongated shoots bearing floating leaves with an alternate leaf arrangement. Submerged leaves rare. Flowers usually in clusters at the end of elongated shoots, hermaphroditic, actinomorphic. Perianth gamopetalous, composed of a calyx in five parts and a coloured corolla, also in five parts. Tips of corolla often fringed. Stamens: five. Carpels: two, united, hypogynous superior. The fruit is a capsule.

General Information: The genus embraces approximately 25 species. All of them colonize still waters, living in the zone of plants with floating leaves as do the water lilies. Some species are able to survive in bogs. A few, e.g. *N. indica* and *N. cristata*, have developed into rice field weeds. The members of the genus are not really suitable for an aquarium as their leaves cast too much shade. But many of the species could easily be accommodated in planthouses and, with increased use of the latter in aquarium plant cultivation, interest in the genus might well rise in future. Some species can be kept on open-air ponds, if not throughout the year, at least during the summer months.

Aquarium literature often mentioned that the flowers arise from the petioles. However, this is not correct. The long stalks at the end of which the flowers are positioned look like petioles but are, in fact, very elongated axial internodes. The actual petiole appears at the place of attachment of the flower.

Many *Nymphoides* species, perhaps all of them, will multiply freely from fully developed leaves, cut off and put onto wet soil in very humid air. The whole surface of the lamina has to be pushed down firmly. After some time adventitious plants develop on the petiole; they grow roots and can be planted once they are sufficiently strong.

Several species are described in greater detail below. But *N. indica* from Africa, south-east Asia and Australia has also been cared for in botanical gardens and by aquarists. The same applies to *N. parviflora* from Africa and south-east Asia; the plant has small, white flowers and some of its varieties have flowers in different colours. Amongst others *N. hydrochari-*

oides occurring in Africa and Australia, could be recommended for cultivation; the species has orange-coloured flowers. The yellow-flowering *N. fallax*, a native plant of Central America, is also worth trying out.

Nymphoides peltata (GMEL.) O. KTZE. (Ill. *46*, 86, 87)

The species was named *Limnanthemum peltatum* by Gmelin in 1770 and moved to the genus *Nymphoides* by O. Kuntze in 1891.

Distribution: Europe, Asia.

Characteristics: A persistent, herbaceous plant with floating leaves, runners and shoots growing erect. Laminae of floating leaves elliptical to egg-shaped, cleft up to the point of insertion of the petiole, up to 15 cm long and up to 10 cm wide, but sometimes larger, with slightly wavy margins, upperside dark-green with brown or blackish markings, underside pale-green—sometimes with a red coating. Flower corolla yellow.

Cultivation and Propagation: A species for open-air cultivation which should be covered with foliage during the winter if the pond has to be drained. Should the soil mixture contain too many nutrients the plants spread out too much because of their many runners and have to be cut back fairly often. Propagation from cut-off runner sections is simple; otherwise seeds can be sown.

46 Nymphoides peltata

Nymphoides aquatica (WALT.) O. KTZE

The species was named *Anonymos aquatica* by Walter in 1788 and moved to the genus *Nymphoides* by O. Kuntze in 1891.

Distribution: South-eastern North America.

Characteristics: Persistent, herbaceous aquatics with runners and erect shoots. Commonly called banana plants because the swollen adventitious roots resemble tiny bunches of bananas. Submerged leaves with long petiole, their laminae heart-shaped, delicately wavy, up to 10 cm long, pale-green to reddish. Upperside of floating leaves olive-green with dark violet spots, their underside reddish. Corolla of flower white.

Cultivation and Propagation: Usable as a show specimen in an aquarium owing to submerged leaves being rather persistent. The plants need good light and temperatures above 20 °C. If it is desired to delay the development of floating leaves, sand only should be used for the substratum. Propagation from separated slips forming on the runners, or from laminae of floating leaves as previously described for the genus.

General Information: The species is a popular aquarium plant in North America but has rarely been cultivated in Europe.

Nymphoides humboldtiana (KUNTH) O. KTZE.

The species was named *Vallisneria humboldtiana* by Kunth in 1818 and moved to the genus *Nymphoides* by O. Kuntze in 1891.

Distribution: Tropical America.

Characteristics: Persistent aquatic plant with floating leaves, runners and erect shoots. Laminae of floating leaves almost kidney-shaped with a maximum width of 15 cm, dark-green. Corolla of flower white.

Cultivation and Propagation: The species can be kept out in the open during the summer but is best suited to the conditions of a planthouse. Propagation from separated slips.

General Information: According to latest investigations, the species is supposed to be identical with *N. indica*. In literature for aquarists a dwarf form is mentioned. Its floating leaves reach a diameter of no more than 6 cm. However, the plant is probably a different species.

Family Scrophulariaceae · Figwort Family

Two hundred genera, 3,000 species. Cosmopolitan. Rarely shrubs or lianas, usually perennial herbs or other persistent and annual, herbaceous plants. Flowers generally with gaily coloured corolla of different forms, often two-lipped.

Several ornamental plants, such as snapdragons and calceolarias, are members of the family. It also includes some species adapted to a special source of nourishment, e.g. semiparasites taking a part of the nutrients they need from their host plants. The Scrophularia-ceae grow in many different habitats, from the plains to the mountains. A number of the species colonize moist and wet habitats as well as the water. It is not always easy to find the exact line of division between plants in wet habitats flooded occasionally for a short period and those regularly flooded for long periods. Unequivocal marsh and aquatic plants, however, are likely to occur in 17 genera.

Several hedge hyssop species of the genus *Gratiola* grow on and near the waters of North America, also the yellow-flowering *Mimulus guttatus*, one of the monkey flowers which has become established in Europe and other parts of the world. The genus *Craterostigma* in southern Africa and Madagascar possesses submerged species, as yet unknown in aquarist circles. Some of the speedwell species, members of the genus *Veronica*, are adapted to living submerged. Thus *V. beccabunga*, widely distributed in the northern hemisphere, has often been used in cold-water aquaria, particularly in the early days of aquarium plant cultivation. In more recent times plants of the genus *Lindernia* which embraces 120 species occurring in all warmer regions have been tested for use in tanks. Success has been varied. Because of the large number of species and their wide area of distribution it is not easy to define each species with exactitude. A *Glossostigma* species has only lately been offered for sale; it is a small marsh plant which forms a turf but does not feel very happy when submerged (Ill. 76). But representatives of the genera *Bacopa*, *Limnophila*, *Hydrotriche*, *Micranthemum* and *Limosella* have been well tried and proved their worth for a long time.

Bacopa

The genus was defined by Aublet in 1775. Its range was increased in 1946 when Pennell included with the genus *Bacopa* several genera formerly independent. The name was taken from the native language of Guyana.

Distribution: In all parts of the world, particularly in America where the plants have spread into the temperate latitudes.

Characteristics: Small perennial or annual herbaceous plants with elongated shoots, creeping on boggy soil, growing erect when submerged, or floating on the surface of the water. Leaves simple, sessile, opposite and decussate or, more rarely—arranged in whorls. Flowers solitary in leaf axils, hermaphroditic, faintly mirror-symmetrical. Perianth usually gamopetalous, normally composed of a calyx in five parts and a coloured corolla, either in four or five parts. Stamens: two to five. Carpels: two, united, hypogynous superior. The fruit is a capsule.

General Information: The genus includes approximately 100 species. Many of them grow in permanently wet or periodically flooded habitats and, thus, should be suitable for aquarium plant cultivation. *B. longipes* from Cuba, *B. najas* from Central America and *B. reflexa* from tropical South America are typical aquatics; yet they have never been cared for in an aquarium.

Bacopa monniera (L.) WETTST.

The species was named *Lysimachia monniera* by Linné in 1756 and moved to the genus *Bacopa* by Wettstein in 1891.

Distribution: In all tropical and subtropical regions.

Characteristics: Herbaceous plants with opposite and decussate leaf arrangement, creeping on boggy soil or growing rigidly erect when submerged. Leaves obovate to wedge-shaped, up to 1.5 cm long and up to 8 mm wide, firm, pale-green. Corolla a pale-violet colour.

Cultivation and Propagation: The species can be kept in temperatures above 18°C and its demands on light are average. In an aquarium the plants look attractive only when planted in clumps as they have such stiff stems. When the species is grown submerged it does not thrive as well as the one described subsequently. Propagation from cuttings.

General Information: A species widely distributed as weeds in rice fields. It has been cultivated in tanks since the turn of the century.

Bacopa amplexicaulis (PURSH) WETTST.

The species was named *Herpestes amplexicaulis* by Pursh in 1814 and moved to the genus *Bacopa* by Wettstein in 1891. Another, but incorrect name for the species is *Bacopa caroliniana*.

Distribution: Atlantic coastal regions of southern and central North America.

Characteristics: Herbaceous plants either creeping on boggy soil or growing rigidly erect when submerged. Leaves arranged opposite and decussate. Submerged leaves elliptical to egg-shaped, almost clasping the stem, up to 2.5 cm long and up to 20 mm wide, delicate, pale-green, in good light with reddish markings. Aerial leaves tougher, pale-green. Corolla of flowers bluish.

Cultivation and Propagation: The species can be kept in a temperature of just above 18 °C but does better in warmer water. The plants look rather pleasing when planted in clumps in the middle or the back, or even in the corners of a tank. Propagation from cuttings.

Bacopa myriophylloides (BENTH.) WETTST.

The species was named *Herpestes myriophylloides* by Bentham and moved to the genus *Bacopa* by Wettstein in 1891.

Distribution: Tropical South America.

Characteristics: Small, herbaceous plants with leaves arranged in whorls, either creeping on boggy soil or growing erect when submerged. Submerged leaves linear, up to 1 cm long and up to 1 mm wide, pale-green. Aerial leaves tougher, dark-green.

Cultivation and Propagation: A little-known, but attractive species which may be kept in a

66 *Ludwigia arcuata*
67 *Ludwigia repens*, narrow-leafed form
68 *Ludwigia repens* x *palustris* (hybrid)
69 *Ludwigia palustris*

 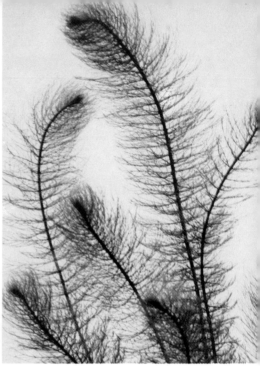

70 *Proserpinaca palustris*
71 *Myriophyllum hippuroides*
72 *Trapa natans*
73 *Rorippa aquatica*
74 *Alternanthera reineckii*

75 *Hydrocotyle verticillata*
76 *Glossostigma diandra*
77 *Hottonia inflata*

temperature of just above 20 °C. Light-loving, otherwise undemanding. To be planted in clumps in the middle of a tank. Propagation from cuttings.

Limnophila

The genus was defined by R. Brown in 1810. The name is derived from limne (Gk) = bog, pond and philos (Gk) = friend. A name for the genus often used in older aquarium literature was *Ambulia,* but the name is no longer applied.

Distribution: Tropical and subtropical Asia and Africa.

Characteristics: Herbaceous plants with shoots creeping on boggy soil or growing erect when submerged. Leaves arranged opposite and decussate or in whorls (Ill. *40*). Leaves sessile, entire or pinnate. Flowers in loose or more compact terminal inflorescences, solitary or in clusters in leaf axils, hermaphroditic, mirror-symmetrical. Perianth gamo-petalous, composed of a calyx in five parts and with a two-lipped and basal tubular corolla in five parts. Stamens: four. Carpels: two, united, hypogynous superior. The fruit is a capsule.

General Information: The species of the genus *Limnophila* grow as marsh plants in bogs, on the edges of lakes and running waters, but also in water and as weeds in rice paddies. Out of the 35 species there are twelve with finely divided submerged leaves, well able to withstand flooding for a longer period. These are the species most suited to aquarium plant cultivation, but so far very few of them have ever been cultivated. Plants like *L. aromatica* grow leaves with entire margins only and are, therefore, of little or no use in an aquarium. A number of species is discussed in greater detail below. But there are others also character-ized by finely divided, submerged leaves, e.g. *L. tillaeoides,* *L. glabra,* *L. heterophylla,* *L. polystachya* and *L. cana* from south-east Asia, as well as *L. ceratophylloides,* *L. bangweo-lensis,* *L. barteri* and *L. dasyantha* from Africa.

Limnophila aquatica (ROXB.) ALSTON (Ill. 88, 89)

Roxburgh named the species *Cyrilla aquatica* in 1798 and Alston moved it to the genus *Limnophila* in 1929.

Distribution: India and the island Sri Lanka (Ceylon).

Characteristics: Herbaceous plants growing in bogs and submerged, with erect-elongated and horizontally creeping shoots. Leaves in whorls of three to ten. Submerged leaves simple pinnate or bipinnate, with very slender tips, up to 5 cm long, upperside pale-green, underside whitish-green. Aerial leaves simple, lanceolate with toothed margins, up to 2.5 cm long, dark-green. Corolla of flower up to 2 cm in length, pale bluish with darker markings.

Cultivation and Propagation: The plant looks really splendid in any aquarium. Its large whorls of finely divided leaves provide an interesting contrast to *Hygrophila* species with a matching colouration. The best effects are achieved if planted in small bunches or as a show specimen against a darker background. The shoots ascend quickly to the surface of the water and have to be trimmed rather frequently. The tips can be re-planted and soon develop roots. The species needs a well-lit position, but it does survive if there is a little shade from other plants. Temperature no less than 20 °C. If the daily period of illumination is less than 12 hours the shoots rise above the surface of the water and develop simple aerial leaves. Propagation from cuttings.

Limnophila sessiliflora BL. (Ill. 81)

The species was named by Blume in 1826. Another name for it, *Ambulia sessiliflora*, can be found in older literature.

Distribution: South-east and east Asia; a few have become established in North America.

Characteristics: Herbaceous plants with elongated shoots growing in marshes and submerged. Leaves arranged in whorls. Submerged leaves simple pinnate or bipinnate, up to 3 cm long, pale-green. Aerial leaves very variable, pinnate, tripartite or lanceolate, smaller and tougher than submerged leaves, dark-green. Flowers have neither stalks nor bracts. Corolla pale-blue with darker markings.

Cultivation and Propagation: With their finely divided foliage the plants are very attractive when planted in small bunches in the middle or back of a heated tank. Temperature no less than 20°C. The plants need a well-it position but are, otherwise, undemanding. Propagation from cuttings.

General Information: There is in existence a hybrid produced by *L. sessiliflora* and *L. indica* (the species described below). Most probably the hybrid was produced in aquarium plant cultivation, and some of the plants have become naturalized in isolated areas of North America. For correct identification the flower characteristics have to be examined.

Limnophila indica (L.) DRUCE

Linné named the species *Hottonia indica* in 1762; it was moved to the genus *Limnophila* by Druce in 1913. In earlier aquarists' literature the plant was denoted *Ambulia indica*. Probably the plants referred to as 'Limnophila gratioloides' previously in aquarium literature belong to the species *L. indica*.

Distribution: Tropical Africa and south-east Asia.

Characteristics: Herbaceous plants with elongated shoot axes growing in bog and submerged. The aquatic form cannot be distinguished easily from the species described above. Flowers with a short stalk and two small bracts, corolla pale-pink.

Cultivation and Propagation: As specified for *L. sessiliflora*.

General Information: Older aquarium literature often noted that if over-long shoots were cut back under water symptoms of poisoning were found in the fishes; some of them even died as a result. Probably the species contains a cardiac poison rather like *Digitalis* (foxglove). It has been recommended, therefore, that the plants be cut out of the water only and cuttings be planted after they have been thoroughly rinsed.

Hydrotriche

The species was defined by Zuccarini in 1932. The name is derived from hydor (Gk) = water and trix, trichos (Gk) = hair. The sole species the genus contains is the one described below.

Hydrotriche hottonniiflora Zucc. (Ill. 80)

The species was named by Zuccarini in 1932 when he defined the genus.

Distribution: Madagascar.

Characteristics: Aquatic plants with elongated shoot axes and leaves arranged in whorls. Leaves awl-shaped, pointed, up to 4 cm long, pale-green. Inflorescences racmose, above the surface of the water. Perianth gamopetalous, composed of a calyx in five parts and a white corolla with yellow markings, also in five parts. Stamens: two. Carpels: two, united, hypogynous superior. The fruit is a capsule.

Cultivation and Propagation: This is a pretty plant with its needle-shaped leaves, needing good light and temperatures above 20 °C. Its success in a tank has been varied. Initially it is often difficult to establish in an aquarium because shoots die off from the top to the bottom. But, after some time, shoots sprout again from the base of the plant. The best use made of the species is by planting it in clumps in the middle, back and front corners of a tank. Propagation from cuttings.

Micranthemum

The genus was defined by Michaux in 1803. The name is derived from mikros (Gk) = small and anthemon (Gk) = flower. The name refers to the tiny flowers.

Distribution: America.

Characteristics: Very small herbaceous plants with elongated shoot axes, forming a turf when growing on boggy soil and growing erect when submerged. The simple, sessile leaves are opposite and decussate or arranged in whorls. Flowers solitary in leaf axils, hermaphroditic, mirror-symmetrical, very small. Perianth gamopetalous, composed of a calyx in four parts and a two-lipped, white corolla in five parts. Stamens: two. Carpels: two, united, hypogynous superior. The fruit is a capsule.

General Information: Probably the genus contains five species only. Two of them are described below, but the others should also be suitable for aquarium cultivation. The species are *M. procerum* and *M. standleyi* from Central America, and *M. rotundatum*. All five species form dense turfs on boggy soil in their homeland where they are periodically flooded.

Micranthemum micranthemoides (NUTT.) WETTST. (Ill. 79)

The species was named *Hemianthus micranthemoides* by Nuttall in 1817 and moved to the genus *Micranthemum* by Wettstein in 1891.
Distribution: Eastern coast of central North America.
Characteristics: Small, herbaceous plants with elongated, intensively branching shoots, creeping on boggy soil and growing erect when submerged. Submerged leaves in whorls of three or four, linear or lanceolate, blunt, up to 8 mm in length and up to 1.5 mm wide, pale-green. Aerial leaves rather tougher.
Cultivation and Propagation: The species thrives in temperatures between 15 °C and 30 °C and is thus very versatile. It needs a well-lit position but, otherwise, it is undemanding. The small-leafed plants form a dense, bushy growth and are best used in the middle part of a tank. They can also be put in the foreground where they must not be allowed to grow too high. Propagation from cuttings.

Micranthemum umbrosum (GMEL.) BLAKE

The species was named *Globifera umbrosa* by Gmelen and moved to the genus *Micranthemum* by Blake *M. orbiculatum* is another name for the species.
Distribution: Central America, south-eastern North America.
Characteristics: As described in the last species, *M. micranthemoides*, but leaves are opposite and decussate, round, with a diameter of 4 to 5 mm, pale-green.
Cultivation and Propagation: As specified for *M. micranthemoides*.

Limosella

The species was defined by Linné in 1753. The name is derived from limosus (L) = boggy.
Distribution: Cosmopolitan.
Characteristics: Small, annual or perennial rosette plants with runners. Leaves awl-shaped or petiolate with small laminae. Flowers solitary, hermaphroditic, actinomorphic, very small. Perianth gamopetalous, composed of a calyx in four to five parts and a corolla in the same number of parts. Stamens: four. Carpels: two, united, hypogynous superior. The fruit comes as a capsule.
General Information: The *Limosella* species are small marsh plants well able to withstand flooding over shorter or longer periods. Those representatives which develop runners tend to form a dense, turf-like growth. The genus includes approximately 10 species. The small-leafed *L. aquatica*, distributed over the whole of the northern hemisphere, and the North American *L. subulata* with its awl-shaped leaves have occasionally been cultivated in aquaria (Ill. 91). Both species love the light, form a good turf and grow to a height of approximately 4 cm. They are well-suited to being grown in the foreground of a tank.

Family Lentibulariaceae · Bladderwort Family

Four genera, 300 species. From the tropics to the temperate latitudes. Small, herbaceous plants of varied appearance, without roots; insectiverous. Two-lipped flowers.

All representatives of the family are food specialists; like the sundew family they are able to provide themselves with an additional source of nitrogen by being able to entrap and digest animal foods. It is only the genus *Utricularia* which is of interest.

Utricularia

The genus was defined by Linné in 1753. The name is derived from utriculus (L) small utricle, and refers to the insect-catching organs of the plants.

Distribution: From the tropics to the temperate latitudes.

Characteristics: Small, herbaceous plants without roots, compressed or elongated shoot axes and leaves arranged in rosettes, whorls, opposite and decussate or alternate. Polymorphic leaves, e.g. shield-shaped or petiolate with kidney-shaped, linear, awl-shaped, but also pinnate laminae. Flowers in inflorescences, hermaphroditic, mirror-symmetrical. Perianth gamopetalous, composed of a calyx in two parts and a two-lipped corolla in five parts. Stamens: two. Carpels: two, united, hypogynous superior. The fruit is a capsule.

General Information: The species of the genus *Utricularia* grow in moors, marshes and in the water, but also colonize other habitats. A number of them, for instance, are epiphytes, living symbiotically attached to other plants. The aquatics of the genus, in which the inflorescences alone reach above the water level, grow either floating in still waters or at the bottom of running waters—sometimes attached to stones. All species are able to entrap and digest small crustaceans and water insects by means of round, egg-shaped or lenticular catching bladders positioned on their leaves. However, the plants can exist quite well without the additional supply of animal nutrients. The bladders (Ill. *47*) are closed by a valve. A slight negative pressure prevails inside the bladders. When prey touches the bristles on the apertures the valves draw inwards, and the prey is sucked into the bladder. Special

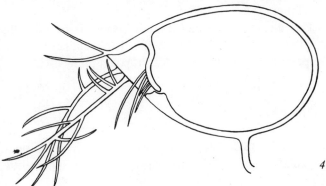

47 Longitudinal section through insect-catching sac of *Utricularia*

glands secrete proteolytic enzymes which not only digest the animal protein but help in the reabsorption of it. Every bladder is capable of functioning several times.

The *Utricularia* species provide an interesting subject for biological study. A grower of aquatic plants, however, is likely to be interested in them only if he is specialised in this field. The genus includes approximately 150 species; 30 species live in water. Some of the latter have been cared for in aquaria, but with varied success so that no reliable information on their cultivation is available. The species of the temperate latitudes form winter buds.

Utricularia spec. 'Johore' (Ill. 90, 97)

So far the species has not been defined properly.

Distribution: Peninsula Malacca.

Characteristics: Rootless plants with elongated, intensively branching shoot axes, streaming in the water. Leaves arranged alternate, several times finely pinnate, up to 5 cm long, pale-green. The characteristic utricles at the tips of leaves are not always developed in aquarium conditions. Flowers yellow.

Cultivation and Propagation: The species needs very good light and thrives best when floating below the surface of the water. As the plants are rootless it would be pointless to put them into the substratum. The higher the content of nutrients in the water the better will be the development of the plants. Optimum temperature lies between 20 °C and 25 °C. Propagation by division of the shoots.

Utricularia gibba L.

The species was named by Linné in 1753. Another and later name for the species is *U. exoleta*.

Distribution: Africa, south-east Asia, Australia.

Characteristics: Dainty, rootless plants with elongated shoot axes and intensive branching, streaming in the water. Leaves alternate, pinnate with many hair-like tips, at most 1 cm long, pale-green. Small bladders for catching prey always present, one to three to each leaf, their diameter approximately 1 mm. Flowers yellow.

Cultivation and Propagation: This undemanding and durable species is occasionally brought in unintentionally with other imported aquatic plants. If left undisturbed the plants will form a dense mat. Temperatures from above 20 °C. Propagation by division.

Family Acanthaceae · Acanthus Family

250 genera, 2,600 species. Tropical to subtropical, very few species in temperate latitudes. Rarely trees or bushes, usually perennial herbs or other herbaceous plants. Hermaphroditic, coloured labiate flowers.

The Acanthus species prefer habitats with a well-balanced water supply. Marsh and aquatic plants, however, occur only in the genus *Justicia*—so far unknown in aquarium plant cultivation—as well as in the genera *Hygrophila* with which *Synnema* is now included, and *Nomaphila*.

All members of the family, at present being cultivated, are characterized by an interesting form of vegetative reproduction. Submerged leaves, cut off and allowed to float on the surface of the water, develop adventitious plantlets after some time. As soon as these have strengthened sufficiently and formed roots they can be planted.

Hygrophila

The genus was defined by R. Brown in 1810; its volume was considerably increased later on when other genera were included with it. The name is derived from hygros (Gk) = wet, moist and philos (Gk) = friend.

Distribution: In all warm regions, but particularly in Africa and south-east Asia.

Characteristics: Perennial or annual, herbaceous plants with erect or creeping shoots and an opposite and decussate leaf arrangement. Submerged leaves simple to pinnate. Aerial leaves usually simple. Flowers (at least in cultivated species) in tight clusters in the leaf axils, very rarely solitary in leaf axils or in terminal inflorescences, hermaphroditic, mirror-symmetrical. Perianth gamopetalous, composed of a calyx in four or five parts, and a two-lipped corolla in five parts. Lower lip usually flat so that the entry to the tube of the corolla is open. Stamens: four. Carpels: two, united, hypogynous superior. The fruit is a capsule.

General Information: Some botanists do not only include the genus *Synnema* but also *Nomaphila* with the genus *Hygrophila*, the reason being that the characteristics of these genera are partly the same. The scientific discussions on the relationships and classification of these groups of plants are still in progress and have not so far led to a satisfactory result. The modifications cannot, therefore, be regarded as final. We believe that the characteristics in the regions of the flowers and inflorescences are yet to be established, but once they are a better definition of the group of kindred genera will become possible. Cultivation and observation of other species is likely to shed more light on the subject. We include the species 'Synnema triflorum' (very popular with aquarists) with the genus *Hygrophila*, whereas we do not agree with the inclusion of the *Nomaphila* species.

The present volume of the genus includes approximately 90 species. All of them grow in wet or boggy habitats. Some even grow submerged. Thus the species are of great interest to the aquarist. A few species occur as weeds in rice fields. The large number of species probably makes their exact classification rather difficult. Besides the species discussed in detail below, some varieties are also cultivated in aquaria. They are not always recognised as independent species and some of them have not yet been defined.

Thus, *H. lacustris* (Ill. 102) can be seen occasionally: it is related to the better-known *H. salicifolia*, but grows better when submerged. The pale-green lanceolate leaves of the former reach a length of up to 10 cm and a width of up to 10 mm. In another form, denoted as 'H. lancea', the lanceolate, submerged leaves are up to 6.5 cm long and up to 7 mm wide; its leaf margins are slightly toothed. This plant resembles *H. polysperma*. Furthermore there is a large-leafed species whose broad lanceolate, submerged leaves may be up to 12 cm long and up to 30 mm wide (Ill. 102).

Hygrophila difformis (L.f.) BL. (Ill. 93, 98, 99)

The species was named *Ruellia difformis* by Linné's son in 1781 and moved to the genus *Hygrophila* by Blume in 1826. A further scientific name under which the plant is known among aquarists, *Synnema triflorum*, dates back to 1891.

Distribution: South-eastern Asiatic mainland.

Characteristics: Medium-sized, herbaceous plants with elongated shoots, creeping to being slanted upwards on boggy soil, and growing erect when submerged, although the shoots may have a horizontal habit over a short distance at the bottom. Leaf arrangement opposite and decussate. Submerged leaves petiolate or sessile, very variable, lamina margins coarsely toothed or with indentations; leaves in one or two pinnate parts, or pinnate, up to 10 cm long and up to 8 cm wide, upperside pale-green, underside whitish green. Aerial leaves always smaller and simple. Flowers pink, solitary or just a few in leaf axils.

Cultivation and Propagation: One of the most beautiful plants when grouped together in the middle or back of a tank. Very good lighting is needed for the development of the pinnate parts or pinnae of the leaves. If the light is insufficient or the daily period of illumination too short the plants will grow simple, undivided leaves only. Temperatures from 20 °C. No particular demands are made on the substratum. Most favourable propagation from cuttings.

General Information: In one variety of *Hygrophila difformis* the pinnate parts and pinnae of the submerged leaves have extremely fine tips (Ill. 98). The form of the aerial leaves is normal. The variety is said to have originated from the Botanical Garden at Prague.

Hygrophila polysperma T. ANDERS (Ill. 6, 53, 100, 102)

The species was named by T. Anderson in 1867.

Distribution: South-eastern Asiatic mainland.

Characteristics: Small, herbaceous plants creeping on boggy soil and growing with erect elongated shoots when submerged. Leaf arrangement opposite and decussate. Submerged leaves sessile, lanceolate to broadly lanceolate, tips rounded, up to 5 cm long and up to 15 mm wide, upperside pale-green, underside whitish green. Aerial leaves smaller and darker in colour. Pale-blue, very small flowers in terminal inflorescences.

Cultivation and Propagation: An undemanding, popular and widely distributed aquarium plant which is particularly effective against a darker background. Can be recommended for planting in groups in the back of the aquarium. Temperature from 20 °C, position in good light, otherwise undemanding. If the illumination is very strong a slight red colouration may occur. Most favourable propagation results from cuttings.

Hygrophila spec. 'Reddish' (Ill. 102)

So far the species has not been defined correctly.

Distribution: Unknown, probably south-eastern Asia.

Characteristics: Small, herbaceous plants creeping on boggy soil and growing with erect, elongated shoots when submerged. Leaf arrangement opposite and decussate. Submerged leaves sessile, lanceolate, blunt, up to 7 cm long and 8 mm wide, with slightly wavy margins, positioned rather irregularly in contrast to *H. polysperma*, upperside olive-green to slightly red, underside whitish-green. Aerial leaves smaller, dark-green. The pale-blue, very small flowers in terminal inflorescences.

Cultivation and Propagation: As specified for *H. polysperma*.

Hygrophila angustifolia R.Br. (Ill. 92, 101, 102)

The species was named by R. Brown in 1810. Another, but scientifically invalid name is *Hygrophila salicifolia*.

Distribution: South-eastern Asiatic mainland.

Characteristics: A larger, herbaceous plant with elongated shoots growing erect in bogs and when submerged. Leaf arrangement opposite and decussate. Submerged leaves sessile or tapering at the base, slender lanceolate, up to 12 cm long and up to 8 mm wide, sometimes slightly curved on one side, upperside pale to medium-green, underside whitish green. Aerial leaves just as large or larger, dark-green. The whitish, very small flowers in dense clusters in leaf axils.

Cultivation and Propagation: As specified for *H. polysperma*, but the plants do not thrive in all conditions.

Nomaphila

The genus was defined by Blume in 1826. Nowadays, some botanists class it with the genus *Hygrophila*. The name is derived from nomos (Gk) = rule and philos (Gk) = friend.

Distribution: Tropics and subtropics of Asia and Africa.

Characteristics: Perennial, herbaceous plants with erect, elongated shoots and opposite and decussate leaves. Submerged and aerial leaves simple in form. Flowers in loosely branched clusters in leaf axils, hermaphroditic, mirror-symmetrical. Perianth composed of a calyx in four or five parts grown together in the lower region, and a two-lipped, gamopetalous corolla. The lower lip is arched in the centre thereby more or less closing the entry to the tube of the corolla. Stamens: four. Carpels: two, united, hypogynous superior. The fruit comes as a capsule.

General Information: The genus is made up of approximately ten species; all of them colonize marshy habitats, and some of them do well in the water. Several species of *Nomaphila* are discussed here in greater detail but, similarly to the genus *Hygrophila*, some *Nomaphila* species are to be seen in tanks without having been properly identified so far. Thus there is a plant which resembles *Nomaphila* spec. 'Thailand', but it has a more compact habit and its leaves are rather longer and noticeably wider. Another species can also be found: it has slender, lanceolate submerged leaves, up to 10 cm long and only 8 mm wide, with a pale-green upperside which in some specimens may be olive-green (Ill. 102).

Nomaphila corymbosa BL. (Ill. 96, 102, 103)

The species was named by Blume in 1826 when he defined the genus *Nomaphila*. The name often used by aquarists, *Nomaphila stricta*, is of more recent date and may, in fact, prove to be the correct one for a different species.

Distribution: South-eastern Asiatic mainland.

Characteristics: Large, herbaceous plants with elongated shoots growing erect on boggy soil and when submerged. Leaf arrangement opposite and decussate. Submerged leaves noticeably petiolate, their laminae broad lanceolate, tips pointed, up to 12 cm long and up to 40 mm wide, upperside pale-green, underside whitish-green. Aerial shoots very hairy, their leaves with egg-shaped pointed laminae, grey-green. Corolla of flower blue.

Cultivation and Propagation: The species may be kept in temperatures from 20 °C, needs a well-lit position but is otherwise undemanding. The plants need a large tank to be shown at their best and several cuttings should be inserted together to obtain good clumps. Single shoots may look attractive in a smaller aquarium. Best propagation results achieved from cuttings.

Nomaphila spec. 'Thailand' (Ill. 102, 104)

So far the species has not been properly defined.

Distribution: Indochina.

Characteristics: Medium-sized herbaceous plants with elongated shoots growing erect on boggy soil and when submerged. Leaf arrangement opposite and decussate. Submerged leaves sessile, lanceolate, up to 10 cm long and up to 20 mm wide, upperside pale-green, underside whitish-green. Aerial leaves have the same shape, but are darker in colour. Corolla of flower blue.

Cultivation and Propagation: As specified for *N. corymbosa*, but better suited to medium-sized and smaller tanks.

Family Plantaginaceae · Plantain Family

Four genera, 280 species. Worldwide distribution. Rarely small bushes, usually perennial herbs, or other persistent or annual plants. Flowers very small and inconspicuous.

The plantain family colonize very varied habitats, some of their members being able to bear a very high content of salt in the soil. The three species of the genus *Litorella* are low-growing, stoloniferous rosette plants of marshy, periodically flooded habitats. In earlier aquarium literature *L. uniflora* of European origin was recommended as a plant forming a good turf in a cold-water aquarium. However, the plant never achieved a wide distribution.

Family Lobeliaceae

Thirty genera, 900 species. Temperate latitudes and subtropics, rare in tropics. Rarely woody plants, usually perennial herbs or other persistent or annual herbaceous plants. Coloured, labiate flowers. In part pollinated by birds. Generally with milky juice in the tissues.

The Lobeliaceae are near in relationship to the Bluebell Family (Campanulaceae). Their representatives colonize varied locations – from the plains to the high mountains. Although marsh and aquatic plants occur in ten genera they have hardly ever been cultivated. So far, the genus *Lobelia* alone has gained some importance.

Lobelia

The genus was defined by Linné in 1753. He named the plants after the Dutch botanist M. de l'Obel (1538—1616).

Distribution: Nearly cosmopolitan; main centre of evolution in America.

Characteristics: Some forms grow to the size of small trees with peculiar tufts of large leaves, but most are perennial herbs or other persistent as well as annual, herbaceous plants. Leaves arranged alternate or in basal rosettes, simple. Flowers in inflorescences, hermaphroditic, mirror-symmetrical. Perianth gamopetalous, composed of a calyx in five parts and a two-lipped, usually coloured corolla, also in five parts. Stamens: five, their anthers grown together as a tube. Carpels: two, united, hypogynous. The fruit is a capsule.

General Information: The genus includes approximately 360 species. Water is very necessary for them and, therefore, most species live on moist or wet soil. A few live in water like *L. dortmanna* from northern Europe and North America. This species is very occasionally cared for in an aquarium and it appears to need a very low *p*H value. The only species which has achieved some importance as a cultivated aquarium plant is the one described in greater detail below. The genus *Lobelia* actually includes a number of perennial and annual ornamental plants, but they were more popular during the last century than they are nowadays. The leaves of some North American species were at one time used like tobacco and smoked by the Red Indians.

Lobelia cardinalis L. (Ill. 124, 125)

The species was named by Linné in 1753.

Distribution: North America.

Characteristics: Herbaceous plants with elongated shoots, an alternate leaf arrangement and growing in the bog as well as submerged. Submerged leaves have a petiole or taper at the base, up to 8 cm long, their laminae elliptical to inverted ovate, up to 3 cm wide, medium-green. The dark-red flowers develop in terminal inflorescences on aerial shoots.

Cultivation and Propagation: In most similar plants the leaves are opposite and decussate. The alternate leaf arrangement of *L. cardinalis* provides a welcome contrast to these species, and thus the plant helps the aquarist in the design of a lively, aquascaped tank. *L. cardinalis* is very suitable for being planted in groups in the middle or the rear of a tank. A temperature of approximately 20°C is adequate, but it may be higher. The plants need a well-lit position, otherwise they are undemanding. Propagation from cuttings.

Family Asteraceae

Nine hundred genera, 20,000 species. Worldwide distribution. Small trees and bushes, succulents and lianas, perennial herbs with rhizomes, tubers and roots, also other perennial and annual, herbaceous plants. Leaves simple to pinnate. Rather small flowers combined in inflorescences, in their totality looking like single flowers. Some have a milky juice in their tissues.

Compositae is the older name for the family. The orchids alone surpass it in the wealth of species. The family includes many ornamental and food plants, such as the dahlias, the sun-flowers, and the lettuce. Although herbaceous plants are predominant, very few genera—probably less than ten—contain marsh and aquatic plants. They have not yet achieved any importance in aquatic plant cultivation. *Gymnocoronis spilanthoides* has been grown occasionally. But, *Cotula myriophylloides* and *Megalodonta beckii* might well be rewarding and interesting as well.

Family Alismataceae · Water Plantain Family

Eleven genera, 100 species. From the tropics to the temperate latitudes, but predominantly in the northern hemisphere and in South America. Perennial herbs, rarely annuals, leaves in basal rosettes. Flowers hermaphroditic or unisexual, in the latter case usually monoecious, actinomorphic, corolla normally white.

The Alismataceae are throughout plants of the marshes and the water. Thus it is likely that genera little-known to date contain species a lover of aquatic plants could use. There are several examples. The three species of the genus *Wiesneria*, distributed from Africa to south-east Asia, have submerged leaves only; they are linear and resemble the leaves of vallisnerias. It is purely the flowers of these plants which reach above the water level. The genus *Burnatia* has a single, dioecious species with submerged and aerial leaves, occurring in central and southern Africa. A fairly large species in south-east Asia belongs to the genus *Ranalisma*. Another species of the same genus resembles *Echinodorus tenellus;* it is very small and a native of tropical Africa. This species, *R. humile*, often colonizes rice fields and has occasionally been cared for in tanks. In the early days of aquarium plant cultivation *Luronium natans* has sometimes been kept in cold-water aquaria. The species is of central and western European origin and, in its natural environment, it is endangered by pollution of the waters. *Caldesia*, *Damasonium* and *Limnophyton* are other, little-known genera. At present, representatives of the genera *Alisma*, *Echinodorus*, *Baldellia* and *Sagittaria* are cultivated in aquaria as well as on ponds.

Alisma

The genus was defined by Linné in 1753. The generic name is probably the old Greek term *Alisma plantago-aquatica*. Initially, several representatives of other genera of the water plantain family were classed with this genus.

Distribution: Almost worldwide, but main evolution in the northern hemisphere.

Characteristics: Tuberous plants with basal leaf rosettes. Submerged leaves linear, aerial leaves petiolate with laminae of varied form. Much-branched inflorescences of complicated structure and shaped like pyramids. Flowers hermaphroditic, actinomorphic. Perianth polysepalous, composed of a green calyx in three parts and a white or pale-violet corolla, also in three parts. Stamens: six. Carpels: many, free, hypogynous superior, arranged in a circle. The fruit is a syncarpous nut.

General Information: The genus includes approximately ten species. Linear submerged leaves are present only in very young plants, as a rule, and are soon succeeded by petiolate leaves with laminae either floating on or reaching above the surface of the water. Only *A. gramineum*, a species which is local in the northern hemisphere, possesses longer persisting, submerged leaves, often only replaced by aerial leaves after the water level has sunk (Ill. 126). The species of this genus are plants of the shallow waters and boggy habitats. We find them on shallow ponds, in pond margins, in ditches and in reed-belts.

Alisma plantago-aquatica L. (Ill. 105)

The species was named by Linné in 1753.

Distribution: Originally in the temperate latitudes of the northern hemisphere. Nowadays established in many regions on earth.

Characteristics: Tuberous plant with basal leaf rosette. Leaves petiolate, up to 60 cm long, their laminae elliptical, egg-shaped or slightly heart-shaped, tips pointed to blunt, medium-green. Petals white. Flowers open in the afternoon.

Cultivation and Propagation: An undemanding, hardy species and very suitable as a border plant on ponds. The flowers should be removed before the fruits have ripened because too many seedlings might develop and become troublesome. Propagation by division of old plants or from seeds.

Alisma lanceolatum WITH.

The species was named by Withering in 1796.

Distribution: Europe, western Asia.

Characteristics: Plants with tubers and basal leaf rosettes. In comparable growth conditions always smaller than *A. plantago-aquatica.* Leaves petiolate, up to 40 cm long, their laminae broad lanceolate, pointed, blue-green. Petals pale-violet. Flowers open in the morning.

Cultivation and Propagation: As specified for *A. plantago-aquatica.*

Echinodorus

The genus was defined by Richard in 1848. The name, literally translated, means 'hedgehog tube' and refers to the spiny syncarpous fruits. Echinos (Gk) = hedgehog, doros (Gk) = tube.

Distribution: The southern part of North America, Central America, Greater Antilles, South America.

Characteristics: Plants with rhizomes and basal leaf rosettes, or rosette plants forming runners; commonly called sword plants. Leaves polymorphic, undivided, slender-lanceolate to noticeably petiolate with variable forms of laminae. Simple or branched inflorescences of complicated structure, some of them developing adventitious plantlets. Flowers hermaphroditic, actinomorphic. Perianth polysepalous, composed of a green calyx in three parts and a usually white corolla, also in three parts. Stamens: from six to approximately 30. Carpels: many but number is indefinite, free, hypogynous superior, arranged as a head. The fruit comes as an aggregate of achenes.

General Information: All the *Echinodorus* species known in cultivation can be distinguished by characteristics of habit and leaves (Ill. 117-119). In imported plants, on the other hand, the characteristics are often unknown and not at the disposal of the aquarist. To define the plants exactly needs a certain amount of experience. For instance, the special areas in the leaves containing a milky juice in pressed herbarium specimens play a role in classification, but these areas show up only under a microscope as transparent dots and lines (Ill. 106). Furthermore, the behaviour of the calyx while the fruit is forming, the number of stamens in the flowers, and the form of the achenes—usually referred to as

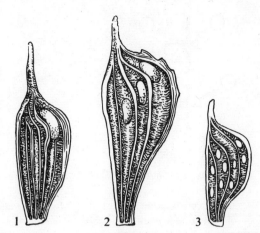

48 Achenes of *Echinodorus berteroi* (1),
   E. cordifolius (2), and *E. tenellus* (3)

seeds—(Ill. *48*) are important factors in determining species, quite apart from other characteristics.

The genus includes approximately 50 species, growing submerged, in boggy habitats with a fluctuating water level, but also on moist meadows. The largest species, e.g. *E. glaucus*, attain a height of 1.50 m including the inflorescence; the smallest species, e.g. *E. tenellus*, measure a few centimetres only. According to their habit of growth the species can be divided into two groups.

One group is made up of small to very large rhizome plants with basal leaf rosettes, branching little under cultivation. For practical reasons aquarists again sub-divide this group. A number of species, e.g. *E. paniculatus*, *E. grandiflorus*, or *E. macrophyllus* are unsuitable for aquarium cultivation. They grow submerged as very young plants, very soon adopt emerse growth and turn into robust, terrestrial plants. Other species, e.g. *E. berteroi*, *E. cordifolius*, or *E. subalatus* depend on photoperiods to a more or less marked degree. In their natural environment the species grow, in turn, as emerse plants when they develop flowers, and as submerged plants according to the length of daylight hours. Characteristic, different forms of leaves develop in these two phases of varied light conditions (see also page 67).

Knowledge of the plant's reaction to photoperiods enables the aquarist to keep them in a tank and, which is also very important, to propagate them. Finally, in some species, e.g. *E. osiris*, *E. parviflorus* and others the form of leaves and the development of inflorescences are subject to photoperiods. Nevertheless, in aquarium conditions, these species do not grow above the surface of the water.

The second group consists of medium-sized and small rosette plants. They produce a profusion of runners and can thus develop dense stocks, made up of single plants, rather like the vallisnerias and some sagittarias. Runners and inflorescences in these *Echinodorus* species have the same basic design initially. But the conditions in which they live, whether it is in or out of the water, as well as the varied amount of light they receive, cause differenti-

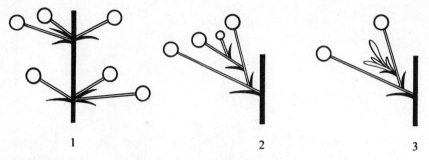

49 Sections of *Echinodorus* inflorescences (schematic representation).

1 Basic construction in three parts. 2 Further branching of a flower. 3 Ditto, but showing development of adventitious plantlet

ations in form. If kept submerged these species never flower and only multiply vegetatively from their runners. In emerse conditions they react to the light by being short-day or long-day plants, or they may be indeterminate. Whilst the plants are flowering they never develop runners. The form of the leaves depends largely on the length of time of lighting (Ill. *51*).

It is quite easy for the aquarist to propagate rosette plants because of their numerous runners. In older specimens of rhizome plants the method of rhizome division may be used when transplanting. But, as a rule, the aquarist depends on the intitiation of inflorescences. These consist of an elongated main axis and whorls which have a basic construction in three parts. Initially, one flower is positioned in the axils of every three bracts. At the base of each flower stalk a small scale-shaped leaf is present and, from its axil, another flower can develop. This process may be repeated several times and explains the multiple flowering capacity of the whorls (Ill. 49, 131). In many *Echinodorus* species adventitious plantlets develop instead of flowers.

In submerged plants the inflorescences capable of forming adventitious plantlets have variable habits of growth. In *E. major* they are stiff and erect; in *E. amazonicus* they grow slanting up to the surface of the water, continue growth just below it and may reach considerable dimensions; in *E. aschersonianus* they grow closely attached to the bottom. The plantlets usually develop quickly and form roots. When the plantlets have attained a size of several centimetres they can be separated from the parent plant and set into the substratum. The plantlets will become detached by themselves when the inflorescences disintegrate at a later stage. If an aquarium is sufficiently spacious, ascending inflorescences can be carefully attached to the bottom with the use of stones or glass pins. Thus the young plantlets can find immediate anchorage.

If adventitious plantlets do not occur we have to rely on sowing the one-seeded achenes. In all species the best germination results have been achieved in a fairly high temperature, between 25-30 °C.

82 *Alternanthera sessilis*
83 From left to right:
   Alternanthera spec.
   'Lilacina',
   A. sessilis,
   A. reineckii

   following double-page:
84 *Alternanthera reineckii*
85 *Menyanthes trifoliata*

90 *Utricularia* spec. 'Johore', flower
91 *Limosella subulata*, flowering

92 *Hygrophila angustifolia*, flowers
93 *Hygrophila difformis*, blossom
94 *Alternanthera* spec. 'Lilacina', flowering
95 *Proserpinaca palustris*, flowering

96 *Nomaphila corymbosa*, flowering
97 *Utricularia* spec. 'Johore'
98 *Hygrophila difformis*, variation in width of leaves

99 *Hygrophila difformis*
100 *Hygrophila polysperma*
101 *Hygrophila angustifolia*, bog form

102 From left to right, upper line: *Nomaphila* spec.
'Long leafed', *N.* spec. 'Thailand', *N.* spec.
'Densely leafed', *N. corymbosa*, *Hygrophila
angustifolia*, *H. lacustris;* bottom line: *H.* spec.
'Big-leafed', *H.* spec. 'Reddish', *H. polysperma*

103 *Nomaphila corymbosa*
104 *Nomaphila* spec. 'Thailand'

105 *Alisma plantago-aquatica*
106 Transparent lines in a leaf blade of *Echinodorus berteroi* (microscopic photograph)
107 *Echinodorus aschersonianus*
108 *Echinodorus berteroi*

109 *Echinodorus amazonicus*
110 *Echinodorus bleheri*

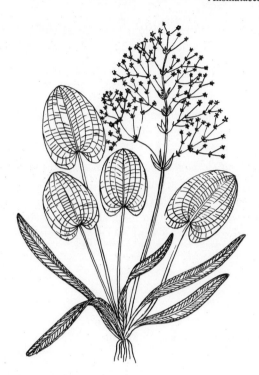

50 Echinodorus nymphaeifolius

    To date, approximately 30 species of the genus have received the attention of botanical gardens and aquarists. Out of the group of rhizome plants some have not yet been cultivated although they might well be interesting. One is *E. nymphaeifolius* (Ill. *50*) from Central America, northern South America and the Greater Antilles; its name has often been mentioned in aquarium literature, but it has been confused with other species. Another is the very small *E. gracilis* from north-eastern South America. Of the well-known rosette plants with runners it is only *E. isthmicus* from Central America and the Greater Antilles which has not yet been imported. Some species are cultivated in botanical gardens but need to be tested for suitability in tanks. But *E. palaefolius* var. *latifolius*, at home in central South America, has been kept in aquaria where it develops submerged leaves with lanceolate, dark-green laminae but, unfortunately, very long petioles. *E. pellucidus* from the southern part of South America is also supposed to be suitable for aquarium cultivation. Finally, it is certain that new and so far unknown species will eventually be discovered.

Echinodorus horizontalis RATAJ

The species was named by Rataj in 1969. It has often been imported under the name of 'E. guianensis'.
    Distribution: South America, Amazon region.

Characteristics: Rhizome plant with basal leaf rosette. Leaves petiolate, up to 25 cm long. Laminae not an elongation of petiole but arranged at an angle to it and orientated more or less horizontally, longish heart-shaped, tough, pale-green. In addition to midrib one to three pairs of parallel veins, dependent on size of lamina; all veins curved at base of lamina. The innermost pair of veins runs from the base to the apex of the lamina, the others reach the margins sooner or later. Young leaves red-brown if light is intensive. Inflorescences form adventitious plantlets. Diameter of flowers 1.5-2 cm. Stamens: 26-30. The ripening fruit is enclosed by the calyx.

Cultivation and Propagation: A medium-sized plant useful as a solitary specimen plant. It needs good light and—at the very least—unwashed sand as a substratum. The temperature should not be below 22 °C because the plant is tropical. Does not grow up above the surface of the water if cultivated in an aquarium. Adventitious plantlets do not form freely. In emerse cultivation and if artificial pollination is used achenes capable of germinating may be produced.

Echinodorus cordifolius (L.) GRISEB. (Ill. *48*)

The species was named *Alisma cordifolia* by Linné in 1753. In ignorance of this Nuttall described the plant for the second time in 1837 and named it *Sagittaria radicans*. In 1857 Grisebach moved the species to the genus *Echinodorus* and, quite correctly, maintained the specific epithet of the first description. Another name for the species, *E. radicans*, used in specialized literature for a long time, was based on the scientifically invalid, specific epithet of the later description.

Distribution: Southern North America; local in northern South America.

Characteristics: Rhizome plant with basal leaf rosette. Submerged leaves petiolate, up to 30 cm long. Laminae of very young plants egg-shaped, later on heart-shaped, tough, pale-green, often with red-brown markings. In addition to midrib one to five pairs of parallel veins, dependent on size of lamina; all veins curved at base of lamina. The innermost pair of veins runs from the base to the apex of the lamina, the others reach the margins sooner or later. Floating and aerial leaves with a longer petiole, but otherwise shaped the same way. Inflorescence with adventitious plantlets. Diameter of flowers 1.5-2.5 cm. Stamens: 24-28.

Cultivation and Propagation: A light-loving solitary show plant. It may be kept in an unheated as well as in a heated tank and also out in the open during the summer months. Hardy in the winter in a sheltered position. All leaves die off in temperatures below 10°C, but the rhizomes produce shoots as soon as the temperature rises. If kept in an aquarium attention has to be paid to the plants' reaction to photoperiods. Sufficiently strong plants form submerged leaves only if the period of illumination is less than 12 hours. In long-day conditions the leaves outgrow the water. A substratum lacking nutrients can delay the process. It has also been recommended that all older leaves be removed, or to put the rhizome tied up in a plastic bag into the substratum so as to hinder the growth of roots.

But if this procedure is followed, the plants are unlikely to develop well. Of course, inflorescences form in long-day conditions only. At first the inflorescences are always erect. In emerse conditions they become procumbent or, if cultivated in the shallow water of an aquarium, they first ascend to the surface of the water and then submerge beneath it. The flower stalks always lengthen sufficiently for the flowers to grow in the air. The seeds do not set easily and, for that reason, artificial pollination is recommended. When the achenes turn brown they should be harvested. After flowering, adventitious plantlets form in the whorls, especially at the tips of inflorescences.

General Information: E. *cordifolius* is one of the oldest, cultivated species of the genus. Many lateral roots are slightly thickened and, like the rhizome, presumably serve the storage of food.

Echinodorus aschersonianus GRAEBN. (Ill. 107, 119)

The species was named by Gräbner in 1911.

Distribution: Southern South America.

Characteristics: Rhizome plant with basal leaf rosette. Submerged leaves with a short petiole, up to 20 cm long. Laminae very variable, elliptical, egg or heart-shaped, rounded or pointed tips, pale to medium-green. All parallel veins curving at the base of lamina and running to its apex. Inflorescences with few adventitious plantlets. Diameter of flowers 2.5-3.5 cm. Stamens: 24-28.

Cultivation and Propagation: Medium-sized solitary show plant needing a light position and a substratum not too poor in nutrients. Optimum temperature between 20 and 25 °C. In aquarium cultivation the species does not grow above the water level. Inflorescences develop when daily periods of illumination are more than 12 hours. The inflorescences are procumbent from the beginning and—compared with other species—produce few adventitious plantlets. In emerse cultivation and if artificially pollinated, numerous achenes capable of germinating are produced.

Echinodorus subalatus (MART.) GRISEB.

The species was named *Alisma subalatum* by Martius in 1830 and moved to the genus *Echinodorus* by Grisebach in 1866.

Distribution: From Central America to the centre of South America.

Characteristics: Rhizome plant with basal leaf rosette. Submerged leaves petiolate, up to 35 cm long, resembling those of E. *amazonicus.* Laminae slender-lanceolate to lanceolate, pointed, up to 3 cm wide, pale-green. In addition to the midrib two pairs of parallel veins. The outer pair curves at the base of the lamina, it is inconspicuous and soon runs to the margins. The inner pair curves in the lowest quarter of the lamina, runs along its surface and reaches the margins shortly before the apex. Inflorescences bear adventitious plantlets. Diameter of flowers approximately 1.5 cm. Stamens: 12.

Cultivation and Propagation: A solitary show plant which needs a position in good light and a substratum of unwashed sand. Temperature 20-25 °C, but it can be higher. In a daily period of more than 12 hours' illumination the plant does not grow up above the water level. Being a short-day plant it produces aerial leaves in moderate daily periods of light. Inflorescences with plantlets also develop in short-day conditions which makes propagation of the plant in an aquarium rather more difficult.

Echinodorus berteroi (Spreng.) Fass. (Ill. *48*, 106, 108, 118)

The species was first named *Alisma berteroi* by Sprengel in 1825. Engelmann coined the name *Echinodorus rostratus* for the same plant in 1848, a name which was accepted in scientific and aquaristic literature. It was not until 1955 that Fassett drew attention to the name of the first description. The second generic name is correct and has been maintained.

Distribution: South-eastern North America, Central America, Greater Antilles, southern South America.

Characteristics: Rhizome plant with basal leaf rosette. Submerged leaves very variable, up to 40 cm long, slender-lanceolate to noticeably petiolate with egg to heart-shaped laminae, flat to slightly wavy, very thin and slightly translucent, dark-green. In addition to the midrib one to four pairs of parallel veins, dependent on the form of leaf and size of lamina. All veins proceed from the base of the lamina, the innermost pair ending in the apex, the others reaching the margins sooner or later. Floating and aerial leaves have a long petiole and heart-shaped, pale-green, tougher laminae. Inflorescence does not bear adventitious plantlets. Diameter of flowers approximately 1.5 cm. Stamens: 12.

Cultivation and Propagation: Because of its variable submerged leaves with their translucent structure a very decorative solitary specimen plant which needs a light to slightly shady position in the tank. Optimum temperature 18-25 °C. The plant is suited to being kept out in the open during the summer months. Its reactions to photoperiods unfortunately make it rather difficult to cultivate in a home aquarium. All the stronger plants, often even quite young ones, develop floating and aerial leaves in daily periods of more than 12 hours' illumination. At the same time, all submerged leaves die off. For delaying the process of leaves growing up above the water see the notes on *E. cordifolius.* It has to be borne in mind, however, that the growth of aerial leaves is the prerequisite for optimum propagation results in this species. It is in the phase of aerial leaf-growth that the erect, branched inflorescences with their numerous flowers appear. They produce ripe achenes even without the aid of artificial pollination. There is no need to worry that these may be lost which often happens with many aquarium plants. The achenes stay firmly attached, even to dead inflorescences, and they germinate very freely.

General Information: The plants occurring in the southern part of South America are fairly small; they are also supposed to be annuals. Otherwise they are indistinguishable from the more northern kinds. These plants have been denoted as *E. berteroi* var. *patagonicus*, but also as an independent species, *E. patagonicus.* It is also possible to cultivate flowering dwarf forms from the North American species. The two distribution areas are far distant from each other. Perhaps migrating birds have spread the seeds.

Echinodorus osiris RATAJ (Ill. 111, 117, 132)

The species was named by Rataj in 1970. Early on it was sometimes traded under the scientifically incorrect names 'E. rubra' and 'E. aureobrunensis'.

Distribution: South America, in the Brazilian state Paraná.

Characteristics: Rhizome plant with basal leaf rosette. Submerged leaves petiolate, up to 40 cm long. Form of laminae varied depending on time of illumination, broad-lanceolate, longish obovate, obcordate or elliptical, obtuse, up to 8 cm wide, flat or slightly wavy, young leaves an intensive red, colour fading as leaves become larger, later olive to dark-green. In addition to the midrib two pairs of parallel veins; one pair curves from the base of the lamina and runs to the margin, the other arises slightly above it and does not reach the margin. Other surface venation reaches the margins shortly below the apex. Aerial leaves elliptical. Inflorescence with plantlets. Diameter of flowers approx. 3 cm. Stamens: 18, rarely up to 24.

Cultivation and Propagation: One of the most beautiful species of the genus. Usable as a solitary show specimen in medium-sized and large aquaria. Bright to slightly shady position. Temperature about 20 °C, but it can be higher or temporarily fall to 10 °C. During warm summer months the species grows satisfactorily out in the open. The substratum should not be too poor in nutrients. In aquarium conditions the species does not grow up above the water, but it can be changed into a marsh plant if the water is withdrawn. In strong plants inflorescences develop—predominantly but not exclusively—in daily periods of more than 12 hours' illumination. In an aquarium the inflorescences grow slanting towards the surface of the water. Should they grow out of the water it is best to push them down to give the profuse plantlets a better chance to develop. Plantlets can be taken off as soon as they have strengthened sufficiently and used for propagation. In conditions of cultivation the flowers rarely open so that sexual propagation cannot be carried out.

General Information: In its native habitat large stocks of the species often grow together with *E. horemanii* in shallow areas of slowly flowing, rather cool waters coming down from the mountains. The two species are related, and *E. osiris* is also related to *E. uruguayensis*.

Echinodorus horemanii RATAJ (Ill. 117, 133)

Rataj named the species in 1960. In aquarist circles it was introduced under the scientifically incorrect name of 'E. undulatus'.

Distribution: South America, in the Brazilian state Paraná.

Characteristics: Rhizome plant with basal leaf rosette. Submerged leaves petiolate, up to 40 cm long. Their laminae lanceolate, flat to slightly wavy, up to 4 cm wide, dark-green.

In addition to the midrib two pairs of parallel veins. The outer pair curves at the base of the lamina and soon reaches the margin, the other pair curves away in the lowest quarter of the lamina and reaches the margin shortly before the apex. Inflorescence with adventitious plantlets. Diameter of flowers approx. 2.5 cm. Stamens: 18.

Cultivation and Propagation: A very decorative show plant for a tank which should not be too small. Bright to slightly shady position. Temperature 20-25 °C, but it can be higher or be allowed to fall to 15°C temporarily. A substratum rich in nutrients will further growth. If kept in an aquarium the species does not grow up above the water level, but it can be forced to adapt to emerse cultivation if the water is withdrawn. In long-day conditions the inflorescences grow up to the water level. If the lighting periods are only moderate flower stems curve and grow near the bottom. Propagation from separated adventitious plantlets.

General Information: In its native habitat the species grows together with *E. osiris* to which it is close in relationship. The species is also related to *E. uruguayensis.*

Echinodorus uruguayensis ARECH. (Ill. 112, 117)

The species was named by Arechavaleta in 1903.
   Distribution: Southern South America.
   Characteristics: Rhizome plant with basal leaf rosette. Submerged leaves petiolate, up to 30 cm long, but sometimes longer. Laminae lanceolate, obtuse, flat to slightly wavy, up to 3 cm wide, olive-green, dark red-green or black-green. In addition to the midrib two pairs of parallel veins. The outer pair curves at the base of the lamina and soon runs to the margin; the inner pair deflects in the lowest quarter of the lamina, runs along the surface and reaches the margin shortly below the apex. Inflorescences with adventitious plantlets. Diameter of flowers 1-1.5 cm. Stamens: 18.

   Cultivation and Propagation: The dark leaves make the species most attractive as show plants, suitable even for medium-sized tanks. Bright to slightly shady position. Temperature 20-25 °C. Use at least unwashed sand as substratum. In aquarium conditions the species does not grow up above the water level, but it can be forced to adapt to emerse cultivation if the water is withdrawn. Propagation by removing the adventitious plantlets which develop in inflorescences.

   General Information: The plant is near in relationship to the two previously described species *E. osiris* and *E. horemanii.*

Echinodorus major (MICH.) RATAJ (Ill. 113, 118)

Micheli denoted the plant as *Echinodorus martii* var. *major* in 1881. But for a long time, in aquaristic literature in Europe the name used for the plant was *E. martii,* and in North America 'E. leopoldina'. Both names are erroneous, and it was not until 1967 that Rataj was able to clarify the relationship and introduce the plant under the now correct name.

Distribution: South America, in the Brazilian states Goiás and Minas Gerais.

Characteristics: Rhizome plant with basal leaf rosette. Leaves petiolate, up to 50 cm long. Commonly called the ruffled sword plant. The blades are long and slightly spatulate, up to 5 cm wide, pale-green, with wavy edges. Depending on leaf size, in addition to the midrib two to three pairs of parallel veins. The outer pair curves at the base and soon reaches the margins; one pair deflects in the lowest quarter and reaches the margins in the upper third of the leaf; the other pair deflects shortly below the middle of the leaf and runs to the apex. Inflorescence with adventitious plantlets. Flowers measure 1.5 cm across. Stamens: 9-12.

Cultivation and Propagation: A solitary specimen plant needing a spacious aquarium to unfold its full beauty. It should be given good light or, at most, a very little shade. Temperature around 25°C. A substratum containing a good supply of food promotes the plant's growth. The species does not grow up above the water level. So far emerse cultivation of the plant has never been satisfactory. The growth of inflorescences is erect and they do grow out of the water. If the flowers are pollinated artificially achenes set quite readily, and they will germinate. The adventitious plantlets which develop in the region of the inflorescences do not develop particularly well in the air. They have a better chance to thrive if the inflorescences are pushed carefully below the water level.

Echinodorus grisebachii SMALL

Small gave the species its scientific name in 1909.

Distribution: Central America, Greater Antilles, northern South America.

Characteristics: Rhizome plant with basal leaf rosette. Submerged leaves petiolate, up to 25 cm long. Laminae longish egg-shaped to broad lanceolate, pointed, up to 4 cm wide, pale to medium-green. In addition to the midrib two pairs of parallel veins. The outer pair curves at the base of the lamina, it is very delicate and ends just before the margins so that it is easily overlooked; the inner pair deflects in the lowest quarter of the lamina, runs along the surface and reaches the margins just below the apex. Inflorescence with adventitious plantlets. Flowers measure 1 cm across. Stamens: generally 12.

Cultivation and Propagation: Among the plants of the genus having rhizomes a relatively small species and therefore usable as a solitary specimen plant in a medium-sized tank. Needs a position in good light. Temperature not below 20°C. Substratum should not be too poor in nutrients and, at least, consist of unwashed sand. In aquarium conditions the species does not grow up above the water. However, if the water is withdrawn, the species can be adapted to emerse cultivation. The inflorescences grow erect and produce plantlets, thus making propagation simple. Plants grown emerse produce fruit with seeds which set easily.

Echinodorus amazonicus RATAJ (Ill. 109, 117)

Although the species has been grown by aquarists and in botanical gardens since 1940 it was not until 1970 that Rataj gave it its scientific name. For a long time the plant was incorrectly classified and known under the name of *E. brevipedicellatus*.

Distribution: South America, Amazon region.

Characteristics: Rhizome plant with basal leaf rosette. Submerged leaves with short petiole and up to 40 cm long. Their laminae slender lanceolate, pointed, often slightly curved on one side, up to 3 cm wide, pale-green, In addition to the midrib two pairs of parallel veins.

The outer pair curves from the base of the lamina and ends close to the margins; the inner pair deflects in the lowest quarter of the lamina and runs on the surface near the margins. Marginal and surface veins combine before they reach the apex. Inflorescence with adventitious plantlets. Diameter of flowers approximately 1 cm. Stamens: as a rule nine, but there may be six or twelve.

Cultivation and Propagation: Light-loving, but otherwise undemanding solitary specimen plant growing to a large size and, therefore, needing adequate space. An enriched substratum furthers growth. In aquarium conditions the plant does not grow up above the water level, but it will grow emerse if the water is withdrawn.

Mature, strong plants produce inflorescences ascending nearly as high as the water surface, then becoming procumbent and continuing growth until they have attained quite a length. These inflorescences are often mistaken for runners. Flowers rarely develop in an aquarium. Numerous plantlets form in the region of the flower whorls. The plantlets grow quickly and develop roots. They can be taken off and planted as soon as they measure a few centimetres.

General Information: According to collectors profuse numbers of the species grow in slowly flowing and still waters of their homeland up to a depth of 1 m. The species is closely related to the two species described below, *E. bleheri* and *E. parviflorus*.

Echinodorus bleheri RATAJ (Ill. 110, 117)

It is probable that the species was introduced to aquarists together with *E. amazonicus*. Like the latter it was also first named scientifically by Rataj in 1970. For a long time the plant was incorrectly classified, being denoted as *E. paniculatus* (Amazon sword plant) in Europe, and traded in North America under the name of 'E. rangeri'.

Distribution: Probably central South America.

Characteristics: Rhizome plant with basal leaf rosette. Submerged leaves with a short petiole and up to 40 cm long. Laminae slender lanceolate to lanceolate, pointed, never curved as *E. amazonicus*, up to 7 cm wide, pale-green. In short-day conditions the leaves are more solid than in long-day conditions. Venation of laminae as in *E. amazonicus*. Inflorescence with adventitious plantlets. Flower characteristics not examined so far.

Cultivation and Propagation: E. *bleheri* is grown and propagated as a large solitary specimen plant and in aquarium conditions it does not grow up above the water. It can be forced to be cultivated as a marsh plant if the water is withdrawn.

General Information: E. *amazonicus* and E. *parviflorus* are closely related. As yet there is no exact information about the natural environment of E. *bleheri*. The imported plants are not collected wild plants, like many other *Echinodorus* species, but are obtained from nurseries.

Echinodorus parviflorus RATAJ (Ill. 117, 119, 134)

Rataj gave the species its scientific name in 1970. Originally the plant was introduced under the scientifically incorrect trade names of 'E. peruensis' and 'E. tocantins'. It is often called the 'Black Amazon plant'.

Distribution: Probably central South America.

Characteristics: Rhizome plant with basal leaf rosette. Submerged leaves in long-day conditions with a short petiole and up to 40 cm long. Laminae lanceolate, pointed, up to 4 cm wide, pale to mid-green. In short-day conditions the petioles are longer and the laminae more solid to being elongated heart-shaped. In addition to the midrib there are two pairs of parallel veins.

The outer pair curves at the base of the lamina and runs very close to the margins; the inner pair deflects in the lowest quarter of the lamina, runs and ends on the leaf surface. Marginal and surface veins do not combine and run separately to the apex of the lamina. Inflorescence with adventitious plantlets. Diameter of flowers around 1 cm. Stamens: as a rule nine.

Cultivation and Propagation: Undemanding solitary specimen plant growing to a considerable size and possessing very durable leaves. Thus, in older plants which have enjoyed undisturbed development, up to 100 well-preserved leaves have been counted. A position in good light is favourable, but the plant can also take a little shade. Temperature 20-25 °C, but a higher one will do no damage. An enriched substratum furthers development. In aquarium conditions the plant does not grow up above the water level, although it can be cultivated emerse if the water is withdrawn. Propagation is a problem, because inflorescences develop only if daily periods of illumination are less than 12 hours. Many aquaria, however, are lit for a longer period.

If cultivated submerged in short-day conditions numerous, adventitious plantlets form on the inflorescences. The plantlets should be treated like those of E. *amazonicus*. In emerse cultivation as marsh plants many achenes are produced. They are capable of germinating and can be harvested.

General Information: At present definite information on the exact area of distribution in the species' homeland is still lacking. According to statements made by collectors the plants seem to occur in large numbers in Bolivia and Peru. The species is related to the two previously described E. *amazonicus* and E. *bleheri*.

Echinodorus amphibius RATAJ (Ill. 114)

The species was named by Rataj in 1967.

Distribution: South America, in the Brazilian states of Pará and Bahia.

Characteristics: Rhizome plant with basal leaf rosette. Submerged leaves very variable, depending on periods of light. In long-day conditions slender lanceolate, up to 25 cm long and up to 1 cm wide, resembling leaves of *E. latifolius* and E. *angustifolius*, flat to wavy, pale-green. In conditions of less light the leaves resemble those of *E. grisebachii;* they are noticeably petiolate, at most 20 cm long, laminae broad lanceolate to elliptical, up to 3 cm wide. In addition to the midrib only one prominent pair of parallel veins which curves from near the base of the lamina, runs towards the apex and ends shortly before it. Inflorescence with adventitious plantlets. Diameter of flowers approx. 0.7 cm. Stamens: six.

Cultivation and Propagation: An inconspicuous species with slender leaves which form in tanks illuminated for more than 12 hours. It looks best when planted with groups of other plants in the middle part of the aquarium. It should be given a position in good light and a temperature of not less than 20 °C. A substratum of unwashed sand is adequate. The species does not grow up above the water level in aquarium conditions, but it can be cultivated emerse as a marsh plant if the water is withdrawn. Inflorescences with adventitious plantlets develop in short-day conditions only, so that propagation in an aquarium is hardly possible. Optimal propagation results may be achieved in emerse cultivation with daily periods of light from nine to ten hours.

Echinodorus portoalegrensis RATAJ (Ill. 115, 119)

The species was named by Rataj in 1970.

Distribution: South America, in the Brazilian state Rio Grande do Sul.

Characteristics: Rhizome plant with basal leaf rosette. Submerged leaves petiolate, up to 20 cm long. Laminae lanceolate to broad lanceolate, pointed, wavy, very tough and stiff, up to 4 cm wide, dark-green. In addition to the midrib often one pair of parallel veins only, curving near the base of the lamina, running on the surface and reaching the margin shortly below the apex. Aerial leaves with a long petiole, their laminae heart-shaped. Characteristics of inflorescences and flowers unknown.

Cultivation and Propagation: Its tough, dark-green leaves make this a very decorative solitary specimen plant. It grows slowly and, as it never becomes large, it is suitable for being kept in a small aquarium. The species needs a bright to slightly shady position and, at least, unwashed sand as substratum. Temperature 20-25 °C. Compared with other *Echinodorus* species E. *portoalegrensis* forms roots rather slowly so that it should be transplanted as little as possible. Growing it emerse as a marsh plant is not always successful. So far propagation has been possible only by division of rhizomes or removal of occasionally developing lateral shoots.

General Information: Very probably the species is rather closely related to *E. opacus.*

Echinodorus opacus RATAJ (Ill. 116, 119)

The species was named by Rataj in 1970.

Distribution: South America, in the Brazilian state Paraná.

Characteristics: Rhizome plant with basal leaf rosette. Submerged leaves with a long petiole and up to 20 cm long. Laminae ovate to heart-shaped, obtuse, slightly wavy, very tough and stiff, up to 5 cm wide, mid to dark-green. In addition to the midrib two pairs of parallel veins. The outer pair curves at the base of the lamina and reaches the margins sooner or later; the inner pair arises slightly further up and runs on the surface to the apex. Characteristics of inflorescence and flowers unknown.

Cultivation and Propagation: To be cultivated as specified for *E. portoalegrensis.* Emerse cultivation of this species as a marsh plant has never yet been successful. Propagation only possible by division of rhizomes. The yield is rather low.

General Information: The species has been observed in its homeland together with *E. osiris* and *E. horemanii.* Probably it is rather closely related to *E. portoalegrensis.*

Echinodorus angustifolius RATAJ (Ill. *51*)

The species was named by Rataj in 1975.

Distribution: Central South America, so far only known from the Brazilian state Mato Grosso.

Characteristics: Rosette plant forming runners. In long-day conditions submerged leaves tapering at the base, very narrow lanceolate with a long pointed tip, up to 40 cm, sometimes even 50 cm long, approx. 5 mm wide, pale-green. Midrib only conspicuous vein. If observed superficially the species can easily be mistaken for vallisnerias or long and slender-leafed sagittarias whom it closely resembles. In comparable growth conditions always larger than *E.* spec. 'longifolius'. Inflorescences in emerse conditions only. Diameter of flowers 1.2-1.5 cm. Stamens: six to nine.

Cultivation and Propagation: Among the runner forming species the one with the longest leaves and very suitable for a group display in the foreground corners of a tank. Slips will develop at some distance from the parent plants and should be removed. Another good use for the species is to plant it in the background where its many slips, produced on the runners, will form a dense growth after some time. It should be given a bright to slightly shady position. Temperature 20-25 °C. Unwashed sand is an adequate substratum. Can be cultivated as a marsh plant if the water is removed. Propagation from slips taken off the runners.

Echinodorus spec. 'longifolius' (Ill. *51*)

The species has not yet been scientifically named.

Distribution: South America, more exact information not at hand.

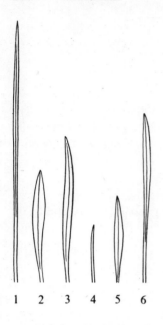

51 Leaf forms of *Echinodorus* species that send out runners—
in long-day conditions

1 *E. angustifolius*, 2 *E.* spec. 'longifolius', 3 *E. latifolius*,
4 *E. quadricostatus*, 5 *E. austroamericanus*, 6 *E. tenellus*

Characteristics: Rosette plant forming runners. Submerged leaves in long-day conditions tapering at the base, narrow lanceolate, pointed, up to 30 cm long and up to 8 mm wide, pale-green. Midrib only conspicuous vein. In comparable growth conditions always smaller than the similar *E. angustifolius*. In short-day conditions leaves less long and divided into petiole and a lanceolate lamina. Inflorescences only if growing emerse. Diameter of flowers 1 cm. Stamens: six to nine.

Cultivation and Propagation: Among the species producing runners this one is relatively long-leafed and suitable for being planted in the front corners of not too tall tanks. It can also be used in the middle or the back of an aquarium. Requires a position in good light. Temperature 20-25 °C or a little higher. Unwashed sand provides an adequate substratum. Can be cultivated emerse as a marsh plant if the water is withdrawn. Propagation from slips taken off the runners.

Echinodorus latifolius (SEUB.) RATAJ (Ill. *51*, 121)

The plant was given the name *Alisma tenellum* forma *latifolia* by Seubert in 1848. Fassett moved it to the genus *Echinodorus* in 1955 and interpreted it as a variety of *E. tenellus*. It was not until 1975 that Rataj gave the plant the status of an independent species. To aquarists it was introduced under the incorrect name 'E. magdalenensis'.

Distribution: Central America, Greater Antilles, northern South America.

Characteristics: Rosette plant producing runners. In long-day conditions submerged leaves without petiole and tapering at the base, narrow lanceolate, pointed, up to 15 cm or—at most—20 cm long and up to 10 mm wide, partly curved on one side, pale-green.

The midrib is the only conspicuous vein. In comparable growth conditions always more narrow-leafed than the similar *E. quadricostatus*. In short-day conditions leaves clearly divided into petiole and lanceolate laminae. Inflorescences only if growing emerse. Diameter of flowers 1.2-1.5 cm. Petals tilted downward. Stamens: six to nine.

Cultivation and Propagation: In the *Echinodorus* group producing runners, it is a medium-sized species like the one described below. It looks very attractive in a group display in the middle part of a medium-sized tank, but can also be used in the foreground of a large one. Requires a position in good light. Temperature 20-25 °C, but it can be higher or go down, temporarily, to 15 °C. Emerse cultivation as a marsh plant possible if water is withdrawn. Propagation from slips taken off the runners.

Echinodorus quadricostatus Fass. (Ill. *51*, 120)

Fassett gave the plant its scientific name in 1955. Up to that time it was usually known to aquarists under the incorrect name of 'E. intermedius' owing to a mistaken definition.

Distribution: From Central America to the middle of South America.

Characteristics: Rosette plant producing runners. In long-day conditions submerged leaves tapering at the base, narrow lanceolate to lanceolate, tip pointed or obtuse, up to 15 cm or—at most—20 cm long and up to 15 mm wide, pale-green. Midrib is the only conspicuous vein. In comparable growth conditions leaves always broader than in the similar *E. latifolius* and leaves never curved on one side. In short-day conditions leaves noticeably divided into petiole and lanceolate lamina. Inflorescences develop in emerse cultivation only. Diameter of flowers 1.5-1.8 cm. Stamens: six to nine.

Cultivation and Propagation: In the *Echinodorus* group producing runners it belongs to the medium-sized species like the previous one, *E. latifolius*. Cultivation and propagation methods are the same for both.

General Information: The plants kept in our aquaria are generally the variety var. *xinguensis* which originates from the Rio Xingu in the Brazilian state of Pará.

Echinodorus austroamericanus Rataj (Ill. *51*)

The species was named by Rataj in 1970.

Distribution: From central South America to the southerly temperate latitudes of the continent.

Characteristics: Rhizome plant producing runners. Submerged leaves very variable, sessile or tapering at the base, very narrow linear, linear, narrow, lanceolate, but also petiolate with lanceolate or curiously shaped laminae, pointed or obtuse tips, up to 12 cm long, pale-green. The midrib is the only conspicuous vein. Inflorescences only if growing as bog plants. Diameter of flower approximately 1.2 cm. Stamens: six to nine.

Cultivation and Propagation: This plant does not grow as tall as the two previous species and is very suitable for a reasonably sized tank where it will form a good turf. However, it can also be planted in groups in the middle part of the aquarium. It is an interesting plant to look after because of the variability of its leaves. Temperature between 15 and 20 °C suffices, but it can go up without hurting the plants or, temporarily sink to 10 °C. Otherwise the species is cultivated and propagated in the same way as *E. latifolius*.

General Information: *E. austroamericanus* is the only member of the genus producing runners. It occurs to the south of the tropic of capricorn and grows in the higher mountain ranges of the Andes.

Echinodorus tenellus (MART.) BUCH. (Ill. *48, 51,* 122)

Martius named the species *Alisma tenellum* in 1830. Buchenau moved it to the genus *Echinodorus* in 1869.

Characteristics: A rosette plant with runners, commonly called the pigmy chain-sword. Submerged leaves narrow linear, tips pointed or obtuse, up to 5 cm or—at most 10 cm long, up to 3 mm wide, mid to dark-green. Venation sometimes difficult to see. Inflorescences produced by marsh plant only. Diameter of flowers 0.6-0.7 cm. Stamens: six to nine.

Cultivation and Propagation: The smallest species of the genus. Valued as a useful plant for the front of an aquarium as it forms a dense turf within a short time. Occasional thinning out is necessary. Sufficient illumination is quite essential for healthy growth. Temperature upwards of 20 °C, but it can be lower temporarily. Unwashed sand is an adequate substratum. Contrary to earlier ideas it grows well in a coarse-grained substratum, but it does not like too high a layer of mulm. The height of the tank is unimportant. Can be changed into a marsh plant by withdrawing the water. Propagation from slips taken off the runners.

General Information: In botanical literature two different varieties are distinguished. In var. *tenellus* the laminae of aerial leaves are said to be broadest in the lowest third and the inflorescences higher than the leaves. This plant appears to be our own perennial aquarium form which originates in Central and South America. In var. *parvulus* the laminae of aerial leaves and the inflorescences are as long as or only a little longer than the leaves. This variety is said to be annual and to occur in North America as well as in Cuba.

Baldellia

The genus was defined by Parlatore in 1854. It contains only the single species described below. Its varieties should probably be given the status of independent species. No explanation has been found for the meaning of the generic name.

Baldellia ranunculoides (L.) PARL.

The species was named *Alisma ranunculoides* by Linné in 1753. Parlatore separated it from the genus *Alisma* and gave it the name *Baldellia ranunculoides* when he defined the genus. In scientific literature it is often denoted as *Echinodorus ranunculoides*.

Distribution: Western and southern Europe, north-west Africa, Canary Islands.

Characteristics: Small rosette plant, partly with runners. Submerged leaves linear, pointed, of varying length, pale-green. In addition to the midrib one pair of parallel veins which runs near the margins. Aerial leaves up to 25 cm long, with a long petiole, their laminae lanceolate, dark to blue-green. Flowers hermaphroditic, actinomorphic, their diameter 1-2 cm. Perianth polysepalous, composed of a green calyx in three parts and a white or pale-violet corolla also in three parts. Stamens: six. Carpels: many, free, hypogynous superior, arranged in a head. The fruit is an aggregate of achenes. In contrast to the genus *Echinodorus* in *Baldellia* the sepals fall off the ripening fruit.

Cultivation and Propagation: The plants prove to be hardy in the winter in open air cultivation. It is advisable to cover them with a light layer of foliage if they grow as bog plants. In a cold-water aquarium they remain vegetative during the winter. As the plants are quite happy in temperatures above 20 °C they can also be used in a heated tank. They are really a very versatile species. The plants do require a position in good light but make no special demands on the substratum. If they are cultivated as bog plants they produce a good yield of seeds. In aquarium cultivation the possibility of vegetative propagation depends on the respective subspecies.

General Information: A distinction is made between three subspecies. The plants of ssp. *ranunculoides* form basal leaf rosettes without runners when submerged. The leaves reach a length of 20 cm, and they are up to 4 mm wide. But in their natural habitat, in deep water, the plants' leaves may grow to a length of 50 cm. The leaves are soft. Vegetative propagation is not possible. In emerse growing marsh plants erect, umbellate inflorescences occur. Submerged and in comparable growth conditions the plants of ssp. *repens* are always smaller. They form basal leaf rosettes and runners. The leaves reach a length up to 10 cm and are 4 mm wide; they are stiff. Vegetative propagation is possible by taking off slips. If the plants grow emerse as marsh plants they develop inflorescences, looking like runners, growing horizontally and possessing adventitious plantlets. The geographical boundary of these two subspecies has not yet been clarified. Another plant, ssp. *alpestris*, has been observed in the mountain ranges of the Spanish peninsula. This is a little-known plant; it is said to be near in relationship to ssp. *repens*.

Sagittaria

The genus was defined by Linné in 1753. The name was chosen because some species have leaves shaped like arrows. Sagitta (L) = arrow.

Distribution: Predominantly America; on the other continents originally three species only, but several more became established later on.

Characteristics: Herbaceous plants with rhizomes, tubers and runners and leaves in basal rosettes. Submerged leaves linear. Floating and aerial leaves petiolate with very variable laminae, lanceolate, elliptical, egg or strap-shaped. Simple racemose inflorescences. Flowers unisexual, as a rule monoecious, actinomorphic. Perianth polysepalous, composed of a green calyx in three parts and a generally white corolla, also in three parts. A very varied number of stamens. Many carpels, free, hypogynous superior. Aggregate fruit of achenes.

General Information: Commonly called arrowhead, the genus includes approximately 20 species. All of them grow in marshy areas or in shallow water, rarely in deeper water. The species show differences in growth form and growing rhythm. In addition to the very large, robust marsh plants like *S. lancifolia* which is often cultivated in botanical gardens, there are other marsh plants suitable for open air or planthouse cultivation. Some of the species are ideal aquarium plants. Many have not yet been tried out in cultures.

The great variability of the leaves is characteristic of the genus. All species possess linear submerged leaves having a more or less long span of life. Linear leaves are also produced by mature plants of some species, e.g. *S. platyphylla*, whereas in other species they are the chief form of leaves, e.g. *S. subulata*. The aerial leaves of mature plants are either in an unbroken line or display the well-known arrow shape. In the second case the first leaves of young plants and those developing on lateral shoots occur in differently shaped preliminary stages (Ill. *17*).

On the whole, the inflorescences stand upright; it is rare that they float underneath the water surface, only single flowers projecting into the air. Three flowers are always present in each whorl of an inflorescence. The flowers are always unisexual and rarely dioecious. In a monoecious arrangement the female flowers are positioned at the base of the inflorescences and the male flowers further up. The female and male flowers rarely blossom at the same time so that at least two inflorescences in different phases of development are needed for a pollination. The ripening fruits should be kept under observation as the seeds drop out while still green and are, thus, easily lost.

Sagittaria montevidensis CHAM. et SCHLECHT. (Ill. 128)

The species was named by Chamisso and Schlechtendal in 1827.

Distribution: Originally in tropical and subtropical South America, but now also established in southern North America, in Africa, Asia and Australia.

Characteristics: Strong rhizome plant with basal leaf rosette. Submerged leaves linear, but only in very young plants. Aerial leaves petiolate, up to 100 cm long, the laminae of young plants and young lateral shoots broad lanceolate to elliptical, later always arrow-shaped, mid-green. Inflorescences erect. Diameter of flowers up to 4 cm. Petals white with a dark-red spot at the base. Male flowers with 12 to very many stamens. The rather flat syncarp partially enclosed by the calyx.

Cultivation and Propagation: This large, robust and undemanding plant is not suitable for aquarium cultivation. It can be grown in a planthouse and spend the summers out in the open. But the species does not stand up to cold winters outside. Propagation from lateral shoots which develop on the more mature plants or by sowing seeds. Plenty of seeds are produced and they set easily.

111 *Enchinodorus osiris*
112 *Echinodorus uruguayensis*

117 From left to right: *Echinodorus uruguayensis*, *E. osiris*, *E. horemanii*, *E. parviflorus*, *E. bleheri*, *E. amazonicus*

118 From left to right: *Echinodorus berteroi*—3 varied forms of submerged leaves, *E. major*—2 submerged leaves

119 From left to right: *Echinodorus opacus*, *E. portoalegrensis*, *E. aschersonianus*, *E. parviflorus*—leaf
in short-day and long-day conditions

120 *Echinodorus quadricostatus*, flowering marsh plants
121 *Echinodorus latifolius*

following page:
122 *Echinodorus tenellus*
123 *Sagittaria graminea*

128 *Sagittaria montevidensis*, female flowers
129 *Sagittaria weatherbiana*, inflorescence in the female phase
130 *Sagittaria weatherbiana*, inflorescence in the male phase

131 Flowers of a species of *Echinodorus*
132 *Echinodorus osiris*, marsh plant
133 *Echinodorus horemanii*
134 *Echinodorus parviflorus*

General Information: The species has become naturalized in some areas of the temperate latitudes. Because it grows so fast it flowers and produces fruit in the first year. Hence the old plants which die in the winter can be replaced by new, young plants in the spring. The small, dormant fruits are not sensitive to frost.

Sagittaria sagittifolia L. (Ill. 127)

The species was named by Linné in 1753.

Distribution: Europa, Asia.

Characteristics: Rosette plant with runners and tubers which last through the winter. Linear submerged leaves produced only when the plants start sprouting in the spring. Floating and aerial leaves petiolate, up to 60 cm long, their laminae arrow-shaped, mid-green. Occasionally transitionary leaves with differently shaped laminae. Inflorescences erect. Diameter of flowers up to 2.5 cm. Petals white. Male flowers with many stamens. The globular syncarps are not enclosed by the calyx.

Cultivation and Propagation: This undemanding species, which dies down during the winter, can only be used in shallow areas of ponds. Underground runners of varying lengths sprout from the plants during the summer. At the end of each runner a tuber develops. The tubers survive the winter whereas the old plants die down. In the following spring runner-like shoots sprout from the tips of the tubers, eventually forming a new rosette. Propagation from dug up dormant tubers or seeds.

General Information: The preferred habitat of the species is in shallow places of still or slowly flowing waters. The distribution area of the species is very large and two subspecies are distinguished. The petals of ssp. *sagittifolia* have a red spot at the base and the pollen-sacs of the plant are violet. It occurs in Europe and western Asia. The habitat of ssp. *leucopetala* lies in eastern Asia; this plant lacks the red spot at the base of the petals and its pollen-sacs are yellow. Cultivated forms of the latter exist in Japan, China and south-east Asia; their tubers, 5-7 cm long, contain starch and are used as a food.

Sagittaria latifolia WILLD.

The species was named by Willdenow in 1805. In scientific literature it has sometimes been denoted *S. variabilis*.

Distribution: From North America to the northern part of South America. Naturalized and local in some areas. Whether the specimens collected in Europe really belong to this species is uncertain.

Characteristics: Rosette plant with runners and tubers lasting through the winter. In comparable growth conditions always bigger than *S. sagittifolia*. Submerged leaves fairly persistent in very young plants only, otherwise they develop in the spring when the plants start to sprout. Floating and aerial leaves petiolate, up to 80 cm long, their laminae very variable, lanceolate, elliptical, egg or arrow-shaped. Inflorescence erect. Diameter of flowers up to 2 cm. Petals white. Male flowers with many stamens, pollen-sacs yellow. The globular fruit is not enclosed by the calyx.

Cultivation and Propagation: As specified for *S. sagittifolia.*

Sagittaria weatherbiana FERN. (Ill. 129, 130, 140)

The species was described by Fernald in 1935. Some botanists consider it to be a variety of *S. graminea.*

Distribution: Atlantic coast of North America. Naturalized in Australia.

Characteristics: Rosette plant producing runners. Small tubercles occasionally only present on end of runners. Submerged leaves up to a length of 50 cm, but normally shorter, up to 2.5 cm wide, tips pointed, mid-green. In addition to the midrib two to six pairs of parallel veins, depending on width of leaf. Aerial leaves petiolate, their laminae broad lanceolate, elliptical or egg-shaped. Inflorescence erect. Diameter of flowers approx. 1.5 cm. Petals white. Male flowers with 15-20 stamens. The fruit is not enclosed by the calyx. The flower stalks are 4—7 cm long, they spread from the central stem and are not recurved.

Cultivation and Propagation: This is an undemanding plant. Optimum temperature 15-25 °C. The plant grows well out in the open during the summer and may be quite hardy in the winter if covered with a layer of foliage. In an aquarium large, broad-leafed forms can be achieved only in very good light. Some plants stay submerged for a long time, whereas others project above the water level if the daily period of illumination exceeds 12 hours. In daylight cultivation and long-day conditions all plants turn into marsh forms. The plants can be propagated from separated slips. Runners grow out of the rosettes and either form new plantlets immediately, or develop swellings on their tips. These swellings are small tubers needing different resting periods and eventually produce young plants. Inflorescences usually appear just after the plants have formed aerial leaves. Achenes can be harvested and they will germinate freely.

Sagittaria platyphylla (ENGELM.) J. G. SM.

Engelmann named the plant *Sagittaria graminea* var. *platyphylla* in 1867. J. G. Smith gave it the status of an independent species in 1894.

Distribution: In North America in the lower region of the Mississippi. Naturalized and local in parts of South America and south-east Asia.

Characteristics: Rosette plant producing runners. Small tubers occur in tips of runners, but only occasionally. Submerged leaves linear, tips pointed or obtuse, up to 40 cm long and up to 2 cm wide, mid-green. Aerial leaves petiolate, their laminae broad lanceolate or egg-shaped. Inflorescences erect. Flowers and fruit characteristics as in *S. weatherbiana,* but the flower stalks are up to 3 cm long and noticeably curved downwards.

Cultivation and Propagation: The same as the previous species.

General Information: Many plants kept in tanks and taken for *S. platyphylla* are actually *S. weatherbiana.*

Sagittaria graminea Michx. (Ill. 123)

The species was named by Michaux in 1803.

Distribution: Southern and central parts of North America.

Characteristics: Rosette plant producing runners. Submerged leaves linear, pointed, up to 25 cm long and up to 1.5 cm wide, mid to dark-green. Aerial leaves petiolate, their laminae narrow lanceolate to lanceolate. Inflorescence erect. Diameter of flowers 1-1.5 cm. Petals white. Male flowers with approx. 15 stamens. The fruit is not enclosed by the calyx.

Cultivation and Propagation: This undemanding species belongs to the sagittarias with broad submerged leaves. It is better suited to aquarium cultivation than the two previous species as it grows up above the water level less easily. Propagation as specified for *S. weatherbiana*.

Sagittaria subulata (L.) Buch. (Ill. 142)

Linné named the species *Alisma subulatum* in 1753. Buchenau moved it to the genus *Sagittaria* in 1871.

Distribution: Atlantic coast of North America; naturalized and local in parts of South America.

Characteristics: Rosette plant producing runners. Small tubers occasionally on the tips of runners. Submerged leaves linear and obtuse at the tip, of very varied length and width according to variety, mid to dark-green. In addition to the midrib two pairs of parallel veins. Healthy, strong plants may develop floating leaves with small elliptical or egg-shaped laminae. Aerial leaves also linear, with obtuse or broadened tips. If growing submerged, inflorescences procumbent below the surface of the water and only single flowers project into the air. Diameter of flowers up to 1.5 cm. Petals white. Male flowers with seven to nine stamens. The fruit is not enclosed by the calyx.

Cultivation and Propagation: An undemanding and fast-growing plant, forming dense stocks in the course of time because of its profuse runners. The species still thrives in washed sand and a position half in the shade in an aquarium. Temperature fluctuations from 15 °C to 30 °C will do no harm. Propagation from separated slips.

General Information: In scientific literature a distinction is made between three varieties of the species. The submerged leaves of var. *subulata*, the variety most widely used in aquaria, grow to a length of up to 30 cm and a width of 6 cm. In aquaristic literature the larger forms are often denoted as 'forma natans' and the smaller forms as 'forma pusilla'. In specific growth conditions, however, the two forms may merge and become one. The submerged leaves of var. *gracillima* attain a length from 30 cm to 90 cm, they are 3 mm wide, rarely up to 5 mm. In older aquarium literature the name 'forma gracillima' was often used for this plant. In var. *kurtziana* the length of submerged leaves varies, but their width is always between 7 mm and 14 mm. The formerly independent species *S. filiformis* now belongs to *Sagittaria subulata*.

Sagittaria teres S. WATS.

The species was named by S. Watson in 1890. Some botanists consider it to be a variety of *Sagittaria graminea*.

Distribution: South-eastern North America, Cuba.

Characteristics: Rosette plant producing runners. Submerged leaves roundish, with pointed tips, up to 20 cm long, dark-green. Aerial leaves petiolate, with narrow lanceolate laminae. Inflorescence erect. Diameter of flowers up to 1 cm. Petals white. Male flowers with 12-15 stamens. The fruit is not enclosed by the calyx.

Cultivation and Propagation: The species has rarely been cultivated in an aquarium and never for any length of time so no definite experience exists. In its natural environment the species is said to occur in relatively acid waters.

Family Butomaceae

Four genera, fifteen species. Predominantly tropical but also occurring in temperate latitudes. Perennial, rarely annual, herbaceous plants of diverse appearance. Leaves in basal rosettes or arranged like rosettes on floating shoots, linear or divided into petioles and blades. Flowers solitary in leaf axils or in umbellate inflorescences, hermaphroditic, actinomorphic, with a colourful flower envelope. All members of the Butomaceae are marsh and aquatic plants.

Hydrocleis nymphoides with its glowing yellow flowers and floating on the surface of the water can often be admired in the aquatic planthouses of botanical gardens. The species originates in South America. The genus *Hydrocleis* includes ten species. However, it is only the genus *Butomus* which has become interesting to growers of aquatic plants.

Butomus

The genus was defined by Linné in 1753. The name is derived from bus (Gk) = ox and temnein (Gk) = cut. Originally it was the name for a marsh plant with cutting leaf edges which could damage grazing cattle. Towards the end of the 16th century the name was transferred to the present-day genus which contains solely the one species described.

Butomus umbellatus L. (Ill. 135)

Linné gave the plant its scientific name when he defined the genus in 1753.

Distribution: Europe, central parts of western Asia, north Africa. Naturalized and local in some areas of North America.

Characteristics: Rhizome plant with basal, bipartite leaf rosette. Leaves linear, up to approx. 100 cm long and up to 1 cm wide, triangular at the base, dark-green. Inflorescence umbellate, with a long stem, normally overtopping the leaves. Flowers hermaphroditic, actinomorphic. Perianth polysepalous, with three persistent, coronal, pink sepals and three similarly shaped, but longer petals. Stamens: six to nine. Carpels: six to nine, slightly united at the base, hypogynous superior. Syncarpous dehiscent fruit.

Cultivation and Propagation: A hardy species well suited to shallow areas of a pond or its borders as long as the soil is sufficiently damp. A good supply of nutrients is essential for optimal development. Inflorescences appear from June until August and their many single flowers look very pleasant indeed. Propagation by dividion of rhizome. Propagation from seeds is also possible, but raising the young plants is rather a protracted process.

General Information: The species grows in reed belts and still or slowly flowing waters. Should the water level be very high floating leaves might develop.

Family Hydrocharitaceae · Frogbit Family

Fifteen genera, 100 species. Predominantly tropical-subtropical, but also occurring in temperate latitudes. Herbaceous, aquatic plants of very varied appearance, their leaves usually in basal rosettes or arranged in whorls. One or several flowers develop within a spathe: they are rarely hermaphroditic, usually unisexual and dioecious, actinomorphic, generally with a white corolla or an inconspicuous perianth.

The members of the Frogbit family grow rooted at the bottom of the waters, stream beneath the water's surface, or float on it. Just a few grow in a marshy habitat. In many species pollination takes place in an unusual manner and, thus a cultivator of aquatic plants is able to make very interesting observations.

Three genera colonise coastal regions near the sea. Representatives of ten freshwater genera have been cultivated in tanks and on ponds. They are the following species: *Ottelia*, *Vallisneria*, *Blyxa*, *Stratiotes*, *Hydrocharis*, *Limnobium*, *Egeria*, *Elodea*, *Hydrilla*, and *Lagarosiphon*. Two further genera, each containing one species only, have not yet been cultivated but might well be rewarding; one genus is *Maidenia* from Australia and the other *Nechamandra* from east Asia.

Ottelia

Persoon defined the genus in 1805. The previously independent genus *Bootia* was later incorporated with *Ottelia*. The latter's name is said to be derived from 'Ottel-ambel', the term used for plants in the native language of the Malabar Coast.

Distribution: Africa and south-east Asia with main centres of evolution in central Africa and on the south-eastern Asiatic mainland. One species apparently occurs in South America.

Characteristics: Aquatic large rhizome plants with basal leaf rosettes, always living submerged. Branching is scanty. Leaves very variable, with long or short petiole, lanceolate,

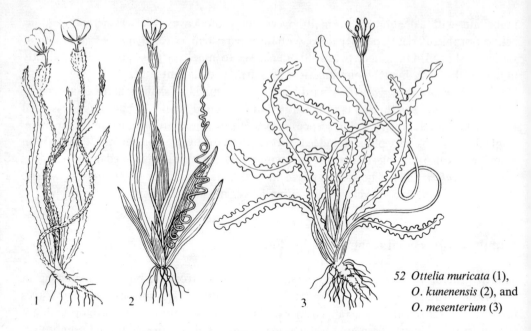

52 *Ottelia muricata* (1),
O. kunenensis (2), and
O. mesenterium (3)

egg or heart-shaped, or narrow lanceolate with toothed, undulated or crisp margins. One or several flowers develop in a green, long-stemmed spathe. They are hermaphroditic or unisexual, in the latter case monoecious or dioecious. Perianth radiated, polysepalous, with a green calyx in three parts and a white or coloured corolla, also in three parts. Hermaphroditic and male flowers with 6-15 stamens. Hermaphroditic and female flowers with three carpels, these united and hypogynous. The fruit is a water berry.

General Information: Because the branching of the rhizome is insignificant a good yield of young plants can only be achieved from seeds. Elongation of the spathe stem sends the flower to the surface so that it projects above the water. Pollination by insects is therefore possible. Self-pollination also occurs. When the fruit ripens it is pulled under the water by the downwards curving spathe.

The genus includes approximately 40 species. Many of them are very attractive plants and some of them should be suitable for aquarium cultivation. To name a few examples: *O. mesenterium* from the island Celebes in south-east Asia; *O. exserta* from south and south-east Africa as well as Madagascar; and *O. kunenensis* from South Africa (Ill. *52*). The African *O. ulvifolius* has been imported from time to time without ever being widely distributed.

Ottelia alismoides (L.) PERS. (Ill. 143)

Linné named the species *Stratiotes alismoides* in 1753; it was moved to the genus *Ottelia* by Persoon in 1805 when he defined the genus.

Distribution: North Africa, south-east Asia, northern Australia. The plant has become established as a weed in southern European rice fields.

Characteristics: Rather large rhizome plant with basal leaf rosette and scanty branching. In very young plants leaves are narrow lanceolate, becoming broad lanceolate later on; in older plants the leaves have a long petiole and egg or heart-shaped laminae, they are up to 50 cm long, pale-green. Leaves often bullate with upturned edges. Single flowers develop within a green, winged spathe, they are hermaphroditic. The three conspicuous petals are white with a yellow base.

Cultivation and Propagation: Light-loving plant which needs light for more than 12 hours. Belief that in our latitudes it is usually impossible to keep the plant alive during the winter goes back to attempts made in botanical gardens in daylight cultivation. Temperature optimum 20-30 °C. An enriched substratum promotes growth. Should be used as a solitary plant as it needs a great deal of space for good development and can therefore be recommended only for very large tanks. The plants should be handled with care as the petioles and leaves are brittle and easily broken.

Propagation is only possible from seeds. The flowers produce seeds through self-pollination, and the seeds set easily. The ripening fruit enlarges very little and does not alter in form. The fruit is ripe after approximately 14 days and—like all water berries—quickly disintegrates. To avoid losing the seeds the fruit should be cut off in good time and stored in a small vessel or tied up in a cloth bag. Germination results are very uncertain regardless of whether the seeds are stored dry or moist. A reliable procedure is not yet available.

Vallisneria

The genus was defined by Linné in 1753. The name was chosen after the Italian botanist Antonio Vallisneri (1661-1730) from Padua.

Distribution: All tropical and subtropical regions, but also in some temperate latitudes.

Characteristics: Rosette plants with runners always living submerged. Leaves long linear with rounded or obtuse tips. Flowers unisexual, dioecious, actinomorphic. Perianth polysepalous, with an inconspicuous green calyx in three parts and a scaly corolla, also in three parts. Numerous male flowers develop within a short-stalked, membranous spathe, with one to two stamens. Single female flowers enclosed by a long-stalked spathe. Carpels: three, united, hypogynous. The fruit is a longish water berry.

General Information: The vallisnerias have adapted their anatomical structure to under-water life to such an extent that they are no longer able to develop land forms. It is solely their sexual reproduction—observable in an aquarium—which still links them to the surface of the water. It is only in some species that both sexes of the plants are being cultivated. The single female flowers develop inside a translucent spathe and on an ascending stem, rise to the surface of the water (Ill. 146) where they float horizontally. Large numbers of male flowers, perhaps 100-250, form in a spathe which is also translucent as well as delicate. But the male

53 Male flower of *Vallisneria spiralis* swimming on the water

inflorescences grow a few centimetres in length only and, thus, stay attached to the base of the plants. The single flower buds gradually detach themselves from the inflorescence and rise to the surface of the water. It may take several days before the spathe has released all the buds. The buds open on the surface of the water by turning back their sepals. The maximum size of these buds is 1 mm so that a fairly strong magnifying glass is needed to observe them (Ill. *53*). Because they are so small they are often overlooked in an aquarium. Swimming freely on the surface of the water the male flowers can reach the anchored female flowers and pollinate them. It is reported in aquaristic literature that after successful pollination the flower stalks coil back in a spiral and pull the ripening fruit below the surface of the water. However, this is not universally so. It has been widely observed that the female flowers remained on the surface and, even when they detached themselves from the stalk, the seeds still ripened. The ripe fruit disintegrates rapidly like all water berries. The seeds germinate freely.

Whereas botanists used to hold the opinion that the genus *Vallisneria* contained only one very variable species—*V. spiralis*—with a worldwide distribution it has now been established that a distinction can be made between approx. 10 species occurring in smaller distribution areas. In addition to the species discussed here *V. asiatica* and *V. denseserrulata* have been described. The habitat of both these species is in Japan; in the latter the runners are said to possess small, spiky hairs. *E. aethiopica* has been observed from Africa. Very likely these species have been cultivated without being recognised as such because of the homogenous habits of the species. Plants of the genus *Vallisneria* are being cared for in our aquaria which vary in some characteristics from the species described below. Thus, there is one variety of *V. spiralis* of a stronger growth with noticeably thicker runners and a second one with narrower, but rather thicker leaves. The genus is in urgent need of revision.

Vallisneria gigantea GRAEBN. (Ill. 144, 145, 146)

The species was named by Graebner in 1913.
   Distribution: South-eastern Asiatic islands.
   Characteristics: Rosette plant with runners. Leaves linear, up to more than 1 m long and 10-20 mm wide, flat, sometimes with slightly swollen margins, mid to dark-green. Five or seven parallel veins present on lamina. Male flowers with one stamen, sometimes cleft in the upper part.

Cultivation and Propagation: As specified for *V. spiralis.* As the species grows to a very large size it is not really suitable for an ordinary tank. The long leaves grow along the surface and take away too much light from the plants further down.

General Information: A. Wendt made an interesting observation. According to him *V. gigantea* has been crossed with *V. spiralis* by gardeners, and the hybrids produced by the two species have found their way into the trade. In his opinion the typical species possesses seven parallel veins and swollen leaf margins, and rarely forms runners, whereas the hybrids show five parallel veins, do not have swollen leaf margins and reproduce intensively from runners (Ill. 144). If this view is correct then the giant vallisnerias at present looked after in our tanks are hybrids. In the original description of the plant, as a matter of fact, seven veins are mentioned.

Vallisneria neotropicalis MARIE–VICT. (Ill. 145)

Marie-Victorin named the species in 1943.

Distribution: North America on the Florida peninsula and Cuba.

Characteristics: Rosette plant with runners. Leaves linear, up to more than 2 m long and 15-30 mm wide, flat, olive-green. Seven reddish to red-brown coloured parallel veins present on lamina. Male flowers with one stamen.

Cultivation and Propagation: In the main as specified for *V. spiralis.* In optimum growth conditions, however, the species grows to be even larger and more robust than the green giant vallisneria and is, therefore, really only suitable for a large display aquarium or for cultivation in a deep pool in a planthouse.

Vallisneria spiralis L. (Ill. 141, 144)

The species was named by Linné in 1753.

Distribution: Southern Europe, local in some areas of central Europe, north Africa, Near East.

Characteristics: Rosette plant with runners. Leaves linear, up to 80 cm long and 4-8 mm wide, normally flat, pale to mid-green. Male flowers with two stamens.

Cultivation and Propagation: This species is one of the most undemanding, most frequently cultivated and oldest aquarium plants. Even washed sand suffices as a substratum. Temperature 15-30 °C. Requires a position in good light. At its most effective in a tall tank. In a low tank the tops of the long leaves bend and lie on the water. The plants are particularly suitable for background decoration, but they are also an adornment in the middle part of the tank grouped with other plants, or in the corners. The species develops a profusion of runners which form a dense turf after some time. Propagation from runners taken off the parent plant. Thus one sex only of the species spreads in the tank.

General Information: In a well-lit position the plants are good oxygenators. Several forms and cultivated strains of *V. spiralis* are to be found under trade names such as 'Vallisneria portugalensis' or 'Vallisneria spiralis Contortionist'. They are plants with tightly twisted spirally leaves. Sometimes the leaves are reddish.

Vallisneria americana MICHX.

The species was named by Michaux in 1803. For a long time aquarium plants of this species went under the name of *Vallisneria spiralis* forma *tortifolia*.

Distribution: Eastern North America, local in some parts of the Greater Antilles.

Characteristics: Rosette plant with runners. Leaves linear, flat to being spirally twisted, up to 40 cm long and 3-8 mm wide, dark-green. Male flowers with one stamen, sometimes cleft in the upper part.

Cultivation and Propagation: As specified for *V. spiralis*.

Vallisneria spec. 'Little'

This species has not yet been clearly identified and has therefore no scientific name so far.

Distribution: Unknown.

Characteristics: Rosette plant with runners. Leaves linear, flat, up to 40 cm long and 1.5—4 mm wide, pale-green.

Cultivation and Propagation: As specified for *V. spiralis*. However, the species is much smaller and is therefore better suited to small and medium-sized tanks.

Blyxa

The genus was defined by Noronha in 1806. The name is said to be derived from blyzein (ancient Gk) = to flow.

Distribution: Tropical and subtropical regions of Africa and Asia, established and local in some parts of North America.

Characteristics: Annual or perennial rosette plants always living submerged, or plants with elongated shoot axes. Leaves linear, usually with a pointed tip, mid or grey-green. Flowers hermaphroditic or unisexual, in the latter case monoecious or dioecious, actinomorphic. Perianth polysepalous, composed of a green calyx in three parts and an inconspicuous corolla also in three parts, or the corolla may be lacking. Up to ten male flowers develop in a membranous spathe, hermaphroditic and female flowers normally single. Hermaphroditic and male flowers with three to nine stamens. Hermaphroditic and female flowers with three carpels, these united, hypogynous. The fruit is a water berry.

General Information: The genus includes approximately ten species; none of them are very well-known. The plants live submerged in still or slowly flowing waters or occur as weeds in rice paddies. Plants of the genus have been imported and cared for in aquaria on a number of occasions. However, they were never widely distributed nor were they ever kept for long enough for reliable experiences to be available. The African *B. radicans* and

B. senegalensis have been described. *B. leiosperma*, *B. novoguinensis*, *B. octandra* and *B. japonica* occur in Asia amongst others. It is particularly *B. auberti* and *B. echinosperma*, both originating from Asia, which have been mentioned in literature for aquarists.

Stratiotes

The genus was defined by Linné in 1753. The name refers to the leaves, shaped like a sword, calling to mind the swords of soldiers. Stratiotes (Gk) = soldier, warrior. The genus contains only the one species described below.

Stratiotes aloides L. (Ill. 136)

The species was named by Linné in 1753 when he defined the genus.

Distribution: Europe, North-West Asia. Local in other areas.

Characteristics: Rosette plant with runners living either floating or submerged. Leaves linear with a long pointed tip, up to 40 cm long and up to 25 mm wide, rarely broader, tough, pale, dark or olive-green. Leaf margins coarsely toothed. Flowers unisexual and dioecious, actinomorphic. Perianth polysepalous, with a green calyx in three parts and a white corolla also in three parts having a diameter of up to 3 cm. Several male flowers develop within a short-stalked, two-leafed spathe, each with 12 stamens. Female flowers singly in the spathe, with three carpels, these hypogynous, united. The fruit is a water berry.

Cultivation and Propagation: A hardy species on ponds during the winter. During the summer the plants float on the water and the upper parts of their leaves project above it. Roots normally free in the water and not anchored. In the autumn the plants sink to the bottom where they stay during the winter. Some plants, however, live in a varied depth of water during the summer. If the pond is drained, the best way of wintering the plants is to place them in vessels filled with water and to store these in a cellar clear of frost. More recently the species has been kept submerged in heated indoor tanks. This method has been employed repeatedly and has proved to be successful. Propagation from runners taken off parent plants.

General Information: In central Europe it is almost impossible for the plants to multiply sexually as large distribution areas are normally colonised by only one sex of the dioecious plants. The female plants are said to be the more abundant. *Stratiotes aloides* is the last remaining species of a genus with a far larger representation in earlier geological periods. To date eight extinct species have been identified from fossil remains.

Hydrocharis

The genus was defined by Linné in 1753. The name means water grace and is derived from hydor (Gk) = water and charis (Gk) = gratitude, joy, grace.

Distribution: Europe, Asia, Africa, Australia.

Characteristics: Rosette plant with runners floating on the water. Floating leaves petiolate, with egg-shaped to roundish laminae. Flowers unisexual and dioecious, actinomorphic. Perianth polysepalous, composed of a green calyx in three parts and a white corolla, also in three parts. One to four male flowers develop in an inconspicuous spathe, each with 9-12 stamens. Female flowers singly in a spathe, three carpels, these united, hypogynous. The fruit is a water berry.

General Information: The genus urgently requires systematic revision. It includes between three and six species. All of them form rosettes of floating leaves. The plants grow in quiet, wind-sheltered places of nutritious still waters, e.g. amongst reeds. They can also exist on boggy soil but their leaves are then closely pressed to the bottom, in contrast to the genus *Limnobium* described as the next genus. So far only one species, referred to below, has been cultivated.

Hydrocharis morsus-ranae L. (Ill. 13)

The species was named by Linné in 1753 when he defined the genus.

Distribution: Europe, central parts of western Asia. Naturalised and local in some areas of North America.

Characteristics: Rosette plant with runners. Floating leaves with a long petiole, their laminae roundish, diameter up to 7 cm, cleft up to the point of insertion of the petiole, with rounded basal lobes, pale-green. Petals white with yellow base.

Cultivation and Propagation: A plant suitable for a well-lit, unheated tank, but better suited to open-air cultivation. In the course of time the plants form a dense cover of floating leaves. If the water level is high the roots hang in the water. If it is low the plants root themselves at the bottom and their growth is then particularly strong. In the autumn egg-shaped winter buds form at the tips of the runners and, when the plants disintegrate, the buds sink to the bottom. The buds can be stored in cold water and young plants will sprout from them in the following spring. Slips develop in profusion, so propagation is no problem.

Limnobium

The genus was defined by L. C. M. Richard in 1814. The name is derived from limne (Gk) = bog, pond, and bios (Gk) = to live.

Distribution: The warmer regions of America.

Characteristics: Rosette plant with runners floating on the surface of the water or rooted at the bottom. Leaves with a petiole varying in length, with more or less rounded laminae, flowers unisexual and dioecious, actinomorphic. Perianth polysepalous, inconspicuous, composed of a calyx in three parts and a corolla, also in three parts. A number of male flowers develop in a membranous spathe, each having 6-12 stamens. Single female flowers enclosed by a spathe, having conspicuously long, white divided stigmata. Carpels: three, united, hypogynous. The fruit is a water berry.

General Information: The genus probably consists of three species: two of them— described below—have been cultivated in botanical gardens for a long time and, occasionally, in aquaria. The plants may float on the surface of the water in which case the leaves lie on it as do those of *Hydrocharis morsus-ranae* and the roots end in the water. Spongy tissue forms on the underside of the leaves. If the water level is very low or if the plants live in a marshy habitat the roots are likely to penetrate the soil and the appearance of the plants alters considerably. The petioles are usually much longer; the leaves are erect and project above the water level.

Limnobium spongia (BOSC) STEUD.

Bosc named the species *Hydrocharis spongia* in 1807. Steudel moved it to the genus *Limnobium* in 1841.

Distribution: South-eastern North America.

Characteristics: Rosette plant with runners. Floating leaves loosely arranged, petiolate, up to 10 cm long, egg to heart-shaped, underside with weakly developed spongy tissue, leaves flat, upperside mid-green with red-brown markings, especially near the margins.

Cultivation and Propagation: Nowadays the species is of little interest for aquarium cultivation as the floating leaves lying on the surface of the water cast too much shade. But in planthouses, aquatic plant nurseries and botanical gardens the shading effect may well be useful during the summer months. In fact, it is quite possible to keep the plants in the open during the summer. In the winter the species tends to be sensitive unless it is given additional, artificial light. The numerous runners which develop make propagation quite easy. If both sexes are present ripe seeds may be produced with the aid of artificial pollination. The seeds should be stored in water.

Limnobium laevigatum (HUMB. et BONPL.) HEINE (Ill. 147)

Humboldt and Bonpland originally mistook the species for a fern and named it *Salvinia laevigata* in 1810. In later literature it was generally referred to as *Limnobium stoloniferum*, but also as *Hydromystria stolonifera* and *Trianea bogotensis*. It was not until 1968 that Heine rediscovered the first description of the plant and the present valid name is based on the first specific epithet.

Distribution: Central America, Greater Antilles, large parts of South America. Naturalised and local on the other continents.

Characteristics: Rosette plant with runners. Floating leaves usually very close to each other, with a short or very short petiole, laminae roundish, heart or egg-shaped, with thick spongy tissue on the underside and, therefore, noticeably arched, mid-green, no markings.

Cultivation and Propagation: The species can be recommended for a planthouse where the floating leaves provide good natural shade. Temperature 20-30 °C. The daily light periods should not be less than 12 hours. Propagation as specified for *L. spongia*.

Egeria

The genus was defined by Planchon in 1849. The name was chosen after a Roman fountain nymph.

Distribution: South America, east of the Paraná and Paraguay.

Characteristics: Permanently submerged plants with elongated shoot axes and a habit similar to that of water weeds. Leaves arranged in whorls, at the base of shoots also opposite. Flowers develop inside a translucent spathe, unisexual and dioecious, actinomorphic. Perianth polysepalous, with a green calyx in three parts and a corolla also in three parts, the latter being conspicuously white in contrast to all other genera resembling water weeds. Male flowers with nine stamens. Female flowers with three carpels, united and hypogynous. The fruit is a water berry.

General Information: Vegetative propagation in the genus is very marked as it is in other plants with unisexual, dioeciously arranged flowers. In *Egeria* as well as in the genera *Elodea*, *Hydrilla* and *Lagarosiphon* vegetative reproduction is brought about by profuse branching and brittle, easily fragmented shoots. Every shoot section, provided it is not too small and irrespective or whether it is rooted at the bottom or streaming in the water, is capable of continued growth. The brittleness of the shoots causes dispersal of the plants to areas outside their natural habitat. The broken off shoots are carried away, and the plants establish themselves in a new environment. Masses of the plants may develop in rather dirty waters as they contain nutritive substances, and thus the plants may harm the fishing industry and shipping.

Sexual propagation of *Egeria* is probably rare, even in nature, because male and female plants do not always occur together in the immediate vicinity. Flowers form on shoot sections near the surface of the water. Two to four male flowers develop in one spathe and, one after another, they project above the water. Female flowers are always single; tubular development and stretching of a part of the floral axis lifts the calyx and corolla above the water. The pistil passes through this tube. In contrast to all other related genera the pollen is transferred to the flowers by insects, attracted by the optical effect of the white corolla.

In recent times also the second species of the genus, the smaller *E. najas*, has come to Europe and is spreading in aquarist circles.

Egeria densa PLANCH. (Ill. 148)

The species was named by Planchon in 1849 when he defined the genus. Later on the species was classed with *Elodea* for a long time.

Distribution: In South America in areas matching the characteristics of the genus. Naturalised and local in some parts of Central and North America, Europe and Australia.

Characteristics: Plants with the habit of water weeds and commonly called Argentinian water weed; the largest member in this group of plants. Leaves at the base of shoots, in whorls of three, later in whorls of three to five, sessile, linear, rounded or pointed tips, usually bent backwards and occasionally slightly twisted, 2-3 cm, rarely up to 4 cm long, up to 4 mm wide, pale to mid-green.

Cultivation and Propagation: An undemanding, but light-loving species. Temperature 15-25°C, but a temporarily higher or lower one will do no harm. It thrives out in the open during the summer months when its growth is particularly strong. Usable in an aquarium grouped with other plants in the background, or at the sides. As the shoots grow rapidly up to the surface they have to be cut back fairly often. Or, better still, the old shoot sections should be removed and the tips planted instead. The plant also grows well when floating on the surface of the water. Here too, older and untidy looking shoot sections have to be removed. With its intensively branching, floating shoots *E. densa* forms dense clusters which makes it a useful plant for spawning tanks of viviparous cyprinoids. Propagation from cut off lateral shoots or division of shoots. In either case dormant buds are stimulated to produce new shoots.

General Information: In strong light the plant produces oxygen which may be seen as small blisters. *E. densa* is used in scientific laboratories and also in guide lines on physiological and biochemical experiments.

Elodea

The genus was defined by L. C. M. Richard in 1803. *Anarchis*, *Serpicula* and *Helodea* are further generic names for it. The name is derived from helos (Gk) = marsh, bog.

Distribution: North and South America, but not in Central America.

Characteristics: Permanently submerged plants, rooted at the bottom or floating in the water, with elongated, much-branched shoot axes. Leaves arranged in whorls, also opposite or alternate at the base of shoots. Flowers usually solitary enclosed by an axillary, bipartite, translucent spathe, rarely hermaphroditic, generally unisexual and dioecious, actinomorphic. Perianth polysepalous, composed of a green or brownish calyx in three parts and a corolla in three parts having petals reduced to colourless, small scales. Hermaphroditic and male flowers with three to nine stamens. Hermaphroditic and female flowers with three carpels, united, hypogynous. The fruit is a water berry.

General Information: Twenty *Elodea* species are known at present; many of them should be suitable for aquarium cultivation. It is quite possible that in addition to the species described here in some detail others have been cultivated without being recognized as *Elodea* plants. Presumably this happened to *E. ernstae*, well distributed to the south of the Rio de la Plata. The most common species in South America is *E. granatensis*; it is known to occur from the north coast to the Amazon and, in the east of the continent, as far as the Rio de la Plata. *E. callitrichoides* may be seen on either side of the Rio de la Plata, *E. matthewsii* in the Andes, north of the equator, and *E. potamogeton* along the west coast, south of the equator. In western North America *E. longivaginata* is well known. The different species are easily distinguishable because of variations in the shape of their leaves.

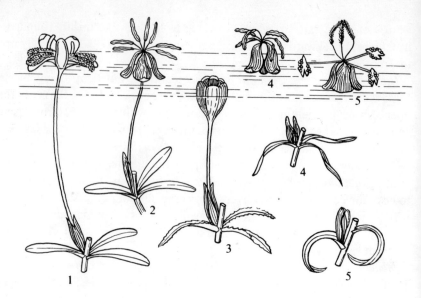

54 Flower biology of some members of the frogbit family

1 Female flower of *Elodea canadensis*. 2 Male flower of *Elodea canadensis*. 3 Female flower of *Hydrilla verticillata*. 4 Male flower of *Elodea nuttallii*. 5 Male flower of *Lagarosiphon major*

All flowers develop in translucent, axillary spathes. In hermaphroditic and female flowers a tubular section of the floral axis stretches up to the point where the perianth reaches the surface of the water when it opens out. The male flowers rise to the surface on elongating petioles. *E. nuttallii* is the only species which does not conform with this pattern of behaviour. The ripe male flower buds detach themselves from the spathe and rise to the surface by means of a gas-filled blister. On the surface of the water the buds open by turning back the sepals of the calyx. Floating on the water gets them in contact with the female flowers. However, the pollen is usually shed before and also floats on the water (Ill. *54*).

Elodea canadensis RICH. (Ill. 54)

The species was named by L. C. M. Richard in 1803.
   Distribution: North America. Naturalised in Europe, Asia and Australia.
   Characteristics: Plants with the habit of water weeds. Leaves in whorls of three to five, sessile, linear, tips obtuse, up to 1 cm long and up to 3 mm wide, slightly curved downwards, mid to dark-green.
   Cultivation and Propagation: An undemanding, hardy plant which should be used in cold-water tanks or on ponds. In a heated aquarium the plant becomes weak and unsightly after some time. Internodes become long and thin and leaves stay very small. Propagation as specified for *Egeria densa*.

140 *Sagittaria weatherbiana*
141 *Vallisneria spiralis*, form with twisted leaves
142 *Sagittaria subulata* var. *subulata*

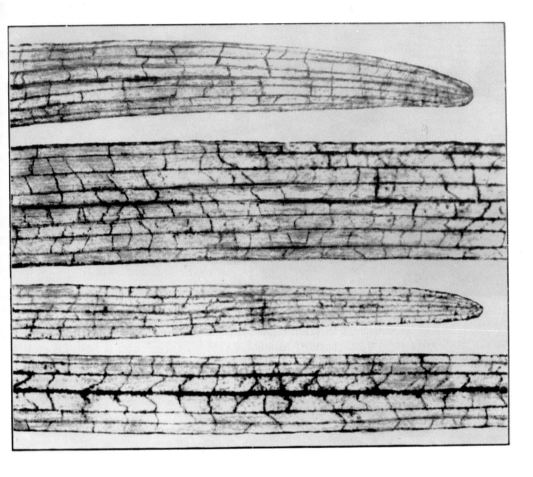

143 *Ottelia alismoides*
144 Top: *Vallisneria gigantea* and below: its hybrid with *V. spiralis* (after Wendt)
145 Top: *Vallisneria neotropicalis*, below: *V. gigantea*

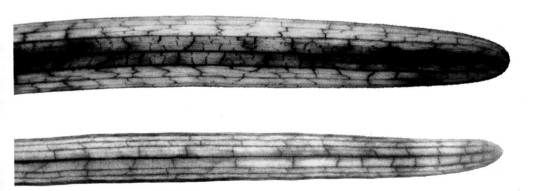

146 *Vallisneria gigantea*, left: female plant with young flower;
right: male plant with young (below) and older (above) inflorescence
147 *Limnobium laevigatum*

148 *Egeria densa*
149 *Hydrilla verticillata*
150 *Lagarosiphon madagascariensis*
151 *Lagarosiphon major*

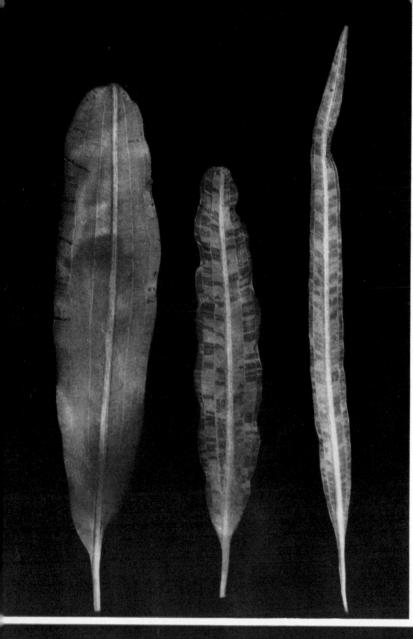

157 *Aponogeton undulatus*, various forms

158 *Aponogeton*, fruiting condition

General Information: In Europe the species was observed for the first time in 1836. Spreading from Ireland to England it soon colonised the European mainland. Only female plants occur in Europe. The species lives predominantly in standing waters. The plants are good oxygenators. If their development on fishponds becomes too widespread it has to be restricted.

Elodea nuttallii (PLANCH.) ŞT. JOHN (Ill. *54*, 152)

Planchon named the species *Anacharis nuttallii* in 1848. St. John moved it to the genus *Elodea* in 1920. A further name for the species is *E. occidentalis*.

Distribution: Eastern North America. Naturalised in some parts of Europe.

Characteristics: Plants with the habit of water weeds. Leaves in whorsl of three to five, sessile, linear, pointed tips, slightly reflexed, up to 1 cm long and up to 3 mm wide, mid to dark-green. Male flowers self detaching.

Cultivation and Propagation: The species is a cold-water plant, but it can stand slightly higher temperatures better than *E. canadensis*. Propagation as specified for *Egeria densa*.

Hydrilla

L. C. M. Richard defined the genus in 1814. Its sole species is the one described below. The name is derived from hydor (Gk) = water and illein (Gk) = to turn.

Hydrilla verticillata (L. fil.) ROYLE (Ill. *54*, 149)

Linné's son named the species *Serpicula verticillata* in 1781. When *Hydrilla* was defined the species was moved to that genus and denoted *H. ovalifolia*. In 1839 Royle went back to the use of the first specific epithet.

Distribution: In warmer areas of Europe, Africa, Asia and Australia, but also in northern Europe. Naturalised and local in North America.

Characteristics: Plants with the habit of water weeds living permanently submerged. Leaves in whorls of three to eight, sessile, linear, rounded or acute tips, straight or slightly curved backwards, with finely toothed margins, maximal up to 2.5 cm long and up to 3 mm wide, mid to dark-green, sometimes red-violet. Flowers develop singly inside a translucent, axillary spathe, unisexual, monoecious or dioecious, actinomorphic. Perianth polysepalous, inconspicuous, with a whitish calyx in three parts and a corolla in the same number of parts, but cup-shaped in female flowers. Male flowers with three stamens detach themselves from the spathe. Female flowers with three carpels, united, hypogynous. The fruit is a water berry.

Cultivation and Propagation: An undemanding, hardy species suitable for ponds, but also a useful and versatile plant in an indoor aquarium as long as this is not too warm. If the temperature is allowed to rise too high the internodes grow too long and the plants look weedy. Some of the plants kept out in the open are said to develop winter buds, whereas those kept in a tank retain their foliage through the winter. The species can be used in group displays or it can be allowed to float. Propagation as specified for *Egeria densa*.

General Information: Some botanists long thought that the plants of northern Europe were an independent species, referred to as *Hydrilla lithuanica*.

The species colonises still and slowly flowing waters and also occurs as a weed in rice fields. Mass development in nutritious waters has to be controlled. In tropical and subtropical plants flowers are said to appear in daily light periods of more than 11 hours. It is believed that the northern plants are indeterminate, i.e. the initiation of their flowers does not depend on the daily periods of light.

Lagarosiphon

Harvey defined the genus in 1841. The name is derived from lagaros (Gk) = limp, slight, thin and siphon (Gk) = tube. It refers to the long, thin tube formed by the floral axis in female flowers.

Distribution: Central and southern parts of Africa, Madagascar.

Characteristics: Permanently submerged plants with elongated shoot axes; the habit is that of water weeds. In contrast to all other genera in this group, the leaves are sparsifolius or in approximate whorls, rarely in real whorls. Flowers develop inside a translucent spathe, they are unisexual and dioecious, actinomorphic. Perianth polysepalous, composed of an inconspicuous, green calyx in three parts and a corolla in three parts with scale-like petals. Large numbers of male flowers develop inside a spathe—there may be as many as 50—and later detach themselves, each male flower has three fertile and three sterile stamens. One to three female flowers develop inside a spathe, each with three carpels, united, hypogynous. The fruit is a water berry.

General Information: The genus contains approximately 15 species, only two of which are at home on Madagascar. Most of the species should be usable in an aquarium, but few—if any—have been cultivated. Species rather well-known to scientists are those from southern Africa, such as *L. major*, *L. muscoides*, *L. verticillifolius*, *L. illicifolius* and *L. crispus*. They are quite easily identified from the form of their leaf margins although a magnifying glass is needed. The male flowers, floating on the surface of the water and approximately 1-3 mm in size, look very bizarre indeed. The fertile stamens are positioned in a line horizontal with the water whereas the sterile ones stand upright. The colour of the stamens is often red-violet and in shape they resemble small sails (Ill. *54*, 5).

Lagarosiphon major (RIDL.) MOSS (Ill. *54*, 151)

Ridley named the species *Lagarosiphon muscoides* var. *major* in 1886. Moss gave it the status of an independent species in 1928. A name found for the species in earlier aquarium literature is 'Elodea crispa'.

Distribution: In large parts of South Africa. Naturalised and local in Europe and New Zealand.

Characteristics: Plants with the habit of water weeds. Leaf arrangement irregular to whorled; leaves sessile, linear, pointed, strongly recurved, up to 3 cm long and up to 3 mm wide, dark-green.

Cultivation and Propagation: The plant develops most beautifully if it is kept out in the open during the summer months. Furthermore, it is suitable for an unheated indoor tank placed in very good light. In temperatures above 20 °C the internodes become over-long and the leaves stay too small. Best use is for group display, but the plant can also be kept floating. Propagation as specified for *Egeria densa.*

Lagarosiphon madagascariensis Casp. (Ill. 150)

The species was named by Caspary.

Characteristics: Plants with the habit of water weeds. Leaves irregular, alternate to whorled, sessile, linear, pointed, standing away from the stem in an almost straight line, up to 2 cm long and up to 1.2 mm wide, pale-green.

Cultivation and Propagation: Needs temperatures above 20 °C and a great deal of light. It is most effective in a group display in the middle part of the aquarium. If pruned repeatedly dense stocks will develop. Floating plants form dense clusters and are useful for spawning tanks containing viviparous cyprinoids. Propagation as specified for *Egeria densa.*

Lagarosiphon spec. 'Little'

It has not yet been possible to classify this species. In specialised literature it has sometimes been labelled as 'Elodea minor'.

Distribution: Central parts of Africa.

Characteristics: Plants with the habit of water weeds. Leaves irregular, alternate to whorled, sessile, linear, blunted tips, slightly or strongly recurved, up to 0.8 cm long and up to 1 mm wide, mid-green.

Cultivation and Propagation: Optimum temperature 18-25 °C, otherwise undemanding and to be cared for like *L. madagascariensis.* Propagation as specified for *Egeria densa.*

Family Aponogetonaceae · Aponogeton Family

The genus *Aponogeton* is the only one belonging to the family.

Aponogeton

The name was introduced by Linné's son in 1781. So far its origin has not been explained satisfactorily. Quite possibly it is a mutation of the generic name *Potamogeton.*

Distribution: Africa, Madagascar, south-east Asia, north and east Australia.

Characteristics: With few exceptions rhizome and tuberous plants with basal leaf rosettes. Commonly called lace plants. Leaves either submerged or floating with variously shaped laminae, rush-like aerial leaves are rare. Inflorescence in one to several spikes, initially enclosed by a protecting spathe. Flowers as a rule hermaphroditic, rarely unisexual and dioecious, mirror-symmetrical. Perianth polysepalous, simple, with one to three petal-like leaves, coloured white, violet or yellow. Stamens: six, rarely more. Carpels: three, rarely more, free, hypogynous superior. The fruit is a water berry.

General Information: The few marsh plants of the genus colonise flooded areas or wet meadows. The majority of the species live in rivers, permanently or periodically conducting water, and in lakes from the lowlands to the mountains. The fact that the plants develop tubers as well as rhizomes, sometimes transitional forms of both, indicates their ability to pass through resting periods. Exact observations and experiments, however, are still lacking. Probably the resting periods are not caused by the plants' physiology but are forced on them by their environment, e.g. if waters dry out in periods of drought or if the water temperature falls below a certain level. In the latter event, some species probably shed all their leaves whereas others retain their foliage but do not add new growth. In cultivated species new growth is particularly strong after resting periods, a phenomenon well-known from tropical water lilies.

Specimens collected in the wild partly possess branched rhizomes and tubers, but in conditions of cultivation lateral shoots which can be taken off and used are rarely produced. Rhizome division for propagation is hardly ever successful. Propagation in this genus is therefore principally by seeds. Here, *A. undulatus* forms an exception as it produces adventitious plantlets. If *Aponogeton* is provided with really favourable conditions it will develop inflorescences continually during its phases of growth, even in an aquarium. The inflorescences grow up to the water's surface on long stalks. Initially the inflorescence is enclosed by a greenish spathe; normally this falls off later on.

In African and Madagascan species the inflorescences are made up of two or more spikes, while Asiatic and Australian species have just one. The spikes open their blossoms from the bottom to the top in the course of several days. The flowers are sessile, their perianth is very reduced. As a rule, this comprises two, rarely one or three coronal leaves. The floral axis and all flower parts are initially white or coloured; they gradually turn green as the flowers fade (Ill. 155).

As soon as the first flowers have opened they should be pollinated artificially, at least once a day, preferably more often. For this purpose the open flowers have to be stroked with a soft brush or the gentle use of fingers. Alternatively, two neighbouring inflorescences can be rubbed against each other. In all species at present in cultivation, with the exception of *A. ulvaceus*, self-pollination is quite feasible. But where cross-pollination is possible, it should be given preference. Success of pollination is very varied, but the reasons for success or failure are not fully understood. A plant which has set seed easily at the first attempt may fail to do so at the second.

Producing fruit and setting seed is often confined to certain sections of the spikes, usually the lower ones. In the process the carpels become noticeably swollen. In most of the cultivated species, even when several ovules can be seen to form, every carpel will produce one seed only. Dependent on the species, the seeds have a simple seed-coat and a well-developed bud of the shoot, or they have a double perisperm combined with an undeveloped bud of the shoot (Ill. 158).

Great care has to be taken of the seeds. As in all water berries the fruitlets and floral axes quickly disintegrate. Thus the seeds are freed and swim on the surface of the water. But just a few hours later the seed coats burst, the embryos emerge and sink to the bottom. The *Aponogeton* seeds begin germinating as soon as they fall and can, therefore, not be stored. The most conspicuous part of the seedling in many species is the usually thickened cotyledon in which the nutrients for the initial period of development are stored. If the seedlings are allowed to float for a time, most species will undergo further development. The foliage leaves enlarge rapidly and adventitious roots form. When the plants are approximately 2 cm in size they should be planted.

The genus includes approximately 40 species. At present fourteen species are known to occur in Africa, ten in Madagascar, eleven in south-east Asia, and four on the Australian continent. The African species are largely plants with floating leaves. Aquarists might well find *A. vallisnerioides* rewarding. The plant originates in central Africa and has linear floating leaves, up to 10 cm long and up to 8 mm wide. Madagascar is the homeland of *A. capuroni*, with its very crimped leaf margins; and *A. longiplumulosus*, which has been cultivated occasionally.

Both species would enrich the vegetation in an aquarium. Among the Australian members of the genus *A. bullosus* with its bullate leaves is particularly ornamental. The species is rare in its natural environment where its stocks are threatened by collectors. In Europe the plant has never been cultivated.

In aquarium cultivation the genus can be divided into four groups. The first group is made up of species which never develop floating leaves and are therefore ideal for cultivation in a tank. Some of them, however, are difficult to cultivate, e.g. the lace plants with foliage resembling the skeletons of leaves. The species in which submerged leaves alternate regularly or irregularly with floating leaves may be regarded as the second group. These species can also be cultivated by an aquarist. The third group is unsuited to tanks but looks very decorative in a planthouse. This group includes species which either never produce submerged leaves or only as very young plants; floating leaves are their characteristic foliage. The fourth group is totally unsuitable. It contains the few marsh plants of the genus having rush-like leaves.

Aponogeton ulvaceus BAK.

The species was named by Baker in 1881.
Distribution: Central and northern Madagascar.

Characteristics: Permanently submerged, tuberous plant with basal leaf rosette. Submerged leaves petiolate and up to 50 cm long, their laminae longish elliptical, rounded at the tips, up to 30 cm long and up to 8 cm wide, with wavy edges, very thin and slightly translucent, pale-green, but reddish in very strong light. In addition to the midrib three to five pairs of parallel veins. Floating leaves lacking. Inflorescence with two spikes, yellow, with densely arranged florets. Sepals: two.

Cultivation and Propagation: Because of its size this very beautiful species can only be recommended for a large tank where it should be used as a solitary display plant. It needs a bright to slightly shady position and temperatures of 18-25 °C. Unwashed sand provides an adequate substratum. Propagation is rather difficult. Two plants flowering at the same time are needed for successful pollination because seeds are not produced from self-pollination. Seedlings are rather small but thrive satisfactorily.

General Information: In its natural environment the species grows in still and slowly flowing waters, but also in rapidly flowing brooks as well as in waters with lime content, in sunny and in shady positions.

Aponogeton boivinianus BAILL. (Ill. 137, 139)

The species was named by Baillon in 1916.

Distribution: Northern Madagascar.

Characteristics: Permanently submerged, tuberous plant with basal leaf rosette. Submerged leaves with petiole up to 45 cm long, their laminae broad-linear, rounded at the tips, up to 30 cm long and up to 5 cm wide, bullate, dark-green. In addition to the midrib three or four pairs of parallel veins. Floating leaves lacking. Inflorescence in two, rarely three spikes, white, usually with densely arranged florets. Sepals: two.

Cultivation and Propagation: A solitary display plant intended for large tanks and not easy to keep. The substratum should contain a reasonable amount of nutrients and the temperature should be above 20 °C. The imported tubers offered for sale initially thrive and produce inflorescences. But, after some time, the plants decline markedly and often die off. Usually the reserve nutrients of the tubers are used up and new tubers have not developed. The reasons for this failure are unknown. Raising of seedlings has rarely been successful so far.

General Information: In its natural environment the species grows in slowly and fast flowing rivers, but also in river rapids, in sunny as well as in shady positions.

Aponogeton longiplumulosus VAN BRUGGEN

The species was named by van Bruggen in 1968.

Distribution: North-west Madagascar.

Characteristics: Permanently submerged, tuberous plant with basal leaf rosette. Submerged leaves petiolate, up to 45 cm long, their laminae lanceolate, tips pointed or rounded, up to 35 cm long and up to 1.5 cm wide, flattened or wavy, pale-green. In addition to the midrib one to three pairs of parallel veins. Floating leaves lacking. Inflorescence in two to three spikes, pale-violet, arranged with dense florets. Sepals: two.

Cultivation and Propagation: A solitary specimen plant for a large tank, easy to care for and to propagate.

Aponogeton madagascariensis (MIRB.) VAN BRUGGEN (Ill. 55, 156)

Mirbel named the species *Uvirandra madagascariensis* in 1802/3. In 1805 Persoon described the species a second time and named it *Hydrogeton fenestralis*. The term used for the species for many years, *Aponogeton fenestralis*, was based on the second specific epithet. In 1968 van Bruggen drew attention to the first description, but as the species had been moved to the genus *Aponogeton* this generic name was retained.

Distribution: Madagascar.

Characteristics: Permanently submerged, tuberous plant with basal leaf rosette. Submerged leaves petiolate, up to 50 cm long, their laminae longish elliptical, sometimes with slightly crenate tips, up to 25 cm long and up to 8 cm wide, lamina surface delicate and evenly cancellate, holes angular, colour mid-green, olive or brown-green. In addition to the midrib five to ten pairs of parallel veins. Floating leaves lacking. Inflorescence in two spikes, white. Sepals: two.

Cultivation and Propagation: A really reliable cultivation method has not yet been found for this species and its kindred, neither in an aquarium nor even in nurseries for aquatic

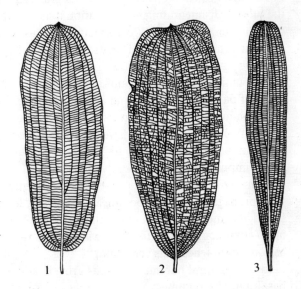

55 Laminae of *Aponogeton madagascariensis* (1), *A. henkelianus* (2), and *A. guillotii* (3)

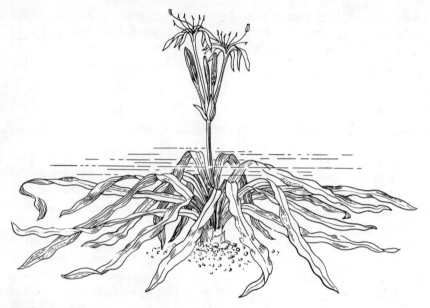

56 Crinum purpurascens of aquarium literature

plants. Over the years many tubers have been imported and the plants have subsequently died. Initially the plants show strong growth and usually produce inflorescences but, after some time, growth stops and the plants gradually die. Generally, it can then be seen that the tuber is disintegrating, an indication that its nutrients have been used up without a new tuber having developed. Why this happens is as yet unknown. When the plants flower they produce a good quantity of seeds. However, the young seedlings also die within a few weeks.

In botanical gardens the plants often last longer. There they are usually planted in barrels made of oak or larch wood and kept fairly dark. Moreover, the barrels are often covered by a lath grid. The temperature fluctuates between 15 °C and 25 °C and the water used is very soft. Part of the water is regularly replaced by fresh water. Aeration causing some water movement is thought to have a favourable effect. The substrate seems to be of minor importance.

General Information : In the first half of this century *A. madagascariensis* has been success-fully propagated in some botanical gardens, at least over a number of years, e.g. in Kew, Leningrad and Rostock. A particularly robust form was raised in Rostock; its laminae were up to 40 cm long and up to 15 cm wide. It was referred to as 'Rostocker Form', but also as 'Aponogeton fenestralis var. major'.

In their natural habitat the plants grow in still waters or rivers which never dry out, on basalt but also on limestone, sometimes in a sunny position, but also often in the shade of wooded areas. In the mountains they occur up to a height of 1,800 m.

More recent scientific literature groups all Madagascan species having cancellate or partly cancellate laminae under *A. madagascariensis* as, apparently, there is much crossing between them. In particular this applies to the two species described below, *A. henkelianus* and *A. guillotii*. However, we believe that a greater degree of independent classification is justified. The position held by 'A. bernerianus' mentioned in aquarium literature does not seem to be at all clear; the plant is not related to the true *A. bernerianus* (Ill. 56).

Aponogeton henkelianus BAUM (Ill. 55)

The species was named by Baum in 1906. Aquaristic literature often denotes it as *A. fenestralis* var. *henkelianus*.

Distribution: Madagascar.

Characteristics: Permanently submerged, tuberous plant with basal leaf rosette. Submerged leaves petiolate and up to 50 cm long, their laminae longish elliptical, usually with noticeably crenate tips, up to 25 cm long and up to 8 cm wide, surface of laminae delicate and unevenly cancellate. Holes varied in shape and size, mid-green to olive-green. In addition to the midrib five to ten pairs of parallel veins. Floating leaves lacking. Inflorescence in twin spikes, white. Sepals: two.

Cultivation and Propagation: As specified for *A. madagascariensis*.

General Information: The species is closely related to *A. madagascarienis*. To date it has rarely been cultivated.

Aponogeton guillotii HOCHR. (Ill. 55, 153)

The species was named by Hochreutiner in 1907. It has also been referred to as *A. fenestralis* var. *guillotii*.

Distribution: Madagascar.

Characteristics: Permanently submerged, tuberous plant with basal leaf rosette. Submerged leaves petiolate, up to 30 cm in length, their laminae broad lanceolate to very elongated obovate, always with rounded tips, up to 25 cm long and up to 4 cm wide, lamina surface tough and evenly cancellate. Holes rounded, sometimes partially missing, dark-green. In addition to the midrib up to five pairs of parallel veins. Floating leaves lacking. Inflorescence in four or five spikes, white. Sepals: two to three.

Cultivation and Propagation: As specified for *A. madagascariensis:* however, the plants are rather more robust and hardy.

General Information: This species is not as closely related to *A. madagascariensis* as to *A. henkelianus*. Compare also with observations under *A. madagascariensis*.

Aponogeton appendiculatus VAN BRUGGEN

The species was named by van Bruggen in 1968.

Distribution: South-west of Peninsular India.

Characteristics: Permanently submerged, tuberous plant with basal leaf rosette. Submerged leaves petiolate, up to 50 cm long, their laminae lanceolate, tips pointed or obtuse, up to 40 cm long and up to 3 cm wide, flat or slightly wavy, pale-green. In addition to the midrib two to four pairs of parallel veins. Floating leaves lacking. Inflorescence in one spike, white. Sepals: two. Plant embryo with a tuft of scale-like leaves.

Cultivation and Propagation: As specified under *A. crispus.*

General Information: In their natural habitat the plants are reported to occur frequently in slightly saline waters. This species has rarely been cultivated, as yet.

Aponogeton rigidifolius VAN BRUGGEN

The species was named by van Bruggen in 1962.

Distribution: Sri Lanka.

Characteristics: Permanently submerged rhizome plant with basal leaf rosette. Submerged petiolate leaves up to 60 cm in length, their laminae broad linear, obtuse, up to 50 cm long and up to 3 cm wide, flat to wavy, dark-green to olive-green. In addition to the midrib three to four pairs of parallel veins. Floating leaves lacking. Inflorescences in one spike. Sepals: two, rarely three.

Cultivation and Propagation: An undemanding, well-growing species which is used as a solitary specimen plant like *A. crispus* and also cultivated like it. With their stiff, narrow and dark leaves these plants provide quite a contrast to most normally cultivated species. Propagation by seeds as specified for the genus, but this species does not flower as frequently.

Aponogeton undulatus ROXB. (Ill. 157, 159)

The species was named by Roxburgh in 1814.

Distribution: South-east Asia, in the lowland of the Ganges and in western areas of Indochina.

Characteristics: Permanently submerged tuberous plant with basal leaf rosette. Submerged leaves petiolate, up to 30 cm in length, their laminae very variable, narrow lanceolate to elliptical, usually with truncated tips, up to 25 cm long and 4.5 cm wide, flat to wavy, lamina surface mid-green to dark-green with transparent looking panels. In addition to the midrib two to four pairs of parallel veins. Floating leaves occur rarely. Inflorescence in one spike, white. Sepals: two, rarely one or three. Inflorescences partly produce plantlets, almost exclusively so in conditions of cultivation.

Cultivation and Propagation: A very lovely plant easy to look after. It tolerates a sunny as well as a shady position and makes no particular demands on the substratum. The temperature should be at least 20 °C, but if it falls temporarily this will do no harm. The adventitious plantlets make propagation an easy task. Strong plants at first appear to develop inflorescences. But, after the spathe has fallen off a plantlet will have developed instead of a flower spike. The plantlet has a small tuber and leaves and soon forms roots. Branching may well produce more plantlets arranged in tiers. These can be taken off and planted as soon as they are strong enough.

General Information: At present, all members of the genus which predominantly produce plantlets in cultivation are grouped together under the name *Aponogeton undulatus.* However, three forms are easily distinguishable and of these the last one almost certainly represents an independent species. A very narrow-leafed form was named *A. stachyosporus* by De Wit in 1958. Its blades are narrow lanceolate, usually pointed, up to 1 cm wide, rarely more. The lamina surface is irregular but completely covered by transparent panels. This form is said to originate from the peninsula Malacca. The second form is the one most widely distributed in aquarium plant cultivation; its laminae are narrow lanceolate to lanceolate, attaining a width of up to 2.5 cm. Here too the whole of the lamina surface is covered with transparent panels. The laminae of the third form are brighter and broad lanceolate to narrow elliptical with rounded tips. Transparent panels are restricted to edges near the tips. The petioles of many of its leaves have a characteristic curvature.

The *Aponogeton undulatus* of earlier aquarium literature belongs to the *Aponogeton crispus* group.

Aponogeton crispus THUNB. (Ill. 138, 154, 161)

The species was named by Thunberg in 1781.

Distribution: South-east Asia.

Characteristics: Permanently submerged rosette plant with basal leaf rosette. Submerged leaves petiolate, up to 40 cm in length but often shorter, their laminae very variable, lanceolate, broad lanceolate or elliptical to longish elliptical, pointed or rounded, up to 30 cm long and up to 4 cm wide, but often smaller, with flat, wavy or crimped edges, pale-green, dark-green or reddish. In addition to the midrib three to four pairs of parallel veins. Floating leaves very rare, almost non-existent in cultivated plants. Inflorescence in one spike, white. Sepals: two.

Cultivation and Propagation: An undemanding species which requires a temperature of 20-25 °C for optimum development. Adding some loam to the substratum promotes growth. Some plants show quite clearly their need for a resting period when they stop growing and often shed their leaves. Usually renewed growth begins after some time. If this does not occur, it is recommended to take the tubers out of the tank and store them in cooler water. When they are re-planted after a resting period of a few weeks they will grow vigorously. The species is best used as a solitary specimen plant in the middle of an aquarium. Smaller specimens can be planted in groups. Propagation from seeds as specified for the genus. The seedlings develop well.

General Information: Van Bruggen who has revised the genus *Aponogeton* very comprehensively limits the species *A. crispus* very closely by attributing to it only the plants endemic to Sri Lanka. But, even given these limitations, he points out a certain variability, particularly in respect of structure and shape of leaf blades. He also emphasizes the close relationship between *A. crispus* and *A. echinatus* (the species described below). He makes an interesting statement, namely that all herbarium records he has examined can be clearly adjoined to the one or the other species, but with the inclusion of the aquarium plants transition forms occur and distinctions are obliterated.

Collection and import of Asiatic plants over the last few years has established that members of the genus resembling *A. crispus* exist in a large variety of forms, particularly on the south-east Asiatic mainland. They vary noticeably in size, form of leaf blade, shape and structure of leaf margins, and colouration. There may be some hybrids among them because in some of them a relationship with *A. echinatus* is apparent. Absolutely definite differences in the region of inflorescences and flowers in these forms have not yet been found. Thus the problems of systematic nomenclature of many of our *Aponogeton* plants are quite evident. We therefore intend to use the name *A. crispus* rather widely and, until there is more up-to-date information on the genus, we shall refer to an *Aponogeton crispus* group in aquarium plants. This group includes the *Aponogeton undulatus* of earlier aquarium literature.

Aponogeton echinatus ROXB.

The species was named by Roxburgh in 1832.

Distribution: Peninsular India.

Characteristics: Permanently submerged tuberous plant with basal leaf rosette. Submerged leaves petiolate, up to 40 cm in length, their laminae longish elliptical, wavy, up to 30 cm long and up to 6 cm wide, delicate, pale-green, resembling *A. ulvaceus*. In addition to the midrib up to four pairs of parallel veins. Laminae of floating leaves elliptical to longish elliptical, tips obtuse, up to 20 cm long and up to 5 cm wide, pale to mid-green. Inflorescence in one spike, white. Sepals: two. Small fruit with irregular thorny appendages.

Cultivation and Propagation: An undemanding plant which grows well; a solitary show plant needing a temperature above 20 °C and a position in good light. A substratum with good nutrients promotes growth. The occasional occurence of floating leaves may be a nuisance, but they are always replaced by submerged leaves after some time. Propagation from seeds as specified for the genus.

General Information: See under *A. crispus* regarding relationship with that species.

Aponogeton elongatus F. v. MUELL.

The species was named by Ferdinand von Müller in 1878.

Distribution: Northern and eastern Australia.

Characteristics: Permanently submerged tuberous plant with basal leaf rosette. Submerged leaves petiolate, up to 50 cm in length, their laminae very variable, lanceolate to elliptical, up to 35 cm long and up to 5 cm wide, flat to wavy, pale-green to brownish. In addition to the midrib two to four pairs of parallel veins. Laminae of floating leaves elliptical, up to 15 cm long and up to 4 cm wide. Inflorescence in one spike, yellowy. Sepals: two.

Cultivation and Propagation: A species rarely cultivated as yet; reliable information on cultivation methods are therefore unobtainable.

General Information: Four varieties of *E. elongatus* have been described.

Aponogeton natans (L) ENGL. et KRAUSE

Linné named the species *Saururus natans* in 1771. Engler and Krause moved it to the genus *Aponogeton* in 1906.

Distribution: South and east of Peninsular India.

Characteristics: Permanently submerged tuberous plant with basal leaf rosette. Submerged leaves relatively small, only up to 10 cm long, their laminae lanceolate, up to 1.5 cm wide, flat, mid-green to dark-green. Laminae of floating leaves elliptical and always with a heart-shaped base, up to 12 cm long and up to 3 cm wide, dark-green. Inflorescence in one spike, white, pink or violet. Sepals: two.

Cultivation and Propagation: This species is not suitable for an aquarium as its submerged leaves are not very attractive and its floating leaves cast too much shade. It can be used in a planthouse. So far the plant has rarely been cultivated so that reliable information is lacking.

General Information: This is probably the most widely distributed *Aponogeton* species in Peninsular India. It may well form hybrids with plants of the *Aponogeton crispus* group, e.g. when pale-violet inflorescences and floating leaves occur.

Aponogeton abyssinicus HOCHST. (Ill. 160)

The species was named by Hochstetter in 1851.

Distribution: Central eastern Africa.

Characteristics: Tuberous plant with basal leaf rosette always growing in water. Submerged leaves linear to slightly egg-shaped, up to 10 cm long, easily declining. Laminae of floating leaves very variable, lanceolate, broad lanceolate or elliptical, up to 16 cm long and up to 5 cm wide, dark-green. Inflorescence in twin spikes, dark-violet. Sepals: two.

Cultivation and Propagation: The species is not suited to the conditions of an aquarium. Its many floating leaves cast too much shade and its submerged leaves do not last. In a planthouse it can look very decorative because of its violet inflorescences. The species is robust and undemanding and has been cultivated occasionally. Propagation is simple; the plants produce seeds even without pollination. In some flowers stamens are completely lacking and the number of carpels in a flower may be increased to seven.

Aponogeton distachyos L. f. (Ill. 162)

The species was named by Linné's son in 1881 when he defined the genus *Aponogeton*.

Distribution: Southern extremity of African continent. Naturalized and local in western Europe, South America and northern Australia.

Characteristics: Tuberous plant with basal leaf rosette growing in water. No submerged leaves. Laminae of floating leaves broad lanceolate to elliptical, with rounded tips, up to more than 20 cm in length and up to 8 cm wide, dark-green. Inflorescence in twin spikes, white. Flowers arranged in two rows. Only one relatively large sepal, 10-15 mm long.

Cultivation and Propagation: A robust and very decorative species. If kept in a planthouse the plants show a definite need for a resting period during the summer months. However, they can also be kept out in the open in which case they remain vegetative in the summer. The tubers are not hardy and do not stand up to the winter. They have to be taken out in the autumn or, in drained ponds, they must be covered with a dense layer of foliage. A well-fertilized substratum is essential for good growth and prolific flowering. If the water is withdrawn the plants can exist as land forms, but then they do not attain their optimum development. Snails are very destructive to the leaves, thus particularly endangering young plants. Propagation from seeds and raising of seedlings. Seeds are produced, even without artificial pollination.

General Information: The natural habitat of the species is a zone with rainfall in the winter where probably many waters dry out in the summer. In botanical gardens the species has been cultivated for almost two centuries. A south African cookery book recommends the use of the inflorescences for flavouring a meat dish.

Family Potamogetonaceae · Pondweed Family

The genus *Potamogeton* is the only one belonging to the family.

Potamogeton

The genus was defined by Linné in 1753. The name is derived from potamos (Gk) = river and geiton (Gk) = neighbour.

Distribution: Worldwide.

Characteristics: Aquatic plants with erect, branched or unbranched shoots with elongated axes, mostly with runners growing in the soil. Leaves arranged in two rows, very varied in form and colouration, formed as submerged or floating leaves, usually with characteristic sheaths. Flowers in spiky inflorescences, hermaphroditic, actinomorphic to slightly mirror-symmetrical. Perianth polysepalous, consisting only of four cup-shaped scales. Stamens: four. Carpels: four, rarely fewer, free, hypogynous superior. The fruit is an aggregate of achenes.

General Information: The genus includes approximately 100 species. They colonise still and running waters, poor or rich in nutrients, either clean and clear or, in part, very dirty. Their suitability for aquarium keeping is little explored as yet. Thus, some years ago, it was often thought that the genus contained no usable aquarium plants. But in the meantime, *Potamogeton gayi*, for instance, has become widely distributed in indoor aquaria. Many species should be particularly suited to being kept on ponds where their decorative submerged leaves would make them valuable plants.

In most species the inflorescences rise above the water level and the flowers are pollinated by the wind. Some species, however, are known to keep their inflorescences submerged and the flowers are pollinated under water. Apparently some of the plants form winter buds in colder areas but, as a rule, the plants get through winters by using the starch stored in their runners.

From a practical viewpoint an aquarist can divide the species into three different groups depending on the character of the leaves. The first group contains species with floating leaves; the second contains species with rather broad and decorative submerged leaves; the third group also contains species with submerged leaves, but these are narrow linear to almost hair-like.

Potamogeton natans L. (Ill. 174)

The species was named by Linné in 1753.

Distribution: Temperate areas of the northern hemisphere.

Characteristics: An aquatic, runner-producing plant with erect, elongated shoots. Submerged leaves at the base of shoots, floating leaves near the top. Leaf laminae or petioles arise at the base of membranous sheaths. Submerged leaves firm but easily declining, very narrow linear, pointed, up to 12 cm long. Laminae of floating leaves firm, elliptical to egg-shaped, up to 12 cm long and up to 7 cm wide. Inflorescence up to 8 cm long.

Cultivation and Propagation: An undemanding species, hardy in the winter; small stocks of it can be used on ponds. If growth is very strong the floating leaves are densely positioned and cast too much shade so that they have to be thinned out fairly frequently. Easiest propagation is from cuttings of erect shoots, the latter forming new runners at the base. This also applies to all other species of *Potamogeton*.

General Information: P. natans is the most widely distributed species of the genus which forms floating leaves. The plants colonise still waters with a good supply of nutrients. This species is often found growing together with *Nymphaea alba* and *Nuphar lutea*, all three species helping to build up the zone of plants with floating leaves around the shallows and shores of our lakes. *P. natans* is able to last for a time if the water dehydrates. Its floating leaves then lie close to the soil.

Potamogeton coloratus VAHL

The species was named by Vahl in 1813.

Distribution: Western Europe, east Africa.

Characteristics: An aquatic plant with runners and erect elongated shoots. Submerged leaves at the base of shoots, floating leaves near the top. Leaf laminae or petioles arise at the base of membranous sheaths. Submerged leaves delicate, lanceolate to broad lanceolate, up to 15 cm long and up to 2.5 cm wide. Laminae of floating leaves also delicate, elliptical to egg-shaped, up to 9 cm long and up to 5 cm wide. All leaves coloured reddish. Inflorescences up to 18 cm in length approximately, but usually shorter.

Cultivation and Propagation: A very attractive, but rarely cultivated species. Reliable information is therefore lacking. The species can only be used out in the open. Propagation as specified for *P. natans*.

Potamogeton gramineus L.

The species was named by Linné in 1753.

Distribution: In all temperate zones of the northern hemisphere.

Characteristics: Aquatic plant with runners and erect elongated shoots. Submerged leaves at the base of shoots, floating leaves often near the top, but not always. Leaf laminae or petioles arise at the base of membranous sheaths. Submerged leaves delicate, linear, with long pointed tips, up to 5 cm long and up to 6 mm wide, dark-green. Laminae of floating leaves firm, elliptical, up to 7 cm long and up to 2.5 cm wide, but occasionally larger. Inflorescence up to 3 cm in length.

Cultivation and Propagation: As specified for *P. natans*.

Potamogeton octandrus POIR.

The species was named by Poiret in 1816.

Distribution: Tropical Africa and Asia.

Characteristics: Aquatic plant with runners and erect elongated shoots. In the main, submerged leaves carried on shoots, but floating leaves occasionally produced near the top. Petioles arise at the base of a membranous sheath. Submerged leaves delicate, with lanceolate laminae, up to 8 cm long, up to 1.5 cm wide, pale to mid-green. Lamina of floating leaves also delicate, elliptical, up to 5 cm long, up to 2.5 cm wide. Inflorescence up to 2.5 cm in length.

Cultivation and Propagation: A species which can be used in a home aquarium. It does, however, quickly grow up to the water surface and should be used as a background plant, planted in groups. In too high a temperature the internodes become very long and the plants lose their optical effect. Propagation as specified for *P. natans*.

Potamogeton lucens L.

The species was named by Linné in 1753.

Distribution: Europe, Asia.

Characteristics: An aquatic plant with runners and erect elongated shoots. The latter only bear submerged leaves and no floating leaves. Leaf blades arise at the base of a membranous sheath; they are delicate, lanceolate, relatively large, up to 25 cm long and up to 5 cm wide, leaf margins often undulate, leaf surface glossy, pale-green. Inflorescence up to 6 cm in length.

Cultivation and Propagation: An undemanding species, hardy in the winter and, therefore, a suitable pond plant. Because of the prolific development of runners dense stocks form within quite a short period of time so that the plants have to be thinned out rather frequently. Propagation from cuttings as specified for *P. natans.*

Potamogeton perfoliatus L. (Ill. 175)

The species was named by Linné in 1753.

Distribution: Temperate zones of the northern hemisphere. Local in some parts of Africa and south-east Asia.

Characteristics: Aquatic plant with runners and erect elongated shoots. Submerged leaves only carried on shoots; no floating leaves. Leaf laminae arise at the base of a membranous sheath; they are delicate, elliptical to egg-shaped with a heart-shaped base, up to 5 cm long and up to 3.5 cm wide. Lamina surface pale-green. Inflorescence up to 3 cm in length.

Cultivation and Propagation: As specified for the previous species, *P. lucens.*

Potamogeton densus L.

The species was named by Linné in 1753. Because of some slight differences, some botanists exclude the species from the genus *Potamogeton* and denote it *Groenlandia densa.*

Distribution: Europe, Asia.

Characteristics: An aquatic plant with runners and erect elongated shoots. These bear submerged leaves; no floating leaves. Leaves without sheaths so that the laminae are sessile on the axis, actually in pairs, almost opposite. Leaf laminae egg-shaped, up to 4 cm long and up to 2 cm wide. Lamina surface pale to mid-green. Inflorescence up to 1.5 cm in length.

Cultivation and Propagation: As specified for *P. lucens.*

Potamogeton crispus L.

The species was named by Linné in 1753.

Distribution: In all temperate zones of the northern hemisphere.

Characteristics: Aquatic plant with runners and erect elongated shoots. These bear only submerged leaves; no floating leaves. Leaf laminae arise at the base of a membranous sheath; they are rather firm, linear, obtuse, up to 10 cm long and up to 1.5 cm wide. Leaf margins finely dentate. Lamina surface wavy, green or red to red-brown. Inflorescence up to 3 cm in length.

Cultivation and Propagation: This attractive species is grown and propagated like *P. lucens.*

Potamogeton zosteriformis FERN.

This species was named by Fernald in 1932.

Distribution: Central parts of North America.

Characteristics: An aquatic plant with runners and erect elongated shoots. These bear submerged leaves only; no floating leaves. Leaf laminae arise at the base of a membranous sheath; they are delicate, linear, up to 10 cm long and up to 5 mm wide. Lamina surface dark-green. Inflorescence up to 3 cm in length.

Cultivation and Propagation: As specified for *P. lucens.*

Potamogeton gayi A. BENNETT (Ill. 176)

The species was named by A. Bennett.

Distribution: South America.

Characteristics: Aquatic plant with runners and erect elongated shoots. These bear submerged leaves only; no floating leaves. Leaf laminae arise at the base of a membranous sheath; they are delicate, linear, up to 6 cm long and up to 4 mm wide. Lamina surface olive-green to brownish. Inflorescence up to 1.5 cm in length.

Cultivation and Propagation: With its slender, dark leaves the plant looks very decorative in the background of a tank. It is advisable to plant it in groups. The species develops a profusion of runners growing at the bottom and, therefore, tends to spread out too much. This can be prevented by frequent removal of shoots from runners. Position should be bright to slightly shady. Temperature from above 18 °C. Propagation from cuttings as specified for *P. natans.*

Potamogeton filiformis PERS.

The species was named by Persoon in 1811.

Distribution: Europe, Asia, northern Africa, Australia, North America.

Characteristics: Aquatic plant with erect elongated shoots. These bear submerged leaves only; no floating leaves. Leaf laminae arise near the tip of a greenish sheath, filiform thin, up to 5 cm long and up to 1 mm wide, pale-green, Inflorescence up to 1 cm in length.

Cultivation and Propagation: A very delicate species which has been recommended for cold water aquaria. Reliable information on its cultivation does not exist. Propagation from cuttings.

Family Ruppiaceae

One genus, approximately seven species. Worldwide distribution. Dainty aquatics with shoots growing horizontally on the ground and erect. Leaves alternate or opposite, with sheaths and usually filiform blades. Flowers in twin-spiked inflorescences, hermaphroditic, inconspicuous, lacking a perianth.

The species of the only genus of the Ruppiaceae, Ruppia, colonize shallow waters of the sea near the coast, brackish water, saline inland waters, but also fresh water. Thus, *R. poly-carpa* occurs in fresh water only in New Zealand. The small flower spikes always rise to the surface of the water and may be wind-pollinated, or the pollen floats on the water until it has reached the stigmata of near-by blossoms. *R. maritima* occurring over the whole of the northern hemisphere has become rare in European inland waters. So far the family has not achieved any importance in the cultivation of aquatic plants.

Family Zannichelliaceae

Three genera, ten species. Cosmopolitan. Dainty aquatics with shoot axes creeping on the ground and erect. Leaf arrangement distichous, more rarely alternate. Leaves narrow linear to filiform, or consisting solely of a leaf sheath. Flowers in small clusters or solitary in leaf axils, unisexual, monoecious or dioecious, inconspicuous. Perianth partly lacking.

In all members of this small family the flowers remain submerged and the pollen is transferred by the water. A few species occur in brackish water. The genera *Althenia* with one species occurring in southern Europe and the Near East, and *Lepilaena* with four species occurring in Australia and New Zealand are rather unknown. Even the genus *Zannichellia* with approx. five species and a worldwide distribution has not produced any aquarium plants of particular importance. *Zanichellia palustris*, however, which remains vegetative even in winter, has been recommended for cold-water tanks.

Family Najadaceae · Najad Family

The family contains only one genus, *Najas*.

Najas

The genus was defined by Linné in 1753. It is named after the Greek fountain nymphs, the Najads.

Distribution: Worldwide.

Characteristics: Annual or persistent plants with elongated, intensively branching, brittle shoots, always living submerged. Leaves opposite or in whorls, composed of a linear lamina and a short sheath. One or several flowers, enclosed by a membranous spathe, produced in leaf axils; flowers unisexual, monoecious or dioecious, inconspicuous. Perianth lacking. Male flowers with one stamen. Female flowers with one carpel, hypogynous superior. The fruit comes as a nut.

General Information: The genus embraces approximately 50 species distinguished by the shape of their foliage, leaves and their carpels as well as by the character of their fruits. The plants colonise all kinds of waters; some occur in brackish water. A few grow at a depth of 5 m. All are characterised by pollination brought to them by the agency of water.

Although many of the species should contain usable aquarium plants very few of them have been tried out as yet. *N. marina, N. graminea* and *N. minor* were considered as being unsuitable in older aquarium literature. In addition to the two species described below— both widely distributed in aquarium plant cultivation—a few others have been grown occasionally in recent years; e.g. *N. interrupta* from tropical east Africa; *N. pectinata* from Africa and Madagascar; and *N. madagascariensis,* also from Madagascar. Apparently, the first-named of these species has proved to be rewarding.

Najas guadelupensis (SPRENG.) MAGN. (Ill. 164)

The species was named *Caulina guadelupensis* by Sprengel in 1835 and moved to the genus *Najas* by Magnus in 1870. A further scientific name for the species is *N. microdon.*

Distribution: North and South America.

Characteristics: Aquatic plant rooted at the bottom or streaming, with elongated much-branched shoot axes. Leaf laminae linear, up to 2 cm long and up to 1.5 mm wide, slightly wavy, mid to dark-green. Leaf margins with sporadic, small teeth.

Cultivation and Propagation: An undemanding plant which can be kept in a position of bright or subdued light and feels happiest in temperatures between 18-25 °C. If the temperature is allowed to rise too high the shoot axes become even more brittle. The species can be put to good use in many different ways. Because it forms dense bushes it is a very decorative background plant. It may also be left streaming and will help to provide a cover of floating leaves which do not cast too much shade. *Najas guadelupensis* also provides an excellent spawning plant in tanks for viviparous cyprinoids; the fish can hide in the much-branched clusters formed by these plants. Propagation from small sections of shoots which can be taken off and may be used either for floating or as cuttings.

Najas indica (WILLD.) CHAM.

Willdenow named the species *Caulina indica* in 1801. Chamisso moved it to the genus *Najas* in 1829. A name used for a long time in aquaristic literature was *N. kingii.*

Distribution: Tropical south-east Asia.

Characteristics: An aquatic plant with elongated shoot axes and much branching, either rooted at the bottom or streaming. In habit it is like *N. guadelupensis*, but the leaf laminae are up to 2.5 cm long and up to 2 mm wide, stiffer, and evenly reflexed. Leaf edges densely, but irregularly toothed. Shoot axes even more brittle.

Cultivation and Propagation: As specified for *N. guadelupensis*.

Family Amaryllidaceae · Narcissus Family

Eighty genera, 1,000 species. Predominantly in the tropics and subtropics of the southern hemisphere, particularly in southern Africa; a few species only in temperate latitudes. Plants with rhizomes, tubers and bulbs, usually with basal leaf rosettes. Conspicuous hermaphroditic flowers.

A number of ornamental plants are members of this family, such as the snowdrop, narcissus and hippeastrum. The plants usually colonise periodically dry habitats where their storage organs enable them to last through periods unfavourable for growth in a state of dormancy. It is only the genus *Crinum* that contains aquatic plants.

Crinum

The genus was defined by Linné in 1753. The name is derived from krinon (Gk) = lily.

Distribution: In all tropical and subtropical areas.

Characteristics: Bulbous plants with linear leaves of varied length arranged in rosettes. Flowers in umbellate inflorescences, hermaphroditic, actinomorphic. Perianth polysepalous consisting of six isomorphic white or reddish leaves. Stamens: six. Carpels: three, united, hypogynous. The fruit comes as a capsule.

General Information: The genus includes approximately 110 species. Some of them grow in water, usually in shallow places in brooks and small rivers. Some of their leaves are submerged, others grow up above the water level. Inflorescences always rise above the water. According to observations made up to date, the waters in which *Crinum* species occur are said to carry water permanently. This is rather astonishing as the presence of bulbs would indicate the plants' ability to endure dry periods. Most normal occurence of *Crinum* is near the coasts.

Crinum purpurascens HERB. (Ill. 57)

Herbert named the species in 1837.

Distribution: Tropical South America, Greater Antilles.

Characteristics: Bulbous aquatic plant with basal leaf rosette. Leaves flat to being slightly grooved, up to 40 cm long and up to 20 mm wide, mid-green or blue-green. Petals white or reddish.

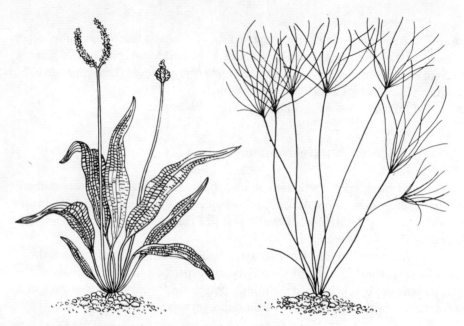

57 Aponogeton 'bernerianus' and *Eleocharis vivipara*

Cultivation and Propagation: Although recommended as an aquarium plant, the species feels happiest as a bog plant or, at least, in very low water so that its leaves can grow in the air. The flowers of *Crinum purpurascens* are really beautiful and a lover of aquatic plants who owns a planthouse would, no doubt, like to care for it and include it with his stock of plants. The species can even be used as a potted plant or in hydroculture. It should be given plenty of nutrients. The bulbs become stronger, but only gradually, and it takes them a few years before they produce flowers. Young plants develop at the base of the bulb eventually; they can be used for multiplication.

Crinum thaianum SCHULZE

The species was named by Schulze in 1971.
Distribution: Indochina.
Characteristics: Aquatic bulbous plant with basal leaf rosette. Leaves linear to being slightly grooved, maximum length 3 m, up to 2.5 cm wide, mid-green. Petals a glowing white.
Cultivation and Propagation: Because the leaves grow to such great length the species cannot be used in a home aquarium; it is suitable for a planthouse. The leaves float on the water so that each plant needs a great deal of space. A nourishing substratum and a temperature of above 20 °C are advisable. The young plants developing at the base of the

bulb yield the best propagation results. Seeds capable of germinating can be obtained from flowering plants if they are artificially pollinated first.

Crinum natans BAKER

The species was named by Baker in 1898.

Distribution: Tropical west Africa.

Characteristics: Bulbous aquatic plant with basal leaf rosette. Leaves linear, very wavy, maximum length 1 m, up to 3 cm wide, pale-green. Petals white.

Cultivation and Propagation: As specified for *C. thaianum.* Young plants of this species may be used as solitary show specimens in large tanks.

Family Iridaceae · Iris Family

Seventy genera, 1,500 species. Tropical-subtropical, with main centres of evolution in America and southern Africa, few species only in the northern temperate latitudes. Predominantly plants with rhizomes and tubers having a two-ranked leaf arrangement. Flowers with a colourful corolla. The Iridaceae colonise dry as well as moist habitats. The family includes numerous ornamental plants such as species of *Crocus, Gladiolus* and *Iris.*

Iris

The genus was defined by Linné in 1753. The name is derived from iris (Gk) = rainbow and refers to the flowers which are often coloured.

Distribution: In the temperate areas of the northern hemisphere.

Characteristics: Perennial herbs with rhizomes or tubers and basal leaf rosettes. Leaves linear, flat or grooved, usually with a long pointed tip. Flowers hermaphroditic, actinomorphic. Perianth polysepalous, consisting of six isomorphic, coronal leaves. Stamens: three or six. Carpels: three, united, hypogynous. The fruit comes as a capsule.

General Information: Several of the approx. 300 species colonise marshy habitats and approximately 10 species grow in shallow water.

Iris pseudacorus L. (Ill. 163)

The species was named by Linné in 1753 when he defined the genus.

Distribution: Europe, western Asia.

Characteristics: Rhizome plant growing in bog and shallow water. The leaves are flat and up to 1 m in length, mid-green. Perianth a glowing yellow. Commonly called yellow flag.

Cultivation and Propagation: An undemanding species, hardy in the winter and suitable for being planted around the edges and in shallow areas of ponds. The plants with their glowing yellow flowers are very handsome. Propagation by division of the rhizome in the autumn or in early spring.

General Information: Various sorts are traded with differing intensively coloured flowers.

Family Orchidaceae · Orchid Family

Seven hundred genera, 20,000 species. Predominantly in the tropics and subtropics, but also in all other areas. Multiform herbaceous plants. Flowers hermaphroditic, mirror-symmetrical, with conspicuously coloured flower envelopes.

The orchids possess complicated mechanisms to ensure pollination. They live symbiotically with certain fungi forming colonies in the orchids' roots. The orchids' seeds are as fine as dust and contain no nutrient tissue. Thus, in nature, they can germinate successfully only if they are able to form a union with these fungi at an early stage.

The members of the family colonise very varied habitats. In the tropics we often find them as epiphytes in trees. Some species occur in wet habitats, and *Spiranthes cernua* (an aquatic form of lady's tresses) from tropical South America is well able to withstand flooding. This plant is occasionally cultivated in aquaria, but with varied success.

Family Pontederiaceae · Pickerelweed Family

Nine genera, 30 species. Tropical-subtropical, penetrating to the temperate latitudes in America. Perennial herbs with rhizomes or runners as well as other persistent or annual, herbaceous plants. Leaves polymorphic. Flowers of varied size, always colourful.

All members of the pickerelweed family are marsh and aquatic plants. It is not surprising, therefore, that this family has become popular with the lover of aquatic plants. Almost certainly the genera not cultivated so far contain usable aquarium plants or plants suited to cultivation in ponds and planthouses. Quite recently, for instance, *Hydrothrix gardneri* has been imported from tropical South America. However, it is particularly the species of the genera *Pontederia*, *Eichhornia*, *Heteranthera* and *Zosterella* that have been cultivated so far.

Pontederia

The genus was defined by Linné in 1753. It was named after the Italian Professor Pontedera (d. in 1757).

Distribution: North and South America.

Characteristics: Perennial herbs with rhizomes and basal leaf rosettes. Leaves arranged in two ranks and formed as submerged, floating and aerial leaves, linear or petiolate with blades of varied shape. Inflorescences in dense spikes. Flowers hermaphroditic, mirror-symmetrical, very small. Perianth labiate, the upper lip consisting of three more or less combined leaves and the lower lip of three free, blue leaves, hairy on the outside. Stamens: six. Carpels: three, united, hypogynous superior. The fruit comes as a nut.

General Information: The genus includes five species all of them thriving in bog or shallow water. *Pontederia lanceolata*, which makes greater demands on temperature than the species described below, is occasionally on view in the culturing houses for aquatic plants in botanical gardens.

Pontederia cordata L.

The species was named by Linné in 1753 when he defined the genus.

Distribution: North and South America.

Characteristics: Rhizome plant with basal leaf rosette. Leaves up to 60 cm in length, petiolate, their laminae lanceolate to heart-shaped, tough, dark-green.

Cultivation and Propagation: Suitable for being planted in margins and shallow areas in ponds. The species needs a good supply of nutrients in the substratum. During the winter it has to be protected by a layer of foliage. Propagation by division of the rootstock of older plants, from lateral shoots or seeds.

Eichhornia

The genus was defined by Kunth in 1842. It was named after the Prussian Minister Eichhorn (1779-1850).

Distribution: Tropical South America.

Characteristics: Herbaceous plants of different appearance growing in marshes and the water. Leaf arrangement two-ranked or in rosettes. Submerged leaves linear, floating and aerial leaves petiolate with laminae of varied shape. Flowers hermaphroditic, mirror-symmetrical, size varied. Perianth consists of six united coronal leaves. Stamens: six. Carpels: three, united, hypogynous superior. The fruit is a capsule.

General Information: The genus embraces seven species all growing either in bog or in the water.

Eichhornia crassipes (MART.) SOLMS (Ill. 166, 178)

Martius named the species *Pontederia crassipes* in 1824; Solms moved it to the genus *Eichhornia* in 1883. A later scientific name for the species is *E. speciosa.*

Distribution: Originally South America, but now established in many tropical and subtropical areas.

Characteristics: Commonly called the water hyacinth. A rosette plant floating on the surface of the water having decorative blue-black roots. Submerged leaves lacking. In a high temperature the aerial leaves are long and slightly swollen. If the temperature is low these leaves are short and the swelling—containing spongy tissue—is thick and knobby. Leaf lamina roundish, up to 15 cm in length and width, mid-green. Flowers large, their corolla pale-violet with a yellow patch.

Cultivation and Propagation: As a rule not a very suitable floating plant for an aquarium as it needs at least 30—40 cm of air space above the water level. But the water hyacinth can be recommended for a planthouse or, in the summer, for ponds where it should be given a sunny position, sheltered from wind. Unfortunately the plants rarely flower if they are kept in the open. During the winter months the short daylight hours endanger the species. To keep it in vegetation in a planthouse additional artificial light is essential. Alternatively a number of specimens can be potted in earth containing sand and peat, and they can then be wintered in a temperature of 15-20 °C, fairly light and moderately moist. Sturdy outdoor plants are the most suitable for this procedure. Propagation from slips which are produced in large numbers from the profuse runners.

General Information: In many areas where the plants have established themselves they have become a serious hazard to the waters. Particularly if the water is dirty and contains a large supply of nutrients the rate of multiplication of the plants is so high that their large numbers may hinder navigation and block up canals. In that event control by mechanical and chemical means is necessary. Those water hyacinths that are removed by mechanical means are partly used as fodder for animals or as green manure on fields. There is actually a publication entitled *Hyacinth Control Journal* devoted especially to the control of this species.

Eichhornia azurea (Sw.) Kunth (Ill. 165)

The species was named *Pontederia azurea* by Swartz in 1788 and moved to the genus *Eichhornia* by Kunth in 1843.

Distribution: Tropical South America.

Characteristics: Herbaceous plant with elongated shoot axes, living submerged, floating on the surface of the water or growing in bogs. Submerged leaves linear, up to 10 cm long and up to 8 mm wide, densely arranged in two ranks, pale-green. Aerial leaves with thick petioles, not crowded, their laminae roundish, up to 8 cm long and up to 7 cm wide, dark-green. Flowers of medium size, their corolla pale-blue, with dark-blue throat.

Cultivation and Propagation: In an aquarium this species needs a great deal of attention as the submerged shoots have the tendency to grow up rapidly to the surface of the water and then develop floating leaves. It is, therefore, necessary to prune the plants rather frequently; the tips of the shoots can be replanted. The plants look their best if displayed in groups near or in the back of the tank. A temperature of above 20 °C and a position in good light are essential. Another use for the species would be in a planthouse where the shoots may be allowed to grow on the surface of the water. They will then develop aerial leaves only and, in all probability, flowers will be produced. The shading effect is insignificant. Propagation from cuttings.

Eichhornia diversifolia (VAHL) URB. (Ill. 179)

The species was named *Heteranthera diversifolia* by Vahl in 1805 and moved to the genus *Eichhornia* by Urban in 1903. It was introduced to aquarists under the trade name of 'Heteranthera matogrossense'.

Distribution: Tropical South America.

Characteristics: Submerged herbaceous plant with elongated shoot axes and two-ranked leaf arrangement. Submerged leaves sessile, linear, up to 6 cm long and up to 4 mm wide, upperside initially pale-green, blue-black later on, underside initially whitish-green and also blue-black later on. Floating leaves petiolate, their laminae elliptical, egg or heart-shaped, up to 4 cm long and up to 2.5 cm wide, dark-green. Aerial leaves probably lacking. Flowers small, their corolla blue.

Cultivation and Propagation: The species resembles *Heteranthera zosteraefolia* but it is not as beautiful. The change of colour to blue-black in the leaves is thought to be rather unsightly. It is unlikely, therefore, that the species will ever become a widely distributed aquarium plant; instead it will interest the specialist. The plants can be used in the middle and back of the aquarium, displayed in groups. They need good light and a temperature of at least 20 °C. Propagation from cuttings.

Heteranthera

The genus was defined by Ruiz and Pavón in 1794. The name is derived from hetero (Gk) = other, different and anthera (Gk) = stamen.

Distribution: Tropical and subtropical America and Africa.

Characteristics: Herbaceous plants with elongated shoot axes and two-ranked leaf arrangement living submerged or in marshes. Submerged leaves linear, floating and aerial leaves also linear, or petiolate with differently shaped laminae. Flowers hermaphroditic, mirror-symmetrical, small. Perianth gamopetalous, consisting of six isomorphic leaves. Stamens: three. Carpels: three, united, hypogynous superior. The fruit comes as a capsule.

General Information: The genus includes approximately ten species. Some of them are certain to contain as yet untried aquarium plants because all species are aquatic or marsh plants. Aquaristic literature frequently mentions *Heteranthera reniformis*, but for aquarium cultivation this plant is of no use. Its shoots grow in bog or float on the surface of the water and its petiolate leaves with kidney-shaped laminae are developed as floating or aerial leaves. This species has been cultivated in botanical gardens since the middle of the last century.

Heteranthera zosteraefolia MART. (Ill. 180)

The species was named by Martius in 1823.

Distribution: Tropical South America.

Characteristics: Herbaceous plants with elongated shoot axes, either submerged or growing in bog. Submerged plants with submerged and floating leaves. Submerged leaves sessile, linear, up to 5 cm long and up to 5 mm wide, upperside pale-green, underside whitish-green. Floating leaves petiolate, their laminae lanceolate to narrow elliptical. Leaves of marsh plants like submerged leaves of submerged plants, but tougher and dark-green. Flowers small, their floral envelope bluish.

Cultivation and Propagation: An undemanding, hardy species and, with its slender, pale-green leaves, it enhances the design of a lively, aquascaped aquarium. It may be used in a group display in the middle or back of a tank, but it also looks attractive in the corners of the aquarium. A position in good light is needed and a temperature of not less than 20 °C. Propagation from cuttings.

Zosterella

The genus was defined by Small in 1913. The name is taken from the generic name of eel-grass, *Zostera.*

Distribution: Southern North America.

Characteristics: Submerged plants with elongated shoot axes and a two-ranked leaf arrangement. Solitary flowers develop in an axillary spathe, hermaphroditic, actino-morphic. Perianth consists of six isomorphic yellow leaves slightly united at the base. Stamens: three. Carpels: three, united, hypogynous superior. The fruit comes as a capsule.

General Information: The genus contains only two species.

Zosterella dubia (JACQ.) SMALL (Ill. 177)

Jacquin named the species *Commelina dubia* in 1764; Small moved it to the genus *Zosterella* in 1913. Some botanists class it with the genus *Heteranthera.* Thus two names for the species are quite commonly used in aquaristic literature, *Heteranthera dubia* or *H. graminea.*

Distribution: Southern North America.

Characteristics: Submerged plants with elongated shoot axes. Leaves linear, up to 10 cm long and up to 5 mm wide, dark-green. Flowers a glowing yellow.

Cultivation and Propagation: An undemanding plant which should be given a bright to slightly shady position. Optimum temperature between 15 and 25 °C. The growth of the plant is so strong that fairly frequent thinning out is necessary. During the summer months it is quite possible to keep the plants out in the open. Propagation from cuttings.

Family Mayacaceae · Mayaca Family

Only the genus *Mayaca* belongs to this family.

Mayaca

The genus was defined by Aublet in 1775. He took the name from the native language of Guyana.

Distribution: South-eastern North America, Central America, South America, Greater Antilles, tropical west-Africa.

Characteristics: Small herbaceous plants with elongated shoot axes and an alternate arrangement of small, simple leaves, growing in bog or submerged in water. Flowers solitary or in small clusters in the leaf axils, hermaphroditic, actinomorphic. Perianth polysepalous, composed of a calyx in three parts and a coloured or white corolla also in three parts. Stamens: three. Carpels: three, united, hypogynous superior. The fruit comes as a capsule.

General Information: The genus consists of approximately ten species. Very little is known about their usefulness as aquarium plants. However, the species described below has been cultivated occasionally.

Mayaca fluviatilis AUBL. (Ill. 181)

The species was named by Aublet in 1775 when he defined the genus. Aquarium literature often refers to it under the name of *M. vandellii.*

Distribution: South-eastern North America, Greater Antilles.

Characteristics: Dainty, herbaceous plant with elongated shoot axes growing horizontally in bog and erect when submerged. Leaves linear, pointed, up to 1 cm long and up to 1 mm wide, pale-green. Flower corolla pale-violet.

Cultivation and Propagation: This pale, very dainty species may be planted in groups in the middle of the aquarium but also in the front to provide some variation. It should be given a light to slightly shady position and a temperature of approximately 25 °C. The plant does not grow satisfactorily in all conditions. The daily period of illumination should never be less than 12 hours. Propagation from cuttings.

Family Juncaceae · Rush Family

Nine genera, 300 species. Predominantly in temperate and cold regions. Usually perennial herbs or other herbaceous plants, often with awl-shaped leaves. Flowers inconspicuous, in more or less crowded inflorescences.

The members of the rush family colonise mainly wet habitats, but that they actually grow in water is exceptional. *Prionium serratum,* however, which forms strong stems, grows in

South African mountain rivers. The species is often cultivated in botanical gardens. The genus *Juncus* contains approximately 225 species with a worldwide distribution. *J. repens* (Ill. 182), a creeping rush from the south-east of North America has occasionally been cultivated in aquaria, but with varying success.

Family Cyperaceae · Sedge Family

Seventy genera, 3,700 species. Distributed throughout the world although particularly abundant in the temperate latitudes. Grass-like, herbaceous plants growing in clusters or forming turfs. Leaves linear. Flowers hermaphroditic or unisexual and monoecious, inconspicuous, arranged in spikelets and these again in spike-like inflorescences.

Marsh plants, partly even aquatic plants occur in approx. 30 genera. Nevertheless, the family has achieved practically no importance in cultivation of aquatic plants so far. The sedges of the genus *Carex* are widely distributed. Although some of the species grow in high mountains, dry habitats and woods, most of them occur in soil which retains water and is poor in air content, e.g. marshes, river banks, silted up zones of lakes and ponds as well as on wet meadows and shallow moors. They often cover large areas. Their greatest occurrence is in the temperate latitudes. The species of the genus *Cyperus* colonise rather similar habitats, but predominantly in the tropics and subtropics. In the early days of aquarium plant cultivation a few species were used in tanks, e.g. *Cyperus alternifolius*, an endemic of Madagascar (Ill. 183). However, the plants always grow up above the water level and, nowadays, they might just be considered a sensible choice for a planthouse. *C. papyrus*, the Egyptian papyrus, belongs to the same genus. This plant was quite an important material in the manufacture of paper in Old Egypt. The only genus of some value in present-day aquarium plant cultivation is *Eleocharis*.

Eleocharis

The genus was defined by R. Brown in 1810. The name is derived from helos (Gk) = marsh and charis (Gk) = favour, joy. Sometimes also referred to as *Heleocheris*.

Distribution: Worldwide.

Characteristics: Small herbaceous plants, partly with runners, rarely with tubers. Leaf arrangement in rosettes. Leaves long and awl-shaped. Flowers hermaphroditic, inconspicuous, grouped together in spikelets. Perianth represented by bristles. Stamens: two to three. Carpels: two to three, united, hypogynous superior. The fruit is a nut.

General Information: The genus includes approximately 200 species occurring in shallow as well as deep water and occasionally as weeds in rice paddies. Thus, a number of species should be usable aquarium plants. Literature for aquarists has recommended several species, such as *E. barrosii* from South America, *E. naumanniana* from tropical west Africa and *E. elongata* from south-eastern North America.

Eleocharis acicularis (L.) ROEM. et SCHULT.

Linné named the species *Scirpus acicularis* in 1753; Roemer and Schultes moved it to the genus *Eleocharis* in 1817.

Distribution: America, Europe, Asia, Australia.

Characteristics: Often known as hair grass, this is a small, herbaceous rosette plant with runners and it grows in bogs and submerged. Submerged leaves awl-shaped, up to 20 cm long and—at most—0.5 mm thick, pale-green.

Cultivation and Propagation: A plant suited to unheated as well as to tropical aquaria. It is quite happy in temperatures up to 25 °C, but will persist during the winter in a cold tank. A position in good light is advisable. In a tall tank the plant can be used in the front, otherwise it should be planted near the middle. If left undisturbed dense stocks develop from the runners in time. To stimulate new growth it may be necessary to thin out the older plants now and again. Propagation from slips taken off parent plants.

Eleocharis parvula (ROEM. et SCHULT.) LINK

Roemer and Schultes named the species *Scirpus parvulus* in 1817; Link moved it to the genus *Eleocharis*.

Distribution: Eastern North America, Cuba.

Characteristics: Herbaceous rosette plant with runners; it grows in bogs and submerged. Very similar to *E. acicularis*, but the runners growing in the soil end in nodules and submerged leaves the latter being only up to 7 cm long, usually even shorter.

Cultivation and Propagation: As specified for *E. acicularis*.

Eleocharis vivipara LINK (Ill. 57)

The species was named by Link in 1827. The name *Eleocharis prolifera* is incorrect.

Distribution: Southern North America.

Characteristics: A herbaceous rosette plant growing in bog and submerged. Submerged leaves up to 10 cm long, pale-green. New rosettes form on foliaceous, erect shoots. This process may be repeated a number of times so that several generations of rosettes are arranged above each other in tiers.

Cultivation and Propagation: The species thrives equally well in heated and unheated tanks. It likes a position in good light but is otherwise undemanding. To allow this beautiful plant full development it should be provided with an aquarium which is not too low. Propagation from plantlets taken off parent plants.

Family Eriocaulaceae

Thirteen genera, 1,200 species. Predominantly tropical—subtropical, a few species only in temperate latitudes. Perennial and annual plants with grass-like, slender leaves. Flowers unisexual, inconspicuous, their inflorescences arranged in crowded heads with many glumes.

The Eriocaulaceae colonise sandy and marshy soil, often in the higher mountain altitudes. Marsh and aquatic plants occur in six genera but, so far, none of them have been tried out in cultivation. Several species of the genus *Eriocaulon* grow submerged e.g. *E. melanocephalum* in South America; *E. bifistulosum* in Africa; and *E. setaceum* in south-east Asia. *Leiothrix fluitans* is a plant of South American rivers, and *Mesanthemum reductum* belongs to the rivers of Central America.

Family Poaceae · Grass Family

Seven hundred genera, 10,000 species. Distribution worldwide. Herbaceous plants growing in tufts or forming turfs, with characteristic narrow leaves arranged in two rows. Flowers as a rule hermaphroditic, inconspicuous, enclosd by glumes, grouped together in spikelets, in inflorescences of various forms.

Gramineae is an older name for this family which represents a high proportion of the vegetation covering the earth. Its members colonise very diverse habitats from the lowlands to the high mountains. In some regions they are the leading feature of the flora, e.g. savannahs and steppes. Grasses also form extended areas of turf. It is not surprising, therefore, that the grasses are not missing from the water as a habitat. Species of approximately 60 genera live in close proximity to water, but not a single species is able to survive for long fully submerged. Therefore, this family cannot be expected to produce plants for the aquarium. Some grasses grow close to the edges of still and running waters and, amongst them, other marsh and aquatic plants may well develop. *Phragmites communis*, the common reed, which grows to a considerable height and has very strong runners, is the most striking of these grasses. Its distribution is worldwide. The common reed characterises the vegetation and reed-belt of silted-up zones of many types of waters. The culms may attain a height of 1-4 m; the paniculate inflorescences appear relatively late in the year. Other species, like *Hygrorhiza aristata*, float with their shoots on the surface of the water and grow from the edges towards the middle of the waters, thus taking part in forming a kind of floating meadow.

The genus *Oryza* needs to be mentioned; it contains approximately 25 species of which the cultivated rice, *O. sativa*, is one (Ill. 184). Rice is the principal tropical-subtropical cereal and, in any case, one of the most important food plants as it represents the main source of nourishment for 60 per cent of mankind. Approximately 90 per cent of the world's rice harvest is produced and also consumed in Asia. Rice is also grown in south and south-east

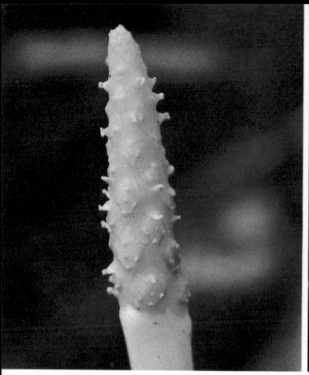
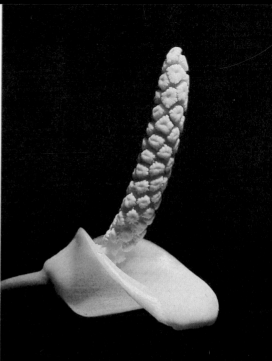

167 *Orontium aquaticum*, inflorescence
168 Inflorescence of a species of *Anubias*
169 *Anubias lanceolata*, flowering
170 *Anubias afzelii*, broad-leafed form, flowering
171 *Anubias afzelii*

172 *Cryptocoryne legroi*
173 *Cryptocoryne petchii*

174 *Potamogeton natans*
175 *Potamogeton perfoliatus*

186 Various species of *Anubias* in an aquarium
187 *Acorus gramineus*
188 *Cryptocoryne petchii*

189 *Cryptocoryne beckettii*
190 *Cryptocoryne willisii*

Europe, tropical west Africa, South America and southern North America. In some areas, early ripening varieties produce three crops a year.

Approximately half the rice is cultivated as hill rice, that is without irrigation. Hill rice makes few demands on moisture in the soil and can even be grown in quite high altitudes. Of course, its yield is not very high. Swamp rice, on the other hand, is normally grown on terraces under irrigation. The rice is pre-cultivated in special seed-beds and the seedlings are then planted out in fields prepared for a flooding and, therefore, provided with dams. In more modern rice cultivation the rice is sown in the field straight away and the field is flooded directly after sowing. The water level in the paddies has to be adjustable and must rise as the rice grows. The influx of water is regulated when the rice begins to ripen and, when it is fully ripe, all the water is drained away.

Numerous other marsh and aquatic plants find the right living conditions in rice fields where they are regarded as weeds. Among them are many species which are nowadays cultivated as aquarium plants. Several aquarium fishes also use the rice fields as a habitat.

Family Araceae · Arum Family

One hundred genera, 1,800 species. Tropical-subtropical, not much represented in temperate latitudes. Perennial herbs with rhizomes and tubers; lianas; epiphytes growing on trees; plants forming runners; and other herbaceous plants. The leaves are feather-veined in contrast to all other monocotyledons. Flowers usually unisexual and monoecious, inconspicuous, arranged on a spike, and more or less enclosed by a usually conspicuously coloured bract, the spathe. Calcium oxalate crystals are often present in the tissues.

Members of the arum family are plants of the woods, swamps and the waters. It is often difficult to find an exact border-line between the species colonising a wet habitat and those colonising a marshy habitat. The poisonous *Calla palustris*, the marsh callas, is a native of Europe, northern Asia and North America; the plant has a white spathe and red berries. It colonises habitats with a low pH-value, and it is difficult to cultivate. *Zantedeschia aethiopica* (a rather well-known calla), a native of South Africa, is also originally a marsh plant. Aquarium literature frequently mentions the genus *Lagenandra*. Its species are small to medium-sized marsh plants from south-east Asia some of which have proved suitable in aquarium cultivation. Species of the genera *Aglaonema* from south-east Asia, and *Spathiphyllum* from the American and Asiatic tropics have been tried out as aquarium plants but have proved themselves to be short-lived and, therefore, unsuitable. In their natural environment they are marsh plants and used to being flooded periodically. The genera that are of great value to the lover of aquatic plants and the aquarist are: *Acorus*, *Peltandra*, *Orontium*, *Anubias*, *Cryptocoryne* and *Pistia*.

Acorus

The genus was defined by Linné in 1753. The name of a Greek plant was chosen for the generic name.

Distribution: Throughout the northern hemisphere.

Characteristics: Perennial herbs with rhizomes, showing great variety in size. Leaves two-rowed, basal, linear, pointed. The spathe like a foliage leaf, the spike-like inflorescence terminal. Flowers hermaphroditic, actinomorphic, inconspicuous. The perianth consists of six very small, greenish leaflets. Stamens: six. Carpels: three, united, hypogynous superior. The fruit is a reddish berry.

General Information: The genus is said to consist of two species. However, very probably it ought to include more because the varieties of *A. gramineus* should almost certainly be given a greater degree of independence. The plants normally grow in bog, but some of them thrive in dry habitats.

Acorus calamus L.

The species was named by Linné when he defined the genus in 1753.

Distribution: Originally in eastern Asia, now naturalised in Europe and North America.

Characteristics: Commonly known as sweet-sedge or sweet-flag. Rhizome plant growing in bog, with basal, two-rowed foliage. Leaves linear, pointed, up to 1 m long and up to 25 mm wide, with distinct midrib, pale to mid-green. The plant exudes an aromatic, strong scent.

Cultivation and Propagation: This robust and undemanding species is suited to the marginal vegetation and shallow areas of ponds. But its foliage is rather dull and plain and it is, therefore, not much in demand. Propagation by division of the rhizome, preferably in spring.

General Information: In Europe the species has been cultivated as a medicinal plant since the 16th century. Often it has been allowed to run wild and dispersed from gardens. The rhizomes were used in various ways, e.g. dried, made into a powder and given to patients suffering from digestive ailments. The European plants are sterile and can multiply only by rhizome division.

Acorus gramineus SOLAND. (Ill. 187)

The species was named by Solander in 1789.

Distribution: Eastern Asia.

Characteristics: Commonly called Japanese rush. Rhizome plant with basal, two-rowed foliage; it grows in bog and dry habitats.

Leaves linear, pointed, up to 40 cm long and up to 10 mm wide, without distinct midrib, mid-green to dark-green.

Cultivation and Propagation: The species is suited to a planthouse where it can be grown emerse or in shallow water. Although offered for sale as an aquarium plant since the early days of aquarium cultivation it cannot really be recommended for a tank. Permanently submerged growth does not suit the plant. It is true, the narrow-leafed forms, in particular, can be kept submerged and will last for a time, but sooner or later they die. Optimum temperature 15-25 °C. Propagation by division of the rhizome.

General Information: The most popular of these plants is the variety *A. gramineus* var. *pussilus* which probably ought to be regarded as an independent species. It is much smaller, the leaves growing to a length of not more than 25 cm and a width of not more than 6 mm. Some of its strains are known to have white or yellow-striped leaves. In eastern Asia they are used as garden plants, particularly for the borders of flower beds. Apparently there are also forms even more restricted in growth.

Peltandra

The genus was defined by Rafin in 1819. The name is derived from pelte (Gk) = shield and andros (Gk) = stamen.

Distribution: Eastern North America.

Characteristics: Perennial herbs with rhizomes and a basal leaf arrangement. Leaves petiolate, up to 40 cm long, their laminae arrow-shaped, mid-green. Spathe grown together at the base, but open further up, enclosing the inflorescence. Flowers unisexual, inconspicuous. Perianth lacking. Male flowers with 4-8 stamens. Female flowers with three carpels, united, hypogynous superior. The fruit is a berry.

General Information: The genus includes three species; all grow in marsh or in water.

Peltandra virginica (L.) KUNTH

Linné named the species *Arum virginicum* in 1753; Kunth moved it to the genus *Peltandra* in 1841.

Distribution: Eastern North America.

Characteristics: A marsh plant with rhizome and basal leaf rosette. The arrow-shaped laminae grow to a length of up to 25 cm and a width of up to 15 cm, colour mid-green. Spathe and fruit green.

Cultivation and Propagation: An interesting plant because of its arrow-shaped leaves, suited to being grown on ponds. It needs a nourishing soil mixture and, in the winter, it has to be protected by a cover of foliage. Propagation by division of the rhizome in spring.

Orontium

The genus was defined by Linné in 1753. It contains only one species, which is described below. It is possible that the plant was named after the river Orontes.

Orontium aquaticum L. (Ill. 167)

The species was named by Linné in 1753 when he defined the genus.

Distribution: Eastern North America.

Characteristics: Runner-producing plant with basal leaf rosette, growing in bog and in the water. Leaves developed as aerial or floating leaves, having a petiole of varying length, their laminae broad lanceolate to elliptical, up to 15 cm long and up to 5 cm wide, tough, dark-green. Spathe small and weak. Peduncle white, flowering spike glowing yellow. Flowers hermaphroditic, inconspicuous. Perianth composed of six very small, isomorphic scales. Stamens: six. Carpels: three, united, hypogynous superior. The fruit is a berry.

Cultivation and Propagation: The species may be used in the margins and shallow areas of ponds. Whilst it is flowering the golden-yellow spikes make it a very attractive plant. It has to be protected by a layer of foliage in the winter. Propagation from slips taken off parent plants.

Anubias

The genus was defined by Schott in 1857. The name was chosen in honour of the Egyptian god Anubis.

Distribution: Tropical west Africa.

Characteristics: Small to medium-sized perennial herbs with rhizomes and basal leaf rosettes. Leaves petiolate, tough, of diverse shape, usually dark-green. Spathe green or whitish, enclosing most of the inflorescence. Flowers unisexual and monoecious, inconspicuous. Perianth lacking. Male flowers with five stamens. Female flowers with one carpel which is hypogynous superior. The fruit is a green berry.

General Information: The species of the genus *Anubias* grow in shallow forest brooks or on their edges and prefer slightly shady places. They either grow permanently outside the water, or their rhizomes grow in the water and the leaves project above it. Some of them are completely flooded for a short time in periods of high water and, thus, they are able to tolerate submerged growth.

Vegetative propagation of the *Anubias* species does not produce a good yield. The lateral shoots that develop can be removed once they are sufficiently strong, or longer rhizomes may be divided. In either case dormant buds will be stimulated into producing new shoots. Multiplication from seeds is more productive. For sexual propagation, however, the plants have to be kept emerse as bog plants which can really only be done in a marsh vivarium, a planthouse, or in a plant box under glass. The *Anubias* will then produce numerous inflorescences quite regularly (Ill. 168, 169). Fruits may develop without intervention, but artificial pollination is more reliable. It has to be borne in mind that the female flowers ripen first. When the male flowers are capable of pollinating the lower part of the spathe closes more or less firmly around the female flowers, thus making self-pollination difficult. But at that time the stigma of the female flower is still receptive. We therefore have to tear open the lower part of the spathe and transfer the pollen from the higher situated male flowers to the stigma.

The genus includes approximately 10 species. Their usefulness for aquarium plant cultivation has been a matter for discussion for a long time. However, a few species have become well adapted to permanently submerged growth and have proved their worth for aquaria (Ill. 186).

Anubias afzelii SCHOTT (Ill. 170, 171, 185)

The species was defined by Schott in 1857. Also named *A. congensis*.
Distribution: Tropical west Africa.
Characteristics: Plant with a thick rhizome growing in bog or, more rarely, submerged. Leaves in basal rosettes,, petiolate. Laminae of submerged leaves elliptical to obovate, flat, tough, up to 20 cm long and up to 10 cm wide, mid-green. Grows to be much larger as a marsh plant.
Cultivation and Propagation: The species is one of the most slow-growing aquarium plants. It should be used as a solitary display specimen. The plant loves light, but a little shade does not hurt it. A substratum containing a good supply of nutrients promotes its growth. Temperature approximately 25 °C. The smaller bog plants tolerate transfer to the aquarium and lose practically no leaves in the process. Propagation from lateral shoots taken off parent plants, division of rhizomes or seeds as specified for the genus.

Anubias lanceolata N. E. BR. (Ill. 169)

The species was named by N. E. Brown in 1901. Certainly only a form of *A. afzelii*.
Distribution: Tropical west Africa.
Characteristics: Plant with a thin rhizome, growing in marsh or, more rarely, submerged. Leaves in basal rosettes, petiolate. Laminae of submerged leaves lanceolate, flat, thin, up to 20 cm long and up to 5 cm wide, mid-green.
Cultivation and Propagation: As specified for *A. afzelii*.

Anubias heterophylla ENGL.

The species was named by Engler in 1879.
Distribution: Tropical west Africa.
Characteristics: Plant with a thick rhizome growing in bog or, more rarely, submerged. Leaves in basal rosettes, petiolate. Laminae of submerged leaves lanceolate, flat or slightly wavy, up to 15 cm long and up to 3 cm wide, dark-green. Definitely larger when growing as a marsh plant.
Cultivation and Propagation: As specified for *A. afzelii*.

Anubias nana ENGL.

The species was named by Engler in 1899.

Characteristics: Plant with thin rhizomes growing in bogs, only rarely submerged. Laminae of submerged leaves elliptical to egg-shaped, flat, up to 8 cm long and up to 3 cm wide, mid-green to dark-green.

Cultivation and Propagation: As specified for *A. afzelii.*

Cryptocoryne

The genus was described by Fischer in 1828. The name is derived from kryptos (Gk) = hidden and koryne (Gk) = club, spadix. The name refers to the club-shaped spadix hidden in the basal inflated section of the spathe.

Distribution: South-east Asia, coastal zones on the mainland and on the islands.

Characteristics: Small, at most medium-sized herbaceous plants with thin rhizomes, runners and intermediate forms of both. Leaves in basal rosettes, with petioles. Their laminae come in various sizes, forms and colours. The inflorescence is enclosed by a coloured spathe having a basal inflated section followed by a more or less long tube expanding into the spathe blade at the top. A characteristically coloured ring may form around the throat. The inflated section at the base and the tube are divided by an operculum. The actual inflorescence is very small and hidden in the basal inflated section of the spathe. Flowers unisexual and monoecious, inconspicuous. Perianth lacking. Male flowers arranged at the top of the spadix; they have only one stamen which varies considerably in structure from the typical stamen. Female flowers arranged at the base of the spadix; they have one carpel, hypogynous superior (Ill. *58*). The fruit is a syncarpous water berry.

General Information: Nowadays, approximately 50 species of this genus have become known, but the figure is steadily rising as more and more species are being discovered. All species are marsh and aquatic plants colonising many different habitats. Thus, there are species that grow most of the time in bog and are submerged in water for only a short period of the year. As a rule they flower in the time they are on land. Other species live permanently or predominantly submerged and then they flower in the submerged form. Their spathes, however, rise above the water level. Finally, there are species living in waters affected by the tides and therefore exposed to daily fluctuations of the water level caused by high and low tides.

All species so far imported are suited to aquarium cultivation. The majority of them thrive satisfactorily if grown submerged, left undisturbed for a long time, and given adequate warmth. After planting they need enough time to become established and send out roots. Patience is needed if, after a fortnight, there is no apparent sign of success. In some species it takes weeks before the first new leaf can be seen. Unwashed sand has proved to be a good substratum. It should not be too low, but at least 5-8 cm deep so that the roots are given a good chance to develop. A cold substratum may retard growth, even if the water has the

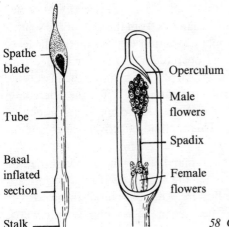

Spathe blade

Tube

Basal inflated section

Stalk

Operculum

Male flowers

Spadix

Female flowers

58 Cryptocoryne: spathe (left), basal inflated section (right)

right temperature. Contrary to former opinions, soft and acid water is not absolutely essential for Cryptocorynes, although many species thrive in it. In aquaristic circles it was also believed for a long time that, in contrast to most other aquarium plants, Cryptocorynes should be given a dark position. Certainly a few species may thrive in very little light whereas some others need subdued light for their well-being. But these are exceptions. Most Cryptocorynes should be given abundant light, irrespective of whether they are cultivated in an aquarium or emerse as bog plants.

If stocks of Cryptocorynes that have been in prime condition for months suddenly decline, if their leaves become soft and glassy and finally collapse they are said to suffer from 'Cryptocoryne disease'. It is usually caused by changes in growth conditions, such as change of water; alternation of light intensivity; change-over from incandescent to fluorescent lighting; adding extra chemicals; an exchange of the filter substratum. The disease may even occur when an aquarist has not introduced any changes of which he is aware. The damaged plants nearly always recover and start sprouting after some time; it is rare that they are irretrievably lost. The susceptibility to the disease varies from species to species. The causes of the phenomenon have been much discussed, but really reliable information does not exist. Some aquarists think that too high a concentration of organic decomposition products causes disintegration whereas others assume a lack of certain nutrients or trace elements is the responsible factor. Yet other aquarists believe that they have traced the origin of the disease to infection by bacteria.

Vegetative propagation of Cryptocorynes is always certain as they produce many slips, and their runners and rhizomes can be divided. Nevertheless, their sexual reproduction deserves some description. It is an interesting example of flower biology and illustrates the mechanisms of insect-pollinated pitfall flowers. Besides, artificial pollination has rarely been attempted as yet so that an aquatic plants enthusiast who is keen on experimenting might well find a new and worthwhile field for his activities.

In the natural environment of the Cryptocorynes suitable pollinating insects are attracted by the colour of the spathe blade and the scent which emanates from the tube of the spathe. The insects crawl through the tube to the basal inflated section but are unable to leave immediately as their return is barred by the inflexed operculum. If they are loaded with pollen on entry this is transferred to the stigmata of the carpels. Afterwards the insects are again loaded with the sticky pollen of the later ripening stamens. When the operculum withers the exit is free and the insects are able to leave. As they have not 'learnt' anything from their captivity they turn to another spathe. This method effectively rules out the possibility of self-pollination.

In species that are suited to being cultivated emerse as marsh plants the following method for artificial pollination has been recommended. After the spathe has fully developed it should be carefully removed to gain access to the flowers. The stigmata of the flowers of a fresh inflorescence are then gently brushed with the stamens of an inflorescence whose spathe has opened three days earlier. It then remains to be seen whether the pollination has been successful. No artificial pollination method has been found as yet for plants that produce inflorescences in conditions of submerged growth. In the natural habitat of these plants insects are able to get into the pit inside the spathe and stay dry as the spathes project above the water.

If pollination has been successful the carpels become distinctly swollen. Before the seeds ripen the stalk of the syncarp elongates. The fruit either disintegrates on the plant and the seeds are thus freed, or the fruit detaches itself from the plant, perhaps floats on the water for a time and then drifts away. In some species seeds germinate immediately, in others they pass through a short resting period, as in the genus *Aponogeton*.

The spathes are indispensable for accurate classification of Cryptocorynes, particularly in newly imported plants. Moreover, all species and their varieties are so well characterised by form and colouration of their foliage that their identification should be possible for someone with sufficient experience. From a practical point of view the Cryptocorynes can be divided into three groups, distinguished by differences in their leaves (Ill. *59*, 207, 210). Most species can be allocated to one of these groups.

The *C. beckettii*-group is characterised by leaves with broad lanceolate to longish egg-shaped laminae. The petioles are nearly as long or rather shorter than the laminae, only rarely longer. In the *C. purpurea* group the laminae are elliptical or egg-shaped, and the petioles are conspicuously long. The leaves of the *C. retrospiralis* group are characterised by rather long narrow-linear or linear blades and, usually, short petioles.

In addition to the species discussed in detail below several others may be seen in aquaria, e.g. *C. auriculata* (Ill. 198), *C. bogneri*, *C. cordata*, *C. dieterici*, *C. gracilis*, *C. longicauda*, *C. sarawacensis*, and *C. tortilis*. Often, only a few specimens of these species are kept by specialists and not much is known about what happens to them. No doubt, some of them will become more widely distributed eventually, whereas others will remain rare or disappear altogether owing to insufficient knowledge about their cultivation. There are also members of the genus which have not as yet been described and are new to science. They

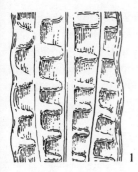 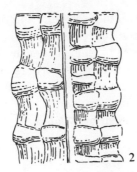 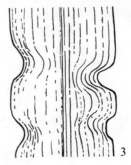

59 Leaves of *Cryptocoryne aponogetifolia* (1), *C. balansae* (2), and *C. retrospiralis* (3)

have been given trade or working names but are in need of scientific examination. New cryptocorynes have been collected, above all on the island Sri Lanka (Ceylon) over the last few years. But a plant which has aroused particular interest is *C.* spec. 'Rosanervis' having dark-green leaf blades with white and red striped venation.

Cryptocoryne lutea ALSTON (Ill. 195, 207)

The species was named by Alston in 1931.

Distribution: Sri Lanka.

Characteristics: Herbaceous plant with runners and thin rhizomes growing in bogs and submerged. Medium-sized species of the *C. beckettii* group. Submerged leaves with olive-green to red-brown petioles. Their laminae elongated egg-shaped to almost lanceolate, wavy at the edge, upperside medium-green to dark-green without markings, underside pale-green and the stronger veins often red-brown. Tube of spathe whitish, its blade flat to slightly twisted, yellow to greenish, throat with a distinct ring coloured like the spathe blade.

Cultivation and Propagation: Like all other Cryptocorynes the species develops best if left undisturbed for as long as possible. It is useful when planted in groups in the middle of a tank, but it can also be used in the front part of a taller aquarium. The stock of the plants will increase gradually from the numerous runners. Position should be light to slightly shady. Temperature from above 20 °C, but a slightly lower one for a short time will do no harm. Can be propagated quite easily by separating slips from parent plants.

General Information: The species is closely related to *C. legroi* described below and also has characteristics in common with *C. walkeri*. At times, therefore, the three species have been grouped together as varieties of one species.

Cryptocoryne legroi DE WIT (Ill. 172, 207)

The species was named by De Wit in 1970.

Distribution: Sri Lanka.

Characteristics: Herbaceous plant with thin rhizomes and runners growing in bogs and submerged. Medium-sized species of the *C. beckettii* group. Submerged leaves with red-brown petioles. Their laminae egg-shaped to elongated ovate, wavy at the edge, upperside olive-green and without markings, underside red-brown or red. Tube of spathe whitish with red-violet lines and dots, spathe blade flat to slightly twisted, yellow to greenish, throat with distinct ring coloured like the blade.

Cultivation and Propagation: As specified for *C. lutea.*

Cryptocoryne walkeri SCHOTT (Ill. 200)

The species was named by Schott in 1857.

Distribution: Sri Lanka.

Characteristics: Herbaceous plant with thin rhizomes and runners growing in bogs and submerged. Medium-sized species of the *C. beckettii* group. Submerged leaves with red-brown petioles. Their laminae egg-shaped to elongated ovate, wavy at the edge, upperside mid-green to olive-green and without markings, underside red-brown. Tube of spathe red-violet, spathe blade flat to slightly twisted, yellow to greenish, the ring around the throat not clearly distinguishable and coloured like the blade.

Cultivation and Propagation: As specified for *C. lutea.*

General Information: See under *C. lutea.*

Cryptocoryne beckettii TRIMEN (Ill. 189, 207)

The species was named by Trimen in 1885.

Distribution: Sri Lanka.

Characteristics: Herbaceous plant with thin rhizomes and runners growing in bogs and submerged. Medium-sized species. Submerged leaves with green petioles, these often having a glimmer of violet. Their laminae elongated ovate to almost lanceolate, wavy at the edge, upperside olive-green with dark-green slanting streaks either side of midrib, sometimes without these markings, underside pale-green to slightly violet. Spathe blade flat, tips slightly twisted, dirty yellow, throat with a brown ring.

Cultivation and Propagation: As specified for *C. lutea.* Once the species has become established as a marsh plant in emerse cultivation it is one of the most freely flowering Cryptocorynes. It can be recommended to the aquarist who likes experimenting.

General Information: The species is amongst the earliest Cryptocorynes ever to have been cultivated in aquaria. It is closely related to the next species, *C. petchii.*

Cryptocoryne petchii ALSTON (Ill. 173, 188, 191, 207)

The species was named by Alston in 1931.

Distribution: Sri Lanka.

Characteristics: Herbaceous plant with thin rhizomes and runners growing in bogs and submerged. Medium-sized species in the *C. beckettii* group. Submerged leaves with olive-green to violet petioles. Their laminae elongated egg-shaped to almost lanceolate, wavy at the edge, upperside dark olive-green to brownish-green and with dark-green striation either side of midrib, but striation often lacking, underside violet, especially in the region of the veins. Spathe blade flat although tip may be slightly twisted, dark olive-green to brown-green, ring of throat dark-brown.

Cultivation and Propagation: As specified for *C. lutea.*

General Information: The species is closely related to *C. beckettii.*

Cryptocoryne versteegii ENGLER

The species was named by Engler in 1910.

Distribution: New Guinea.

Characteristics: A small herbaceous plant with runners growing in bogs and submerged. Petioles thick, green and growing from a membraneous sheath. Laminae thick fleshy, green, ovate to nearly spatulate-triangular, base truncate or cordately lobate, tip blunt. A distinctive and slow-growing species, providing a contrast to other species in the genus.

Cultivation and Propagation: It does not usually do well submerged but successful results have been achieved growing the plant in bog conditions in a medium of loam with clay pellets and receiving partially shaded sunlight.

Cryptocoryne wendtii DE WIT

The species was named by De Wit in 1958.

Distribution: Sri Lanka.

Characteristics: Herbaceous plant with thin rhizomes and runners growing in bogs and submerged. Medium-sized species of *C. beckettii* group. Submerged leaves with green to brown petioles. Laminae very variable in size, form and colouration depending on variety and growth conditions. Spathe blade almost flat to slightly twisted, curved on one side, medium brown, throat with dark-brown to dark-violet ring.

Cultivation and Propagation: As specified for *C. lutea.*

General Information: *C. wendtii* includes a large number of forms, varying from each other in shape and colouration of the leaves, but in the region of the spathes they show little, or even no differences. Exact delimitation of the various forms of this species is therefore difficult to achieve and may well take some time. Some of the forms are considered to be varieties whereas others have only been given trade or working names. Diagnosis of these forms with any certainty is rendered difficult by variation in the colouration of the lamina in particular. Such variations depend on the period of light and probably also on the intensivity of the light.

The typical variety *C. wendtii* var. *wendtii* has egg-shaped to elongated ovate laminae with a wavy edge and often a slightly bullate surface. The upperside is pale-green to olive-green with faint, dark-green striation either side of the midrib. In contrast to the variety described below the colours blend evenly over the whole surface of the leaf upperside. The underside is pale-green to pale-violet in colour. This plant is one of the earliest forms of the species under cultivation and the type form after which De Wit named it.

C. wendtii var. *krauteri* has elongated egg-shaped to almost lanceolate laminae, usually flat and not bullate. The colouration of the upperside is pale-green to olive-green with faint dark-green striation. In contrast to the previous variety the colours blend only partially so that leaves occur with laminae flecked olive-green to dark-green. The underside is pale-green to pale-reddish.

In *C. wendtii* var. *jahnelii* the leaf lamina is elongated egg-shaped with a wavy edge. The upperside is a dark olive-green to brown and the underside more or less red. In comparable growth conditions this is the largest form. In aquarist circles it is often known under the name of '*Braune Wendtii*'.

C. wendtii var. *rubella* is characterised by longish egg-shaped to almost lanceolate laminae with a wavy edge. The upperside is dark olive-green, often with a faint, darker striation. The underside is reddish. The leaf may also be paler. This plant is a small form of the species, known to aquarists for years under the name of *Cryptocoryne* spec. 'Rubella'.

The above are just a few examples of the wealth of forms belonging to *C. wendtii*.

Cryptocoryne willisii BAUM (Ill. 190, 199, 207)

The species was named by Baum in 1909, but its nomenclature is still doubtful. In 1975 it was given another name, *C. axelrodii*, and it has also been taken for *C. undulata*. However, *C. undulata* is definitely another plant which has not been cultivated for some years. It may well have turned up again among the species of cryptocorynes lately discovered and collected in Sri Lanka but not yet delimited.

Distribution: Sri Lanka.

Characteristics: Herbaceous plant with thin rhizomes and runners growing in bogs and submerged. Medium-sized species of *C. beckettii* group. Submerged leaves with brownish petioles. Their laminae very elongated egg-shaped to almost lanceolate with wavy margin, upperside medium-green to pale olive-green with dark striation and markings, underside pale-green to reddish. Spathe blade slightly twisted, ochre to pale-brown in colour, the throat has no ring.

Cultivation and Propagation: As specified for *C. lutea*.

Cryptocoryne nevillii HOOK. f. (Ill. 193, 210)

The species was named by Hooker's son in 1898. At the beginning of the century aquarium literature often referred to the plant as *C. willisii*.

Distribution: Sri Lanka.

Characteristics: Herbaceous plant with thin rhizomes and runners growing in bogs and submerged. Small species in *C. beckettii* group. Submerged leaves with green petioles. Their laminae long egg-shaped, flat and smooth, rarely wavy at the edge, upperside mid-green without markings, underside pale-green. Spathe blade flat, erect, tips only might be slightly twisted, reddish-brown, throat with a dirty-yellow ring.

Cultivation and Propagation: *C. nevillii* is a popular, widely distributed aquarium plant, well-known for a long time. It is cultivated and propagated in much the same way as *C. lutea*. Because it is small the plant is suited to decoration of the front part of tanks entirely planted with Cryptocorynes, but it can also be used in tanks planted with a variety of species.

General Information: The colouration and form of foliage leaves of *C. nevillii* and the two species described below, *C. lucens* and *C. parva*, are very similar. The three species are therefore regarded as being closely related. But as the throat of the spathe of *C. nevillii* has a yellow ring this species probably has a greater degree of independence.

Cryptocoryne lucens DE WIT (Ill. 196, 208, 210)

The species was named by De Wit in 1962. Before it received its scientific description it was regarded as a narrow-leafed form of *C. nevillii*.

Distribution: Sri Lanka.

Characteristics: Herbaceous plant with thin rhizomes and runners growing in bogs and submerged. Small species of *C. beckettii* group. Submerged leaves with green petioles. Their laminae very long drawn-out, egg-shaped to lanceolate, flat and smooth, upperside mid-green without markings, underside pale-green. Spathe blade flat, erect, rather short, medium-brown, throat with a dark-brown to violet ring.

Cultivation and Propagation: As specified for *C. lutea*.

General Information: See under *C. nevillii*.

Cryptocoryne parva DE WIT (Ill. 209, 210)

The species was named by De Wit in 1970.

Distribution: Sri Lanka.

Characteristics: Herbaceous plant with thin rhizomes and runners growing in bogs and submerged. Medium-sized species of *C. beckettii* group. Submerged leaves with green petioles. Their laminae relatively small, lanceolate, flat and smooth, upperside mid-green without markings, underside pale-green. Spathe blade very short, twisted, dark-brown to dark-violet, throat with black-violet ring.

Cultivation and Propagation: In all essentials as specified for *C. lutea*. This is a small species and therefore suitable for being planted in groups in the front of a tank.

General Information: See under *C. nevillii*.

Cryptocoryne bullosa BECC. (Ill. 192)

The species was named by Beccari in 1877.

Distribution: North-western Kalimantan (Indonesia).

Characteristics: Herbaceous plant with thin rhizomes and runners growing in bogs and submerged. Medium-sized species in *C. beckettii* group. Submerged leaves with green to red-brown petioles. Their laminae egg-shaped to elongated ovate, very bullate, upperside dark-green without markings, underside paler in colour. Spathe blade flat, the tip only might be twisted, dark-violet, throat without a ring.

Cultivation and Propagation: A species which has as yet rarely been cultivated and does not thrive in all aquarium conditions. It should be planted in groups in the middle part of the aquarium.

Cryptocoryne thwaitesii SCHOTT

The species was named by Schott in 1857.

Distribution: Sri Lanka.

Characteristics: Herbaceous plant with thin rhizomes and runners growing in bogs and submerged. Submerged leaves with brown petioles. Their laminae egg-shaped to longish ovate, flat to slightly wavy, finely toothed at the margin, upperside dark-green, olive-green or brown with faint darker striation and markings, underside pale-green to reddish. Spathe blade with a very long tail, whitish or red with violet spots.

Cultivation and Propagation: As specified for *C. lutea.*

General Information: Its characteristics isolate the species from other Cryptocorynes found in Sri Lanka.

Cryptocoryne affinis HOOK. f. (Ill. 217, 219)

The species was named by Hooker's son in 1893. For a long time it was known as *Cryptocoryne haerteliana* among aquarists.

Distribution: Malay Peninsula.

Characteristics: Herbaceous plant with thin rhizomes and runners predominantly growing submerged. Medium-sized species of *C. beckettii* group, although the form of its spathe shows common characteristics with the *C. retrospiralis* group. Submerged leaves with green or red-brown petioles. Their laminae varied in form and shape, upperside glossy dark-green without markings, underside pale-green to red-violet. Spathe blade very elongated and tightly twisted several times, dark violet or whitish with violet markings, throat without ring.

Cultivation and Propagation: This is one of the most widely distributed and undemanding species of the genus. It thrives even in a shady position. Temperature from 18 °C. To be planted in groups and particularly suitable for the middle part of the aquarium. If left undisturbed quite large plants may develop; the axis of the shoot with slightly elongated internodes grows up above the substratum. Most favourable propagation results are obtained from slips separated from parent plants.

General Information: A distinction can be made between two varieties of this species. The typical variety, *C. affinis* var. *affinis*, has submerged leaves with laminae long ovate to almost elliptical. The lamina surface is nearly smooth to very bullate. The aerial leaves have egg-shaped laminae which are always very bullate. In aquarist circles this plant has often been denoted as *C.* spec. 'Pseudobullosa'. The submerged leaves of *C. affinis* var. *haerteliana* have longish ovate laminae; these are rarely bullate or only slightly so. The laminae of the aerial leaves of this plant are also never more than slightly bullate.

Cryptocoryne pontederiifolia SCHOTT (Ill. 197, 214)

The species was named by Schott in 1863.

Distribution: Sumatra, northern Kalimantan (Indonesia).

Characteristics: Herbaceous plant with thin rhizomes and runners growing in bogs and submerged. Large species in the *C. purpurea* group. Submerged leaves with long, olive-green to pale-brownish petioles. Their laminae heart-shaped, slightly bullate, upperside glossy medium to dark-green without markings, underside pale green or with a pale reddish gleam. Spathe blade flat, yellow, throat with an upper rim coloured like the blade.

Cultivation and Propagation: A very large and robust species which grows well and is easily cultivated, either in bright light or in a slightly shady position. Temperature from 20°C, but a temporarily lower one will do no harm.

It can be used as a solitary show specimen, but also planted in groups in the middle or back of large tanks. In an aquarium that is not tall enough the leaves unfold on the surface and have a shading effect. The plant can be propagated most easily by separating slips from parent plants.

Cryptocoryne purpurea RIDL.

The species was named by Ridley in 1902. *C. hejnyi* is a later name for the plant.

Distribution: Malay Peninsula.

Characteristics: Herbaceous plant with thin rhizomes and runners predominantly growing submerged. Large species. Submerged leaves with long, red-brown petioles. Their laminae elliptical, egg-shaped or heart-shaped, flat to slightly wavy, upperside mid-green to dark-green with a more or less intensive pattern of dots, streaks and patches, underside pale-green to violet and also patterned. Spathe blade with short tail, red, throat ring not clearly distinguishable, coloured yellow-orange or red.

Cultivation and Propagation: The species requires moderate to good lighting and, for optimum development, needs to be left undisturbed. Temperature approximately 25°C. The plants suffer in hard water and become rather stunted. Depending on the size of the aquarium the species may be used as solitary specimens or planted in groups. The simplest way to propagate them is from slips separated from parent plants.

General Information: There are several other species closely related to *C. purpurea*, but their systematic arrangement is as yet doubtful. Nearly all the plants termed *C. cordata* or *C. griffithii* in aquarist circles really belong to *C. purpurea*.

Cryptocoryne blassii DE WIT

The species was named by De Wit in 1960. Originally the plant was imported under the name of *C.* spec. 'Braune von Bangkok'.

Distribution: Western Indochina.

Characteristics: Herbaceous plant with thin rhizomes and runners predominantly growing submerged. Large species of the *C. purpurea* group. Submerged leaves with long red-brown petioles. Their laminae elliptical, egg-shaped or heart-shaped, flat to slightly bullate, upperside olive-green to brownish-green lacking a pattern, underside red-violet. Spathe blade short-tailed, yellow, without throat ring.

Cultivation and Propagation: A large species that grows well in good light or a slightly shady position. Temperature approximately 25 °C. Suitable as a solitary show plant or in groups depending on the size of the aquarium. The simplest method of propagating the plants is from slips separated from parent plants.

General Information: The species is closely related to the one below, *C. siamensis.*

Cryptocoryne siamensis GAGNEP. (Ill. 4)

The species was named by Gagnepain in 1941. Among some aquarists it was first known under the name *C.* spec. 'Narrow-leafed Blassii'.

Distribution: Western Indochina.

Characteristics: Herbaceous plant with thin rhizomes and runners predominantly growing submerged. Large species of the *C. purpurea* group. Submerged leaves with long, dark-green to red-brown petioles. Their laminae elliptical with pointed tips, upperside dark-green to grey-green without markings, underside pale-green or pale-reddish. Spathe blade yellow and without throat ring like *C. blassii,* but longer and with a more pronounced tail.

Cultivation and Propagation: As specified for *C. blassii.*

General Information: The species is closely related to the one previously described, *C. blassii.*

Cryptocoryne spiralis (RETZ.) SCHOTT (Ill. 206, 211)

Retzius named the species *Arum spirale* in 1779. Schott moved it to the genus *Cryptocoryne* in 1832.

Distribution: Peninsular India.

191 *Cryptocoryne petchii*, as a bog plant
192 *Sparganium erectum*

193 *Cryptocoryne nevillii*
194 *Cryptocoryne bullosa*
195 *Cryptocoryne lutea*, spathe blade
196 *Cryptocoryne lucens*, spathe

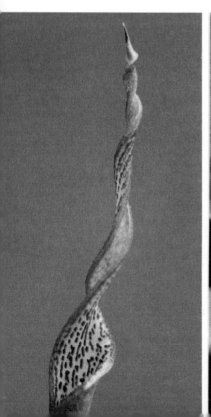

207 From left to right: leaves of *Cryptocoryne legroi, C. lutea, C. beckettii, C. petchii, C. willisii*

208 *Cryptocoryne lucens*
209 *Cryptocoryne parva*

210 From left to right:
Cryptocoryne ciliata, var. *latifolia* and var. *ciliata*, *C. lucens*, *C. nevillii*, *C. parva*

211 *Cryptocoryne spiralis*
212 *Cryptocoryne lingua*

213 *Cryptocoryne albida*
214 *Cryptocoryne pontederiifolia*
215 *Cryptocoryne purpurea*, spathe blade
216 *Cryptocoryne affinis*, spathe

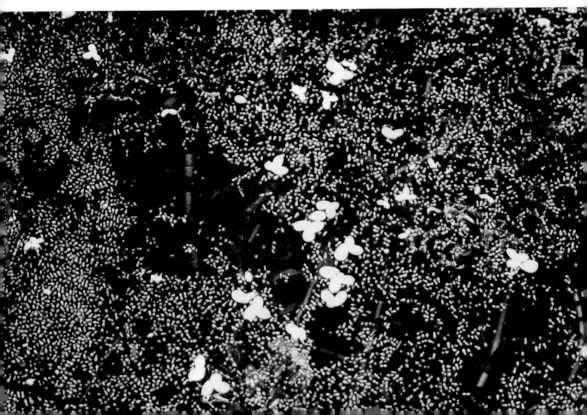

Characteristics: Herbaceous plant with thin rhizomes and runners growing in bogs and submerged. Medium-sized species in the *C. retrospiralis* group. Submerged leaves with green to red-brown petioles. Their laminae narrow lanceolate, flat to slightly wavy, upper-side mid-green without markings, underside pale-green. Spathe lacks a tube, its blade very elongated and pointed, brown-violet.

Cultivation and Propagation: Contrary to some aquarium literature, the plant does thrive in an aquarium. It requires good light and a temperature above 20 °C. It can be recommended for being planted in groups in the middle of a tank. The simple, narrow-leafed foliage of the species provides a good contrast to the broad-leafed foliage of its relatives in a tank planted entirely with Cryptocorynes. The plant is propagated most easily from slips separated from parent plants.

General Information: The lacking tube of the spathe shows that the species is a primitive one in the evolutionary history of the genus.

Cryptocoryne costata GAGNEP. (Ill. 217)

The species was named by Gagnepain in 1941.

Distribution: Western Indochina.

Characteristics: Herbaceous plant with thin rhizomes and runners growing in bogs and submerged. Medium-sized species in the *C. retrospiralis* group. Submerged leaves with red-brown petioles. Their laminae lanceolate, flat to slightly wavy, upperside brownish with darker striation either side of the midrib, underside pale-brownish. Spathe blade short with the hint of a tip, dirty white with violet dots, throat without ring.

Cultivation and Propagation: As specified for *C. spiralis*. Because of its brown leaves this is a very attractive plant.

Cryptocoryne albida PARKER (Ill. 204, 213)

The species was named by Parker in 1931. *C. korthausae* is a later name for the plant.

Distribution: North-western Indochina.

Characteristics: Herbaceous plant with thin rhizomes and runners growing in bogs and submerged. Medium-sized species in the *C. retrospiralis* group. Submerged leaves with green petioles. Their laminae lanceolate, flat to slightly wavy, upperside mid-green without markings, underside whitish-green. Spathe blade short-twisted, dirty white with violet spots, throat lacks a ring.

Cultivation and Propagation: As specified for *C. spiralis*.

Cryptocoryne balansae GAGNEP. (Ill. 59, 201, 202)

The species was named by Gagnepain in 1941. It was introduced to the trade under the name of *C.* spec. 'Somphongsii'.

Distribution: Indochina.

Characteristics: Herbaceous plant with thin rhizomes and runners growing in bogs and submerged. Medium-sized to large species in the *C. retrospiralis* group. Submerged leaves with red-brown petioles. Their laminae linear lanceolate, finely but irregularly crinkled, pale-green on both sides. No markings. Spathe elongated with blade attenuated and tightly twisted, dirty white with violet spots, without ring to the throat.

Cultivation and Propagation: A beautiful and popular long-leafed species which should be planted in groups and needs a tall tank to be shown to best advantage. It is particularly suitable for decoration of the background, or it may be planted in the middle of a tank to make the vegetation look less rigid. The plant requires a bright to slightly shady position. Temperature from 20 °C. The species does not thrive in all conditions. It sends out few runners in an aquarium. Propagation is easiest from slips separated from parent plants.

Cryptocoryne retrospiralis (ROXB.) KUNTH (Ill. 59)

Roxburgh named the species *Ambrosinia retrospiralis* in 1832. Kunth moved it to the genus *Cryptocoryne* in 1841. There are still doubts as to the exact classification of this plant. The names *C. longispatha* and *C. tonkinensis* are also used for it.

Distribution: Peninsular India and Indochina.

Characteristics: Herbaceous plant with thin rhizomes and runners predominantly growing submerged. Large species. Submerged leaves with green to red-brown and, usually, short petioles. Their laminae linear, up to 50 cm long, wavy, olive-green on both sides. Spathe blade long and tightly twisted, dirty white, with or without violet spots, the throat lacks a ring.

Cultivation and Propagation: A species with long, slender leaves very suitable for tanks planted only with Cryptocorynes, but also those containing a number of species. It can be displayed in a number of ways. It looks best planted in groups in the back or front corners of an aquarium. The plant requires a temperature of at least 20 °C, but it is otherwise undemanding and grows well. It is propagated most easily from slips taken off parent plants. But, as the thin rhizomes of this species grow up above the substratum, they can be topped and their tips planted out. Lateral shoots normally develop on the remaining pieces of rhizomes. These, too, can be separated and used for multiplication when they are strong enough.

Cryptocoryne aponogetifolia MERR. (Ill. 59)

The species was named by Merril in 1919. By some botanists it is denoted as *C. usteriana* under which name it has also been introduced to the trade.

Distribution: Philippines.

Characteristics: Herbaceous plant with thin rhizomes and runners predominantly growing submerged. Very large species in the *C. retrospiralis* group. Submerged leaves with long, red-brown petioles. Their laminae lanceolate, up to 70 cm long, very bullate, upperside dark-green, underside a slightly paler green. Spathe blade oblong and slightly twisted, reddish-violet with throat ring in the same colour.

Cultivation and Propagation: This very large species is only suitable for a tall aquarium where it looks very beautiful as a solitary show plant. If the tank is too low the leaf laminae lie on the surface of the water and cast too much shade. Temperature from 20 °C. The species thrives best in good light and a nourishing substratum. Most easily propagated from slips separated from parent plants.

Cryptocoryne lingua ENGL. (Ill. 212)

The species was named by Engler in 1897.

Distribution: Kalimantan (Indonesia).

Characteristics: Herbaceous plant with thin rhizomes and runners growing in bogs and submerged. Small to medium-sized species which does not really fit in with any one of the three groups mentioned. Submerged leaves with green petioles. Their laminae egg-shaped, elliptical or broad lanceolate, relatively tough, pale-green to medium-green without markings on upper and underside. Spathe blade with violet spots and a violet tail, throat ring lacking.

Cultivation and Propagation: An undemanding species. However, it grows very slowly. It is suitable for planting in groups in the middle of a tall aquarium and also in the front. In an aquarium planted entirely with *Cryptocoryne* species the simple, green leaves of the plant provide a pleasant contrast to species having leaves of a different colouration or markings. Temperature from 20 °C. Requires a position in good light. Multiplies quite easily from slips.

Cryptocoryne ciliata (ROXB.) SCHOTT (Ill. 203, 205, 210)

Roxburgh named the species *Ambrosinia ciliata* in 1819; Schott moved it to the genus *Cryptocoryne* in 1832.

Distribution: Areas near the coast on the south-east Asiatic mainland, Kalimantan, Java, Sumatra, Celebes, Moluccas Islands, New Guinea.

Characteristics: Herbaceous plant with thicker rhizomes predominantly growing in bogs. Large species which does not really fit in with any one of the three groups mentioned. Leaves with thick, green petioles. Their laminae variable in form depending on the race of the species, relatively tough, upperside pale-green to dark-green without markings, underside usually slightly paler in colour. Spathe blade brownish with a yellow throat, its edge with simple or branched cilia.

Cultivation and Propagation: This strong marsh plant grows very slowly indeed when submerged. It can be used as a solitary show specimen. If the substratum contains too many nutrients the plant may well grow up above the water level which should be avoided.

It requires a temperature from 20 °C and sufficient light. In an aquarium the species rarely develops runners or lateral shoots usable for propagation.

General Information: Two varieties of the species are readily distinguishable. The typical variety, *C. ciliata* var. *ciliata*, possesses lanceolate to broad lanceolate leaf laminae. It forms long, creeping runners eventually producing slips. In *C. ciliata* var. *latifolia* the leaf laminae are egg-shaped or heart-shaped. The plant forms no runners, but many short, lateral shoots. These break off after some time and can be used for propagation.

Pistia

The genus was defined by Linné in 1753. The name is derived from pistos (Gk) = watery. The genus contains only the one species described below.

Pistia stratiotes L. (Ill. 219)

The species was named by Linné in 1753 when he defined the genus.

Distribution: In nearly all tropical and subtropical areas.

Characteristics: Commonly called water lettuce. Rosette plants either floating on the surface of the water or rooted in bog, sending out a profusion of runners. Roots initially whitish, later on blue-black. Leaves wedge-shaped with slightly crenate tips, up to 10 cm long and wide, spongy, upperside bluish-green, underside pale-green. White flowers unisexual, very small and reduced, enclosed by an inconspicuous, delicate spathe. Perianth lacking. Male flowers with two stamens. Female flowers with one carpel, the latter hypogynous superior. The fruit is a water berry.

Cultivation and Propagation: This floating plant is interesting but really only suitable for a planthouse. In an aquarium it casts too much shade, needs a great deal of air space and is also sensitive to drip water. Temperature from 20 °C. The daily period of illumination should not be allowed to fall much below 12 hours. Because the plant produces a profusion of slips on its runners it is easily propagated. However, it also produces seeds capable of germinating. Often these are overlooked owing to the sessile, inconspicuous inflorescences hidden in the axils of the leaves. It is therefore often a surprise when young plants are found on the water's surface. These young plants bear some resemblance to duckweed.

General Information: In many areas the species has become a troublesome weed, particularly on polluted waters. It has to be kept under control, either by mechanical or by chemical means.

Family Lemnaceae · Duckweed Family

Six genera, 30 species. Their distribution is almost worldwide. Very small plants with a simple plant body not showing much differentiation. Its various parts (or fronds), however, have a more complicated structure and consist of a shoot axis and a leaf. The flowers are very simple indeed and, in any case, are rarely found.

The duckweeds are the smallest flowering plants. Their species occur either floating on the water or submerged beneath it. They are characterised by profuse vegetative multiplication due to early isolation of the daughter segments which will develop. Duckweeds tend to enjoy wide-spread distribution, but occasionally they occur for only a short period. Very probably migrating waterfowl are the cause of their dispersal.

Species of *Pseudowolffia*, *Wolffiella* and *Wolffiopsis* have never been cultivated so far. But representatives of the genera *Spirodela*, *Lemna* and *Wolffia* are well-known to the aquarist.

Spirodela

The genus was defined by von Schleiden in 1839. The name is derived from speira (Gk) = spiral and delos (Gk) = distinct.

Distribution: Almost worldwide.

Characteristics: Very small, perennial plants with a very simple plant body. Daughter segments develop in two lateral pockets of the fronds. Each frond has several roots. Flowers unisexual, inconspicuous. Two male flowers and one female flower are enclosed by a membranous spathe. Perianth Lacking. Male flowers with one stamen. Female flowers with one carpel, the latter hypogynous superior. The fruit is a water berry.

General Information: The genus includes three species.

Spirodela polyrrhiza (L.) SCHLEID.

Linné named the species *Lemna polyrrhiza* in 1753. Von Schleiden moved it to *Spirodela* in 1839 when he defined the genus.

Distribution: Almost worldwide.

Characteristics: A plant floating on the surface of the water having a very simple plant body. Fronds flat, round, their diameter up to 1 cm, green to red.

Cultivation and Propagation: The species may be used on ponds. It is pleasing and does not grow as rapidly as most *Lemna* species. In the temperate zones the fronds sink to the bottom in the late autumn and keep there over the winter. The plants multiply abundantly.

Lemna

The genus was defined by Linné in 1753. The name is derived from limne (Gk) = pond.

Distribution: Nearly worldwide.

Characteristics: Very small, perennial plants with simple plant bodies. Daughter segments grow two lateral pockets of single fronds. Every segment has one root. Flowers unisexual, inconspicuous, arranged and formed as in *Spirodela*. The fruit is a water berry.

General Information: The genus includes ten species. In addition to the two species described below *Lemna gibba*, the thick duckweed, occurs in the northern hemisphere; it has thickened, spongy fronds.

Lemna minor L. (Ill. 220)

The species was named by Linné in 1753.

Distribution: Almost worldwide.

Characteristics: The common duckweed which floats on the water and has a very simple plant body. Fronds flat, ovate, up to 0.5 cm in length, pale-green.

Cultivation and Propagation: The species grows very vigorously indeed. In botanical gardens and nurseries for aquatic plants it has become a troublesome weed. Constant, mechanical removal alone will keep it under control.

Lemna trisulca L.

The species was named by Linné in 1753.

Distribution: Almost worldwide.

Characteristics: An aquatic with a very simple plant body, commonly called the ivy-leafed duckweed. Fronds flat, diamond-shaped to elliptical, petiolate, delicate, dark-green, remaining united for quite a long time.

Cultivation and Propagation: Undemanding and interesting, the plant is suitable for little cold-water aquaria only.

Wolffia

The genus was defined by von Schleiden in 1844. The name was chosen in honour of a German physician, J. F. Wolff (1778-1806).

Distribution: In all tropical and subtropical areas.

Characteristics: Very small perennial plants with a very simple plant body. Daughter segments grow from a retroverted pocket of the frond. Roots lacking. Flowers unisexual, inconspicuous. One male and one female flower enclosed by a membranous spathe. Flower parts like those of *Spirodela*. The fruit is a water berry.

General Information: The genus includes approximately seven species.

Wolffia arrhiza (L.) Wimm. (Ill. 220)

Linné named the species *Lemna arrhiza* in 1771; Wimmer moved it to the genus *Wolffia* in 1857.

Distribution: In nearly all tropical and subtropical zones, local and temporary in the temperate zones.

Characteristics: Very small duckweeds with very simple plant bodies, floating on the surface of the water or submerged. Fronds egg-shaped, up to 1.5 mm long, dark-green.

Cultivation and Propagation: A harmless plant which is easily brought in by chance. Its growth is particularly strong in a daily period of less than 12 hours.

General Information: Some fishes are fond of eating the plants.

Family Sparganiaceae

Only one genus, *Sparganium*, belongs to the family.

Sparganium

The genus was defined by Linné in 1753. The name is probably derived from sparganon (Gk) = ribbon.

Distribution: Mainly in temperate and cold areas of the northern hemisphere.

Characteristics: Perennial herbs with rhizomes. Leaves linear and arranged in two rows. Flowers unisexual and monoecious; inflorescences of varied form composed of small flower clusters of the same sex. Perianth polysepalous, consisting of three to six greenish scales. Male flowers with one to eight stamens, female flowers with one to three carpels, these united, hypogynous superior. Stone fruit.

General Information: The genus includes approximately 20 species. They grow on the edges of still and running waters as well as in marshes, some even in the water. Waterfowl like using stocks of *Sparganium* for building their nests; the fruits provide them with food in the autumn. In addition to the species described below others are also suitable for cultivation near and on ponds, e.g. *S. minimum*, a dwarf form distributed over the whole of the northern hemisphere, and *S. emersum* which occurs in tropical south-east Asia as well as in the northern hemisphere.

Sparganium erectum L. (Ill. 192)

The species was named by Linné in 1753.

Distribution: Europe, northern Asia.

Characteristics: Strong perennial herbs with rhizomes, growing in bogs, up to 60 cm in height. Leaves linear, triangular at the base and up to 15 mm wide, tough, pale-green. Clusters of female flowers at the base, clusters of male flowers at the top of branched inflorescences.

Cultivation and Propagation: A plant which may be used in the marginal vegetation of ponds. It needs a good supply of nutrients in the soil. Propagation by division of the rhizomes in autumn or early spring, or from seeds.

Family Typhaceae · Cattail Family

Only the genus *Typha* belongs to the family. The name is derived from typhos (Gk) = smoke.

Typha

The genus was defined by Linné in 1753.

Distribution: Worldwide.

Characteristics: Perennial herbs growing in bogs; their leaf arrangement is two-rowed and the plants send out runners. Flowers unisexual and monoecious, in spadiceous inflorescences of complicated structure. Perianth lacking. Male flowers with variable number of stamens, sometimes united. Female flowers with one carpel, hypogynous superior. The fruit comes as a capsule.

General Information: The genus includes 10-15 species in urgent need of revision. All species colonise marshy habitats where they help in building up reed-banks. In the temperate latitudes shoots bearing spadices are collected in many places and sold for decorative purposes. Some tropical species grow in such profusion in canals and on ponds that they have become troublesome weeds which have to be kept under control.

Two widely-spread species, *T. latifolia*, a broad-leafed form, and *T. angustifolia*, a narrow-leafed form, are not really suitable for cultivation as they may attain a height of 2-3 m in favourable conditions. However, there are smaller species like the one described below.

Typha minima HOPPE

The species was named by Hoppe.

Distribution: Europe, northern Asia.

Characteristics: A perennial herb which sends out runners, has linear leaves and is up to 75 cm high. Spadix short, egg-shaped.

Cultivation and Propagation: An undemanding species, it is suitable to be planted around the edges of ponds. In the autumn the spadix is brown and then the plants look really decorative. Propagation by division of the plant at the base in autumn or early spring, or from seeds.

Explanation of Specific Epithets

abyssinicus	Abyssinian, growing in the region of present-day Ethiopia	*austroamericanus*	southern American, growing in South America
acicularis	pointed, like a needle	*azurea*	azure-blue
adscendens	ascending	*balansae*	named after the French botanist Balansa
affinis	akin to, related		
afzelii	named after the Swedish botanist Afzel	*beckettii*	named after Beckett who discovered the plant
alba	white	*berteroi*	named after the Italian physician and botanist Bertero
albida	whitish		
alismoides	water-plantain like		
aloides	aloe like	*blassii*	named after Blass, the German importer and breeder of aquatic plants
amazonicus	growing in the region of the Amazon		
americanus	American growing in America	*bleheri*	named after Frau Bleher, the founder of the nursery for aquatic plants, 'Lotus Osiris', in Brazil
amphibius	amphibious, living in water and on land		
amplexicaulis	stem-clasping	*boivinianus*	named after the Canadian botanist Boivin
angustifolia	narrow-leafed		
antipyretica	allaying fever	*brasiliensis*	Brazilian, growing in Brazil
aponogetifolia	with leaves resembling those of species of *Aponogeton*	*brevipes*	short-stemmed
		bullosa	inflated, bladder-like
appendiculatus	with small appendages		
aquatica, -cum, -lis	water, living in water	*calamus*	reed-like
		cardinalis	scarlet-red
arcuata	curved like a bow	*caroliniana*	from Carolina (North America)
arrhiza	rootless		
aschersonianus	named after the German botanist Ascherson	*ciliata*	fringed, as with eye lashes
		circinatus	rolled circularly
auriculata	furnished with ear-like appendages	*coloratus*	coloured
		cordata	heart-shaped
australis	southern	*cordifolius*	with heart-shaped leaves

cornuta	horned or spurred	henkelianus	named after Henkel, a German nursery for aquatic plants
corymbosa	arranged in corymbs, clusters		
costata	ribbed	heterophylla, -um	bearing leaves of more than one kind
crassipes	with thick stem		
crenata	having rounded teeth	heudelotii	named after Heudelot, the collector of the plant
crispus	crisp		
		hippuroides	resembling mare's tail (Hippuris)
demersum	submerged		
densus	dense	horemanii	named after the British aquarist Horeman, a collector of the plant
diandra	with two stamens		
difformis	differently formed		
distachyos	with two spikes or ears	horizontalis	horizontal
diversifolia	with leaves of different shapes	hottoniiflora	resembling the flowers of the genus Hottonia
dubia	doubtful	humboldtiana	named after the German naturalist Humboldt
dubyana	named after Duby, the Swiss theologian and botanist		
		indica	growing in India
		inflata	inflated
echinatus	echinate, with numerous rigid hairs or spines		
		japonica	Japanese, growing in Japan
elongatus	elongated		
erectum	erect		
		lacustris	living in ponds or lakes
filiformis	shaped like threads	laevigatum	smooth
fluitans	floating, swimming	lanceolata, -um	lanceolate
fluviatilis	river-, living in rivers	latifolium, -us	with broad leaves
		legroi	named after the Dutch botanist Legro
gayi	named after the French botanist Gay		
		leucocephala	with white heads
gibba	humped, hunch-backed	longifolia, -us	having long leaves
gigantea	gigantic	longiplumolosus	having a long plumula (shoot vegetation cone on the embryo in the seed)
globulifera	bearing small globes (buds)		
graminea, -us	grass-like		
grisebachii	named after the German botanist Grisebach	lucens	shining, glistening
		lutea	yellow
guadalupensis	from Guadelupe, Mexico	lyrata	lyre-shaped
guillottii	named after the French botanist Guillott	macrandra	with large anthers
		madagascariensis	from the Island Madagascar
hederaceus	ivy-like	maior, major	large
helmsii	named after the Australian botanist Helms	malinverniana	named after Malinverni who discovered the plant

micranthemoides	resembling the genus *Micranthemum*
minima	very small
minor	small
monniera	named after Monnier, the French physician and botanist
montevidensis	growing near Montevideo (South America)
monticola	growing on hills
morsus-ranae	frogbit (an old plant name)
myriophylloides	resembling water milfoil (*Myriophyllum*)
nana	dwarf-like
natans	swimming
neotropicalis	neotropical, growing in South America
nevillii	named after Nevill who discovered the plant
nummularia	round and flat, like a coin
nuttallii	named after the British botanist Nuttall
octandrus	having eight stamens
opacus	dark, with a dull surface
osiris	named after the nursery for aquatic plants, 'Lotus Osiris', in Brazil
palustris	bog, swamp loving
parva	small
parviflorus	having small flowers
parvula	very small
peltata	shield-shaped
perfoliatus	having the stem passing through the leaf
petchii	named after the British botanist Petch
piauhyensis	growing in the Brazilian state Piaui (formerly Piauhy)
plantago-aquatica	plantain in water (an old plant name)
platyphylla	having broad leaves
polyrrhiza	thickly rooted
polysperma	bearing many seeds
pontederiifolia	with leaves resembling species of *Pontederia*
portoalegrensis	growing near Porto Alegre (South America)
pseudacorus	false *Acorus*
pteridioides	resembling the genus *Pteridium*
pteropus	having a winged stem
pulcherrima	most beautiful
pumila	low or little
purpurascens	turning purple
purpurea	purple
quadricostatus	four-ribbed
quadrifolius	having four leaves
ranunculoides	resembling *Ranunculus*
reineckii	named after Reineck, the collector of the plant
repens	creeping
retrospiralis	coiled backwards
rigidifolius	with stiff leaves
rotundifolius	with round leaves
sagittifolia	with arrow-shaped leaves
salicaria	willows, resembling willow (*Salix*)
scabratum	rough, sharp
schreberi	named after the German botanist Schreber
senegalensis	growing in Senegal
sessiliflora	bearing sessile flowers
sessilis	sessile, lacking a stalk
setacea	bristly
siamensis	Siamese, growing in Thailand (formerly Siam)
spicatum	spike-like
spiralis	coiled
spongia	spongy
stratiotes	sword-shaped
subulatus	slightly winged
submersum	submerged
subulata	awl-shaped

tenellus	very tender, soft	*vesiculosa*	covered with little blisters or bladders
teres	cylindrical		
tetragona	four-sided	*virginica*	growing in the North American state Virginia
thaianum	growing in Thailand		
thalictroides	resembling *Thalictrum*	*vivipara*	live-bearing
thwaitesii	named after the British botanist Thwaites	*vulgaris*	common, ordinary
trichophyllum	with hairy leaves	*walkeri*	named after the North American botanist Walker
trifoliata	trifoliate		
trisulca	with three grooves	*wallichii*	named after the Danish botanist Wallich
ulvaceus	resembling *Ulva*, a genus of marine algae	*weatherbiana*	named after the North American botanist Weatherby
umbellatus	umbellate		
umbrosum	shade loving	*wendtii*	named after Wendt, the German aquarist and expert on aquatic plants
undulatus	wavy		
uruguayensis	growing in Uruguay		
ussuriense	growing in the region of the eastern Asiatic river Ussuri	*willisii*	named after the Australian botanist Willis
valerandi	named after the botanist Valerand	*zosterifolia*	with leaves resembling eelgrass *(Zostera)*
verticillata, -um	whorled	*zosteriformis*	eelgrass-like *(Zostera)*

List of Authorities

All. Allioni, C. Italian botanist (1728—1804)

Alston Alston, A.H.G. English botanist (1902—1958). Worked at the Botanic Garden, Paradeniya (Sri Lanka) and at the British Museum, London

Anders, T. Anders, T. English botanist (1832—1870). Curator of Botanic Garden, Calcutta

Arech. Arechavaleta, J. Uruguayan botanist (1838—1912)

Aubl. Aublet, J.B.C.F. French pharmacist, botanist (1720—1778)

Baill. Baillon, H.E. French botanist (1827—1895). Curator of Botanic Garden, Paris

Bak. Baker, G.J.G. English botanist (1834—1920). Worked at the Herbarium, Kew

Baum Baum, H. German gardener (1867—1950). Curator of Botanic Garden, Rostock

Beauv. Beauvois, A.M.F.J.P.de. French botanist (1752—1820)

Becc. Beccari, O. Italian botanist (1843—1920)

Benn., A. Bennett, A.W. English botanist (1833—1902)

Benth. Bentham, G. English botanist (1800—1884)

Blake Blake, S.F. North American botanist (1892—1959)

Bl. Blume, C.L. Dutch botanist (1796—1862). Curator of the Herbarium, Leyden

Bonpl. Bonpland, A.J.A.G. French physician and botanist (1773—1858). Accompanied Humboldt on his travels

Bosc Bosc, L.A.G. French botanist (1759—1828). Curator of Botanic Garden, Paris

Briq. Briquet, J. Swiss botanist (1870—1931). Curator of Botanic Garden, Geneva

Brongn. Brongniart, A.T. French botanist (1801—1876)

Broth. Brotherus, V.F. Finnish botanist (1849—1934)

Br.N.E. Brown, N.E. English botanist (1849—1934)

Br., R. Brown, R. English botanist (1773—1858). Worked at the British Museum, London

Bruggen, van Bruggen, H.W.E. van. Contemporary Dutch aquarist who has made a special study of the genus *Aponogeton*

Buch. Buchenau, F. German headmaster and botanist (1831—1906)

Bunge Bunge, A. A. von. Russian physician and botanist (1803—1890)

Cambess. Cambessedes, J. French botanist (1799—1863)

Casp.	Caspary, J.X.R. German botanist (1818—1887)
Ces.	Cesati, V.B.de. Italian botanist (1806—1883). Curator of Botanic Gardens, Naples
Chaix	Chaix, D. French theologian and botanist (1731—1800)
Cham.	Chammisso, L.A. von. German poet and botanist (1781—1838). Worked at Botanic Museum, Berlin
Ching	Ching, R.–C. Contemporary Chinese botanist. Specialist in ferns
DC.	De Candolle, A.P. Swiss botanist (1778—1841)
De Notaris	De Notaris, G. Italian botanist (1805—1877)
De Wit	De Wit, H.C.D. Contemporary Dutch botanist. Expert in determining the genus *Cryptocoryne*
Druce	Druce, G.L. British botanist (1850—1932)
Eames, E.H.	Eames, E.H. North American botanist (1865—1948)
Eat.	Eaton, A. North American botanist (1776—1842)
Ell.	Elliot, S. North American botanist (1771—1830)
Engelm.	Engelmann, G. North American physician and botanist (1809—1884)
Engl.	Engler, H.G.A. German botanist (1844—1930). Curator of Botanic Garden and Museum, Berlin
Fass.	Fassett, N.C. North American botanist (1900—1954)
Fée	Fée, A.L.A. French pharmacist and botanist (1789—1874)
Fern.	Fernald, M.L. North American botanist (1873—1950)
Forsk.	Forskål, P. Swedish natural historian (1732—1768)
Forst.	Forster, J.R. German theologian and botanist (1729—1798)
Gagnep.	Gagnepain, F. French botanist (1866—1952). Worked at the National Museum, Paris
Gardn.	Gardner, J.G. English botanist (1812—1849). Curator of Botanic Gardens, Paradeniya (Sri Lanka)
Georgi	Georgi, J.G. German botanist (1729—1802). Worked in Russia
Gmel.	Gmelen, J.F. German physician and botanist (1748—1804)
Graebn.	Graebner, P.P. German botanist (1871—1933). Worked at the Botanic Garden and Museum, Berlin
Gray	Gray, A. North American botanist (1810—1888)
Greene	Greene, E.L. North American botanist (1843—1915)
Griseb.	Grisebach, A.H.R. German botanist (1814—1879)
Hara	Hara, H. Contemporary Japanese botanist
Harper	Harper, R.M. North American botanist (1878—1966)
Hartog	Hartog, C. den. Contemporary Dutch botanist
Harv.	Harvey, W.H. Irish botanist (1811—1866)
Hedw.	Hedwig, J. German botanist (1730—1799)
Heine	Heine, H. Contemporary French botanist
Herb.	Herbert, W. British theologian and botanist (1778—1847)
Hieron.	Hieronymus, G.H.E. German botanist (1846—1920). Worked at the Botanic Museum, Berlin

Hill	Hill, J. English physician and botanist (1716—1775)	L.	Linné, C. von. Swedish naturalist (1707—1778)
Hochreut.	Hochreutiner, B.P.G. Swiss botanist (1873—1959)	L. f.	Linné, C. von. Swedish naturalist (1741—1783). Son of above
Hochst.	Hochstetter, C.F. German theologian and botanist (1787—1860)	Long	Long, B.H. American botanist (1885—?)
Hook.	Hooker, W.J. English botanist (1785—1865). Curator of Botanic Gardens, Kew	Magn.	Magnus, P.W. German botanist (1844—1914)
Hook. f.	Hooker, J.D. English botanist (1817—1865). Son of the above. Curator of Botanic Gardens, Kew	Marie-Vict.	Marie-Victorin, F. Contemporary Canadian botanist
		Mart.	Martius, C.F.P. von. German botanist (1794—1868). Curator of Botanic Gardens, Munich
Hoppe	Hoppe, D.H. German physician and botanist (1760—1846)	Maxim.	Maximovicz, D.J. Russian botanist (1827—1891)
Humb.	Humboldt, F.H.A. von. German naturalist (1769—1859). His major expeditions took him to Central and South America	Merr.	Merrill, E.D. North American botanist (1876—1956)
		Michx.	Michaux, A. French botanist (1746–1802)
Jacq.	Jacquin, N.J. von. Austrian botanist (1727—1817)	Mich.	Micheli, M. Swiss botanist (1844—1902)
John, St.	John, H. St. North American botanist (died circa 1960)	Mirb.	Mirbel, C.F. French botanist (1776—1854)
		Moss	Moss, E. Contemporary Canadian botanist
Kirk	Kirk, T. New Zealand botanist (1828—1898)	Muell. Arg.	Müller, I. (from Aargau). Swiss botanist (1828—1896)
Koehne	Koehne, B.A.E. German teacher and botanist (1848—1918)	Muell., C.	Müller, I.K.A. German botanist (1818—1899)
Krause	Krause, K. German botanist (1883—?)	Muell. F. v.	Müller, F.S.H. von. German botanist (1825—1896). Worked in Australia
Kunth	Kunth, C.S. German botanist (1788—1850)		
Ktze. O.	Kuntze, C. E. O. German botanist (1843—1907)	Noronha	Noronha, F. de. Spanish botanist (died 1788)
		Nutt.	Nuttall, T. North American botanist (1786—1859)
Lam.	Lamarck, J.B.B.A.M. de. French naturalist (1744—1820)	Palm.	Palmer, E.J. North American botanist (born 1875)
Lepr.	Leprieur, F.R. French botanist (?—1869)	Parker	Parker, R.N. English botanist (1884—1958)
Link	Link, J.H.F. German botanist (1767—1851). Curator of Botanic Garden, Berlin	Parl.	Parlatore, F. Italian botanist (1816—1877)

Pav.   Pavón, J. Spanish botanist (1750—1844)

Pers.   Persoon, C.H. English botanist (1755—1837)

Planch.   Planchon, J.E. French botanist (1823—1888)

Poir.   Poiret, J.L.M. French theologian and botanist (1755—1834)

Presl   Presl, K.B. Czechoslovakian botanist (1794—1852)

Pursh   Pursh, F.D. Canadian botanist (1774—1820)

Rataj   Rataj, K.C. Contemporary Czechoslovakian biologist. Engaged in revising the genera *Echinodorus* and *Cryptocoryne*

Reg.   Regel, E. German botanist (1815—1892)

Retz.   Retzius, A.J. Swedish botanist (1742—1821)

Rich.   Richard, L.C.M. French botanist (1754—1821)

Ridl.   Ridley, H.N. English botanist (1855—1956)

Roem.   Roemer, J.J. Swiss botanist (1763—1819)

Roxb.   Roxburgh, W. English botanist (1759—1815)

Royle   Royle, J.F. English physician and botanist (1799—1858)

Ruiz   Ruiz, L.H. Spanish botanist (1764—1815)

Schlecht.   Schlechtendal, D.F.L.von. German botanist (1794—1866)

Schleid.   Schleiden, M.J. German botanist (1804—1881)

Schott   Schott, H.W. German botanist (1794—1865)

Schreb.   Schreber, J.D.C. German botanist (1739—1810)

Schult.   Schultes, I.A. German botanist (1773—1831)

Schulze   Schulze, J. Contemporary aquarist in Berlin (West)

Schweinf.   Schweinfurth, G.A. German explorer of Africa (1836—1925)

Scop.   Scopolius, G.A.di. Austrian naturalist (1723—1788)

Seguier   Seguier, J.F. French botanist (1703—1784)

Seub.   Seubert, M.A. German botanist (1818—1878)

Sibth.   Sibthorp, J. English botanist (1758—1796)

Small   Small, J.K. North American botanist (1869—1938). Curator of Botanic Gardens, New York

Sm.   Smith, J.E. English botanist (1759—1828)

Sm., I. G.   Smith, I.G. North American botanist (1866—?)

Soland.   Solander, D.C. English botanist (1736–1782)

Solms   Solms, H.M.C.L.F. von. German botanist (1842—1915)

Speg.   Spegazzini, C. Argentinian botanist (1858—1926)

Spreng.   Sprengel, K. German botanist (1766–1833)

Steud.   Steudel, E.G. German physician and botanist (1783—1856)

Steyerm.   Steyermark, J.A. Contemporary North American botanist

Sw.   Swartz, O. Swedish botanist (1760—1818)

Thunb.   Thunberg, C.P. Swedish botanist (1743—1822)

Timm   Timm, J.C. German botanist (1734—1805)

Torr.   Torrey, J. North American botanist (1796—1873)

Trimen   Trimen, H. English botanist (1843—1896). Curator of Botanic Gardens, Paradeniya (Sri Lanka)

Urb.	Urban, J. German botanist (1848—1931)	Wettst.	Wettstein, R. von. Austrian botanist (1862—1931)
		Willd.	Willdenow, K.L. German botanist (1765—1812)
Vahl	Vahl, M.H. Danish botanist (1749—1804)	Wimm.	Wimmer, C.F.H. German botanist (1809—1868)
		With.	Withering, W. British physician and botanist (1741—1799)
Wall.	Wallich, N. Danish physician and botanist (1786—1854)		
Walt.	Walter, T. North American botanist (1740—1788)	Zucc.	Zuccarini, J.G. German botanist (1797—1848)
Wats. S.	Watson, S. North American botanist (1825—1892)		

Bibliography

Arber, A. *Water plants: a study of aquatic angiosperms.* Cambridge 1920 (Reprint Weinheim 1963)

Bhadri, B., Singh, B., Desai, B. L. *Water plants.* New Delhi 1962

Brünner, G. *Aquarienpflanzen.* Stuttgart 1964

Cook, D. K. *Water plants of the world.* The Hague 1974

De Wit, H. C. D. *Aquariumplanten.* Baarn 1966

De Wit, H. C. D. *Aquarienpflanzen.* Stuttgart 1971

Fehse, F. *Das Freilandaquarium.* Stuttgart 1975

François, M. *Décors exotiques et plantes d'aquarium.* Argenteuil 1951

Friesen, G. *Botanik für Aquarianer.* Stuttgart 1953

Gessner, F. *Hydrobotanik: Die physiologischen Grundlagen der Pflanzenverbreitung im Wasser.* Vol. I Berlin 1955, Vol. II Berlin 1959

Hoehne, F. C. *Plantas aquáticas.* São Paulo 1955

Jacobsen, N. *Akvarieplanter i farver.* Copenhagen 1977

Mönkemeyer, W. *Die Sumpf- und Wasserpflanzen.* Berlin 1897

Mühlberg, H. *Vermehrung der Aquarienpflanzen.* Leipzig, Jena, Berlin 1977

Paffrath, K. *Bestimmung und Pflege von Aquarienpflanzen.* Hanover 1977

Perry, F. *Water gardens.* Harmondsworth 1962

Ramshorst, J. D. van *Planten vor het tropisch aquarium.* Amsterdam 1953

Roe, C. D. *A manual of aquarium plants.* Solihull 1966

Roe, C. D. *Handbuch der Aquarienpflanzen.* Frankfurt/M. 1967

Schöpfel, H. *Schöne Aquarien – aber wie?* Leipzig, Jena, Berlin 1977

Sculthorpe, C. D. *The biology of aquatic vascular plants.* London 1971

Wachter, K. *Der Wassergarten.* Stuttgart 1977

Wendt, A. *Die Aquarienpflanzen in Wort und Bild.* Stuttgart 1952–58

Index of Scientific Names of the Species

Semi-bold figures refer to text pages, those in Roman type to illustration numbers of photographs, and figures in italics to illustration numbers of drawings in the text.

Sources of Illustrations

The numbers refer to colour plates

Barth, Dessau 88, 124

Birnbaum, Halle (Saale) 14, 15, 17, 19, 20, 25–27, 33, 34, 36–38, 40, 41, 46–48, 53–55, 57, 61, 63, 64, 72, 74–83, 85, 89, 96–106, 109–121, 126, 127, 132–134, 140–143, 145, 146, 148–152, 157, 158, 164, 165, 171–175, 178, 180, 181, 184, 187–190, 192, 199, 200, 207–214, 218, 220, 221

Böhme, Pohritzsch (GDR) 62

Bruggen, Heemskerk (Netherlands) 49, 86, 87, 137, 159, 160

Ebel, Halle (Saale) 3

Helbig, Gera (GDR) 12, 186, 194

Hertel, Bad Langensalza (GDR) 11, 138, 168, 169, 198

Horst, Lohmar (FRG) 1, 2, 4

Mühlberg, Halle (Saale) 6, 13, 16, 29, 39, 51, 58–60, 65, 73, 90–95, 125, 128–131, 191, 195, 196, 201, 202, 204–206

Nieuwenhuizen, Zevenaar (Netherlands) 7–10, 50, 56

Paffrath, Cologne 156

Schöpfel, Waltershausen (GDR) 52, 84, 136, 139, 162, 167, 193, 197, 215, 216

Schubert, Halle (Saale) 5

Schütze-Rodemann, Halle (Saale) 18, 21–24, 28, 30–32, 35, 42–45, 66–71, 107, 108, 122, 123, 135, 147, 153–155, 161, 170, 176, 177, 179, 182, 183, 185, 203, 217, 219

Weber, Leipzig 163, 166